MOIETY OF A GINGERBREAD MAN

BY
LARRY WM. CARLSON

 The events described in this book are factual but not immune to the limitations of memory/recollection. Some names have been changed or withheld for privacy purposes.
Inquiries: Melanie Lech at Lechmc1@gmail.com
ISBN: 978-1-7375809-4-2

TABLE OF CONTENTS

FOREWORD/PREFACE

VIGNETTES

The Irish are reputed to have an especially devious curse that simply goes: "May you have an interesting life." I definitely have been influenced up to this point in my life, and it seems not to have been lifted yet! One must consider that one's interactions with other "interesting" people will have consequence. So, my story will contain bits and pieces of other people's stories. None of us walk alone in our journey through life. Interactions with others occur naturally as our paths cross and rejoin for a while before diverging again. We have small snippets, snatches, and sketches in commonality for a time. They might represent individual vignettes that linger in memory. Some of us have been fortunate to walk "hallowed halls" of the great who walked before us. Some even more fortunate have walked in their footsteps, laid down expressly for us to follow. We most fortunate are those who were carried along on the backs of other greater men. Some of the truly blessed have known all along that, in their pathway, they walked with God. Sadly, I found God's presence late in life. But he had known me early, and I benefitted nonetheless.

I have known and benefitted from some of the good, the great, and the truly great men who went before me, so my story contains parts of their stories: some good, some bad, and some inconsequential. (Although, hopefully, each story will carry with it a point of some sort!) I acknowledge my debt to some people I've known. When I finally found that no one was in debt to me, I was emotionally freed. That's the way it played out!

As a young man, I never considered the ramifications of ever "growing old." The concept was entirely foreign – just as it must have seemed for most of my generation. Or I was much too busy striving to get somewhere, never noticing time going by. But where was I heading? I certainly didn't know. Running scared most of the time, I was not following a purpose-driven life. I was merely trying to survive long enough to find out what to do in my immediate future – maybe just weeks, months, or years ahead. As you'll later read, I had a tremendous obstacle to overcome and no faith to help me through that phase of my life. I did not know there can be defining moments in life, often triggered by inconsequential prior decisions. It might be like the trivial example of the rock that breaks your windshield – and would not have if you had only slowed down a little before it happened. A big enough rock could take your life!

Now as I dwell in my mid-eighties, I have to reflect on some places I've been and some of the things I learned along the way. I learned there can be positive purpose where none appears. And those times in life that seemed so oppressive might have actually been a blessing, albeit in disguise. Sometimes, the "universe around us" seems to have a "schizoid duality." Good can be bad and vice-versa. Now I see that some of those times "when my intuition saved me" were really times of help from above. In my early years as an engineer, I went from seriously doubting my ability to rash and heady overconfidence, finally, to an acceptance that I was merely an instrument of a higher power's will. That epiphany took immeasurable burdens off my shoulders and soul. I wonder if anything can be done to save and share some of this knowledge I gained, sometimes at great expense, so others can benefit. Vignettes I share may be disconnected, but there is usually a story within each bearing a moral or a technical lesson I had to learn "my way."

WHAT IS AN ENGINEER?

Perhaps a better question might be: Who am I? The former is easy to answer. The latter, not so much, because our personalities are formed mostly by our interactive experiences with others.

So, what is an engineer? After all, there are many kinds of engineers – electrical, mechanical, civil, aerospace, structural, etc. – it all depends on what subjects an individual might have studied. And then there is a further distinction of being primarily a theoretician, experimentalist, a designer, a "hardware guy," or some combination of specialties. To explain, I'll add that one becomes an effective "engineer" only after considerable time passes following graduation. At least, that's what happened to me. There are "pulls and tugs" from various managers who have their own agendas for you. So, the average engineer becomes a pawn of sorts – both to satisfy management, but also with respect to the specific paths (s)he'll eventually take in her/his profession. (I'm going to be a male chauvinist here to avoid the tedium of having to desexualize the profession, going forward. Read "him" as "her" if you wish.) Will an engineer be a "hardware man," a rare person who can take a design concept in theory, make a prototype, test it, and make it work in reality? As a mechanical engineer, I wound up being "everything to everyone."

Versatility isn't all bad, but sometimes a manager wants your full attention while another might require the same commitment to another project. It's akin to getting carved up into little pieces while several people share a gingerbread cookie. You learn to live with the situation, though you do not like it. Read "Dilbert" in the comics to get an accurate perception of the problem as depicted by Scott Adams, who has "been there." Incompetent management and coworkers, impossibly scheduled deadlines, inadequate funding, and a myriad of other problems are common to the practicing engineer. And this fact is especially true if you are a project engineer who is responsible for a project's eventual success, as measured by being on time, within budget, and getting the "right results" reported to whomever paid you.

It is not an easy life, but it can be rewarding. Given supervision by an older, more experienced engineer, one can learn much more than what was taught "in college." If you are lucky and find an experienced engineer who will mentor you, your career will be immeasurably aided. I was extremely lucky having Tom Coultas as my first real manager. He was incessantly demanding "more from me" – more schooling, more output, more attention to detail, and more faith in myself so that I could be everything an engineer needs to be in order to be effective. When I lacked confidence as an analyst, Tom forced me to continually take coursework emphasizing analysis. I was finally able to overcome the stricture laid on me by my thesis advisor, Tom Irvine, while I was still in graduate school: that I "would be 'OK' as an experimentalist, but [I] should never try analysis." It took significant time and learning ways around archaic mathematics to break the confining mold. I found "finite difference" methodology to be a great substitute for the process of integrating differential equations, using computers instead. So, even though I became a "cut-up" gingerbread man, I managed to patch myself together each time and continue toward becoming an engineer.

Now, as to "who am I?" – "Who am I?" is a question, a "simple" question, that has to be answered by each of us one way or another to our own satisfaction. It behooves us to know who we are and how we got where we are in life, whether by genes, by family interactions, by friends or teachers' influence, or by those who had some sway over us. I can only say that each of us has a personality that is largely formed by our experiences with others as we go through life. Some aspects are taught early by parents or church or school. But, we are who we are, largely not knowing "how we got there." It just didn't happen in a vacuum. Each of us needs to analyze and evaluate particular behavior patterns for ourselves. This memoir is my attempt to do just that! Maybe it will show you who I really am.

TRIBUTE TO A GREAT MAN

There are good men, there are great men, and there are giants among men. My friend Jack Breiby was a gentle giant among men. It is with great sadness that I report he died April 19, 2021. Jack was humble to an extreme. He was rated as second highest in intelligence in all of Grand Rapids, MN high schools' experience where he graduated in 1953.

I now fondly identify him as "Gomer" throughout this book, since he no longer can shun fame, honor, or glory, which he so richly deserves. Jack was an "aw shucks, taint nothin'," kind of guy throughout his career, refusing my identifying him in this book by name. He chose anonymity though his life was replete with great accomplishments wherever he went in a forty-plus year career. In no way could Jack be thought of as a nitwit as portrayed by Jim Nabors in his Gomer Pyle TV show. He grew up in a one-room log cabin out in the woods during WWII, living with his maternal Grandma. We met at his 12th birthday party, became chums, and went through high school together. We parted for a few years when I went to college in Duluth and he went to a local junior college, then roomed together at the University of Minnesota, Minneapolis for three years. He graduated in June of 1959 with a BS in Aeronautical Engineering. He had worked at various jobs (primarily at the US Post Office), paying his own way totally through college to get a five-year degree.

Jack landed a job with Lockheed in Burbank, California helping to convert their floundering Electra Turboprop passenger aircraft into the P-3 Orion plane, which has been in use throughout the world over the past 60 years. Later, he quit Lockheed to go to Seattle, WA to work for Boeing. On the day he quit, he was informed Lockheed wanted him to stay and work at Kelly Johnson's Skunk Works, helping to design the SR71 supersonic spy plane, affectionately known as the "Blackbird."

Our paths diverged for quite a while as Jack "job hopped" for five years. Working at Boeing, he designed the wing root transitions for Boeing's 737 passenger jet. Board work at Boeing was too hard on his eyes, so he quit and went to work at Vandenberg AFB, getting Atlas missiles ready to launch spy satellites. That work wasn't satisfying, so he went to Utah where he worked for Thiokol and streamlined their entire engineering department, saving a lot of money. Thiokol got rid of several dozen personnel because Jack did all their jobs by himself!

Jack met his wife Joyce while they worked together at Thiokol and courted her by driving many weekends to eastern Nebraska where she attended college. He married Joyce in Utah. They then moved to Belmont, California, as he had been hired to work for Lockheed Sunnyvale. There, he did orbital mechanics calculations to determine when to eject spy-photo packages that would be snagged by aircraft as parachutes floated to earth over the ocean. He held a top-secret clearance for some of these jobs. He could not and would not discuss any of his work, except in the most general terms as outlined above. I suspect Jack could have made secret determinations that no one without a "need to know" could know. He had a mystical sense of vision, how to "look" at things, a prescience I believe he got from his mother.

By the mid '60s, he decided to go to NASA Houston, Johnson Space Center (JSC). He shone as a great test engineer, cutting turnaround time at the largest vacuum chamber from a week to one day. He soon led the crew doing check-out tests of various spacecraft. He and Joyce traveled extensively, spending months at a time at Grumman on Long Island for LEM module design monitoring and in Downey, CA for North American Aviation's Apollo command module liaison. He admired Grumman engineering. He helped Grumman by designing a portion of the LEM system while "visiting" them. By this time, Jack was heading a crew testing LEM and Command Module (CM) hardware in the big vacuum chamber at JSC. Jack noted a bad design feature of the Block 1 Command Module access and egress door. It had too many bolts to undo and do to open or close quickly. He suggested a quick release design, but was overridden by low-level NASA management. Grissom, Chaffee, and White burned to death on the pad at Kennedy Space Center, FL because they could not escape the Command Module quickly enough. Only then was the Apollo Command Module design changed to have a quick-release door, and also to eliminate much of the interior flammable materials. Jack told me he had heard that the fellow at NASA who countermanded his suggestion to have a quick release on the Apollo CM Block 1 door had felt so guilt ridden, he committed suicide. Jack also related that the astronauts did not die quickly as has been stated in the press. Observers related to him that they heard screaming inside the CM for many minutes as they died burning.

Jack headed tests of NASA space probes. The Cassini probe going to Saturn was a multibillion-dollar program employing many hundreds, if not thousands, of scientists from many countries, each working a considerable portion of their lives on Cassini. They had designed the craft and all its experiments, building and testing it before it went off to Saturn, a seven-year mission. During test setup, Jack discovered a fatal design flaw in the propulsion system that would be used for attitude and course corrections when it reached Saturn. It would have lost all of its propellant by the time it got there. He was "listened to" this time; the flaw was corrected, and Cassini went on to fulfill all its design goals and establish that life exists on other planetary bodies.

Jack, his wife, and daughter Kristen had constant severe allergies in Houston. He asked for a transfer to a place that had clean air. Bob Gilruth, head of NASA JSC, got him a job at NASA's White Sands facility in New Mexico. Jack quickly rose to head the entire engineering section. Jack transformed his group from designing with slide rules to using computer-aided design (CAD) software. His group built facilities for many small rocket engine tests. He also designed a facility to test the new chemical laser weapons hardware being developed for the US military. Jack retired three times from NASA. TWICE he was called back to do special jobs that no one else could do. I will miss him. The world just lost an exceptionally gifted and truly great man.

EARLY YEARS

CHILDHOOD

The very first memory I have, when I was two and a half years old, is pounding nails into a board on the second landing going upstairs in the new house. I was kept occupied this way while my Dad and brothers worked, though a neighbor, Fred Harwood, objected that I was "wasting nails." Dad is reputed to have replied, "a pound of nails cost twenty-five cents. I get more enjoyment watching the boy pound nails than I would drinking a shot of whiskey" (50 cents). Fred was a drinker who regularly stopped at a local bar on the way home each night, consuming several shots of whiskey. Dad and my two older brothers, Ken (17 years older) and Vincent (whom I called Bing, 22 years older) were helping Dad put up framing on the upper level. It was a one-and-a-half story, 28-foot-square house with a full cement basement, a front room (including a dining area), our parent's bedroom, a kitchen, and a small bathroom on the first floor. Four small bedrooms were on the second (half) story. It replaced a house built from logs that Dad claimed was one story high and seven stories long.

Apparently, as kids came along, more rooms were added to the basic log house. With me coming unexpectedly, I guess Mother had had enough of living in an "added-to" log cabin. She began lobbying Dad to build her a "new house." After two years, she gave up asking him. I understand she took a double-bitted axe to start chopping off the front porch. When Dad, Ken, and Bing came home from work and Dad saw Mom's handiwork, he purportedly said, "Well boys, I guess we are going to build your mother a new house." My sisters tell a story that Mother used a crowbar to take down the front porch. I like the "axe" story better – it more accurately fits Mom's personality.

This would have been in 1938 when the Great Depression was still in full swing. Dad had had a job at the paper mill for only a few years. Before the Great Depression, he had been an independent cement contractor putting in cement sidewalks and basements in and around town (Grand Rapids, Minnesota). After the depression hit and the banks went "bust" in the early 1930s, he lost everything in his business and all family savings (amounting to $8,000).

Before WWII, there were 11 people in our family, including my great Uncle Ted. I heard many times how Ken, Bing, and Uncle Ted slept on the unheated back porch year 'round. In the middle of winter, our mother would preheat their beds with hot bricks taken off the stove. They slept under heavy blankets in the coldest weather – often reaching 40 below zero outside. I was the last of eight surviving children, born to John Paul and Jennie Augusta on September 10, 1935. Mother had twenty-two pregnancies. One baby of each of two sets of twins died shortly after birth. In addition to Bing and Kenny, I had five sisters. Irene was the oldest, followed by Ruth, Agnes, Edythe (Edy), and Doris (Dode). Edythe and Doris were nine and seven years older than me, respectively. All my siblings are deceased. I am the only survivor.

We lived only a short distance from the Great Northern Railroad tracks. Each morning around 5:00 AM, one of the large steam locomotives called "Mallies," weighing 200 tons apiece, would pass our house, shaking it severely and waking most everyone. Dad said it was too late to go back to sleep and too early to get up. So, that's why we had a large family!

I guess Ken and Bing must have contributed to the family income during the last part of the depression because I believe there was no debt after the new house was mostly finished in 1939. Ken enlisted in the Navy in 1941 and Bing joined the Army Air Corps in 1942. Ken was on his way to Pearl Harbor when it was bombed by the Japanese on December 7, 1941. Bing was shipped off to Europe and stayed in England during the war. Ken was on ships that resupplied PT boats and submarines, following these fighting ships wherever they went. My five sisters got married and moved from the new house within a few years after it was built. Only Mom, Dad, and I lived in the new house during the war. I remember Mom looking sad much of the time. She had two stars in the front room window, worrying constantly for her two older sons' safety. Dad worked long hours almost every day of the week. There was a bad labor shortage during WWII. Women could not be expected to do the hardest physical labor, so he was one of the men doing those jobs at the paper mill. He usually worked in the "wood room," handling the heavy logs as they were being processed into paper. On a typical day, he loaded 400 cords (perhaps 600 tons) of wood onto the chain that carried them to the saws and debarking machine.

Another early memory was chasing after my sisters Dode and Edy and their girl friends when I was four or five. To keep me from following, they would say, "You'd better go home or the train will jump the tracks and eat you up." I was deathly afraid and would then run back home. I later became friends with train engineers who would sometimes throw a candy bar to me as they went on by. We only lived 50 yards from the railroad tracks in front of our house. Once in a while (after all, a penny was a lot of money then), we would place a penny on the track and let a train squash it down to keep in our pocket as a special souvenir!

I got a single shot "BB" gun when I was seven. We always had a "mud puddle" in the empty lot across the street after a heavy rain. My sister Dode and some of her friends were wading in the puddle when I decided to shoot at a pebble I saw under the water. The BB ricocheted off the surface of the water and hit Dode in her rump. She screamed and started after me. I just barely made it home in time, hollering, "Mother, Dode is going to kill me!" I lost privileges of having the BB gun for a while. Sixty-five years later, Dode didn't remember the incident. I was always careful with guns later on. I did shoot a robin one summer with that BB gun. I felt so bad I had to hold a funeral for it. Mom gave me a matchbox and a little piece of cloth to wrap it in. I never could get myself to kill anything else when I "plinked targets" as a teenager with a .22 rifle and several handguns I owned.

I remember two important things about Dad when I was growing up: he loved the girls without reservation, and he was "hard" on my brothers. I was too small to be badgered for some time, but it did come later. I heard that Bing "ran away from home" for a couple years when he was 16 and found a job in International Falls, MN. He came back and got a job in the local Blandin paper mill. Kenny also worked at the mill before the war. Dad had been raised on a farm under a very strict father. His favorite quote when he was exhorting us to work hard was: "When I was a boy, I spent 13 hours a day behind the plow," alluding that he had a harder life than we did. If I remember correctly, Dad frequently hugged my sisters and mother and told them they were pretty. I find it easy to do the same thing with "my girls" now.

Dad had become bald early. As I grew up, I was subjected to the same "bribery inducement" that my siblings had been given: "If you rub my head and make my hair grow back, I will get you a pony!" None of us eight kids ever got a pony, but Dad must have had thousands of hours of free head rubs, which he obviously enjoyed.

Dad loved his "lutefisk." What is lutefisk? Well, in the old countries of Sweden and Norway before refrigeration, people had to have some way to preserve cod fish they caught during summer months to eat in the winter. Their solution to this problem was to soak cod in strong lye water. The lye ate away some part of the fish as it leached into the flesh and the remainder was put out in the sun to dry. Once dried, no animal or insect would touch the hard-as-rock slabs of cod now called "lutefisk." The slabs could be stored outside in piles much like cordwood. During the winter, when other meat was not available, they would retrieve some lutefisk slabs, soak them sequentially in tubs of fresh water to leach out the lye, and then boil the "rehydrated" lutefisk. Mother made Dad his lutefisk only on special occasions – Thanksgiving and Christmas. I didn't mind Thanksgiving so much, since northern Minnesota wasn't especially cold yet. However, by Christmas, we had 20 and 30 below zero degrees Fahrenheit weather. These temperatures were preferable to staying in the house – the stench from the boiling lutefisk was just too much to take. I left home and stayed outside until I was told that dinner was ready. Once Mother smothered the lutefisk in white gravy, the smell wasn't so bad. I could at least tolerate that. Dad had to have his lutefisk!

MY FIRST ENGINEERING EXPERIMENT: THE BIKE PROPELLER

Sometime before I was 14, my brother Kenneth shared a salient story with me about when he was young. He and a buddy had put a motorcycle engine with a propeller on an ice sled so that they could go whizzing around frozen lakes in northern Minnesota in winter! I was envious of their achievement. I wanted to build an ice boat! However, it was summertime. I thought maybe I could put a motor on my bicycle with a propeller mounted in back.

I had just been given a half-horsepower Briggs & Stratton engine from a friend who no longer needed it. I proceeded to test my "invention" first in our house basement, where I mounted it on my Dad's workbench. I made a propeller by using my dad's spokeshave on a two-foot length of 2x4 that had no knots or bad grain. I don't know how I did this because Dad had a very strict rule: "You do not put any nails or screws into my workbench!" But somehow, I got the motor mounted on the bench. I could twirl the prop and start the motor. It blew a really big blast of air, so I figured it was going to work on my bike.

The next step was to build a platform on the back of my bike. I fastened a board that had the holes already drilled in the right places for mounting this motor and connected it to the seat post. I had two legs that went down from the board to either side and connected with the rear wheel axle hubs. After I had this all set up, I got the propeller mounted on the motor and the motor mounted on the bicycle, then went out to the road.

We had recently gotten the road paved in front of our house. Before, it had been an old, rough, pot-holed road going into town, but now it was a nice smooth surface to ride on. We had a little bit of an upslope going into town, but after a short distance, it became a downslope. I started on the upslope, got the motor started, climbed on board my bike, and took off. I had to pedal a little bit to get started, but when I got to the top of the hill and started going downhill, I was flying fast. And then, all of a sudden, the propeller flew off the engine! I braked to a stop, stopped the motor, and wondered what had gone wrong.

Not being familiar with mechanical things yet, I had neglected to put a set screw into the pipe section that was the shaft for the propeller. I had just drilled the pipe out enough to let the motor shaft fit inside. I had pounded it together, thinking this would be good enough! Well, it wasn't. The tiniest of details blew the experiment. I came to the conclusion that I was not going to be making an ice boat. My bike experiment wasn't a total flop, but it was not going to be something I would do again because it was too hazardous.

AN OLD FRIEND

I was reminded the other day that Jack Peavey is still alive. He must be past 80 now since I'm past 85. We were kids together. Jack Peavey was a couple years younger, but he kind of followed my friend Gomer and me around when we were doing things. I almost drowned him, so I'm glad that he's survived this long.

We must've been in sophomore or junior year of high school when the paper mill dam went out. The Mississippi River had been bottled up by a dam that crossed at the downtown site of the paper mill and probably held back waters that were anywhere from a third of a mile wide up (in some places, there were bays that extended that by quite a bit), so there was an immense amount of water that gushed out and went downriver. The immediate effect was that the paper mill found an awful lot of "dead heads," or logs that had sunk mostly, then finally went down to the bottom and settled. All were tree sections intended for the mill that had never made it, so the mill sent crews out on the riverbed to retrieve the waterlogged monstrosities. Eventually, they ran these logs through the saws and de-barkers to make, I presume, ordinary paper that was substandard to their usual magazine-grade glossy paper, which was for such publications as *Look Life*, *Time*, *The Saturday Evening Post*, and others. They also had a diver who did some work with a hand-pumped air supply, but when the dam went out again, he lost it. And as fate would have it, somebody found it, and nobody wanted it, so I got it.

I fixed up the leathers on the mechanism to seal the two air chambers. When you hand pumped it, you could get up to 10 PSI at a fairly good flowrate of air. We connected that to a ten-gallon steel drum, stood back to make sure that it didn't blow up when we pressurized it (that was our safety check), and then, I made Herman The Helmet.

Herman was a fiberglass head that would fit over your shoulders, down a bit on your chest and back, and strapped down to a waist with a bunch of lead weights. It had probably a three-inch by five-inch window of plain plexiglass in front to look out of and a microphone that you spoke into and earphones that you could hear from, all connected to a war surplus two-way telephone system that I had gotten from war surplus through some magazine for very little money. And it worked, so we were all set.

Gomer and I went down to the lake one day and talked Jack Peavey into donning the suit. We added some extra lead weights around his ankles to keep his feet down and he waded out into the lake. It was fairly shallow and the slope was gradual. I had about 50 feet of the smallest garden hose that I could buy – I think it was probably ⅜ inch – that served as our air hose, and taped along that were our electrical lines. Well, Peavey got out so that he was submerged and then, all of the sudden, we heard *GLUG, GLUG, GLUG!* I scarcely had time to feel apprehension, Gomer and I hauled him back in so fast. To our relief, Peavey was sputtering and cussing, but otherwise, he was okay. Herman, however, was not so lucky. He never got tested again.

Later, I could not understand where I had "gone wrong" with the design. I analyzed it and said to myself, "I should have…" added a cloth shirt section that sealed the shoulders and torso – it could have been zippered shut down the front. However, I wondered further if that would have made the unit difficult to remove when getting a diver out. In the end, I did not have any inclination to redo the design, though, in later life, that went against one of my hallmarks: Never leave a job half done! Analysis and experiment go hand in hand to get valid results.

Although we almost killed poor Peavey, I didn't feel like a failure. In retrospect, I was a teenage boy with no training or experience in this area. Dumb luck or divine guidance were responsible for a favorable outcome. However, I carried the memory of this incident and used it with other more tragic incidents later on to develop a philosophy: Always have someone else check my work. In those cases (several occurred) where others were responsible for buildup and acquiring the equipment, but I was involved in some way, I had to learn the hard way: Never trust that materials are as stated.

Herman sat down in the basement where I was living with my sister Irene and brother-in-law, Reino, for years, and he probably got tossed out when they cleaned out their basement. But it was an interesting thing that a young kid who didn't know a damn thing about anything would come up with, and I often wonder what would've happened if I'd had some smarts on how to design the thing to make a suit that would've worked. Of course, it wasn't going to be a space suit, but you still have to wonder!

MY FIRST THREE JOBS

My first job, my dad got for me. It was at a little resort up in northern Minnesota. I was 13. He had always pontificated that he had to work 13 hours behind the plow when he was 13, so he said, "You've got to get a job."

Well, I was taken out to this resort. And Minnesota has, or had, a lot of these little mom-and-pop resorts. A couple would usually have half a dozen little cabins on a lake and they'd have fishing boats to go out onto the water. They needed someone to maintain the boats, paint them occasionally. And also, they had a little gazebo I guess you'd call it in which people brought their haul. There, they could gut and scale the fish. It became a really stinky place and it had to be cleaned quite often, usually once a day. So that was my job. I hated it.

It wasn't just the work; the fellow was very finicky. I couldn't do anything right. I didn't paint right and I didn't clean his fish place right. He was not satisfied with what I was doing. The worst part of it was that he and his wife were both skinny little people and his wife didn't feed him very much, so she didn't feed me very much either. I was constantly starving. I believe it was about a year after mother died when he was visited by a woman who had been his sweetheart way back before he met mother. She was a French Catholic. Her name was Irene Gravell Kossow. And since her folks were against her seeing anybody who wasn't Catholic, they had to split up. But she found out that dad was available, and I guess came to see him after her husband had been dead a year or so. A week after I was on the job, Dad and Irene came out to visit and I told Dad, "I don't like this place. I want to come home." So, he said, "Well, you got to have a job." Irene said, "Let the boy come home." So, I did. I don't remember anything more about that summer.

When I was 14, I was able to skip summer work. And the reason was that we took a road trip to California and spent a lot of time visiting our relatives out there. Toward the end of the summer, we left and went up through Oregon and Washington and across Montana and North Dakota and came back home in time for me to go to school. That year was otherwise unmemorable.

When I was 15, I had two brothers as friends: Gene and Ray Finberg. Ray was into cars and into fixing them. Gene was into getting work outside his home. He said, “I’m setting pins at the bowling alley and they need guys – do you wanna come down and see if you want to do it?” So, I did. All that school year, I set pins at the bowling alley. We got 10 cents a line, which is one game per person. Between leagues five days a week and some weekend bowling where we could go to work setting pins, I averaged about $15 a week, which was pretty good money in those days. I got paid Wednesday night like everybody else. We always used to go down to a cafe called Mickey’s after work at 10:30 or 11:00.

Mickey’s had the most wonderful hamburgers. Of course, they had French fries and Coca-Cola. A hamburger with French fries and Coke was 50 cents. Their hamburgers were unique, I think. Mickey had this flat grill on which he fried everything. Onions were sauteed at the top of the grill, which was slanted, so that onion juice ran down through the hamburger patties, giving them a special flavor. The hamburgers were really tasty. They were great hamburgers, especially with a slice of cheddar cheese and including the lettuce, tomato, and mustard that came with them. So, every Wednesday, we would spend 50 cents getting a meal of the week as a reward. I remember that time with great fondness.

I think at the end of that school year, Gene moved on to work at the Coca-Cola bottling plant. Once again, he came to me and said, “Larry, there’s a day job opening at the Coca-Cola bottling plant east of town. Do you want to come see about it?” So, I did. That summer, I worked at the Coca-Cola plant putting bottles on the cleaning machine. I also put bottles on a viewing device to see if anything was in the bottle that was not supposed to be there after they'd been filled with soda pop. Every bottle was thus screened and boxed in 24-bottle wood "flats" going to customers. I also did odd jobs as needed, making 50 cents an hour. I worked all summer and probably a little bit into the year as I turned 16 and began junior year of high school.

The following summer, I got a day job out at the Coke plant pretty much full-time, and I got 75 cents an hour. The owner was Maurice Costello. He asked me if I would also like to load trucks at night. At this time, I was beginning my senior year. Dad and Irene had left Minnesota for California as I turned 17. I did not want to change schools, so I stayed with my sister Irene, her husband Reino, and their three little boys. So, I agreed. I loaded five trucks each weekday night with 600 "flats" during the fall of my senior year from 4:30 in the afternoon until 9:30 at night. I closed the place up, bringing all trucks inside, locking all exterior doors, tossing keys onto the boss' desk. I got in good shape. I could lean down (without bending my knees) and touch the floor with the palms of my hands. I could lift one of those "flats" of Coke (or any soda pop) with one hand and throw it into the truck. I usually made it OK, but sometimes I broke a few bottles and then I had to clean up the mess, sweeping up glass shards and hosing down the floor and truck with water.

We could drink all the free Coke or soda pop we wanted, but after a short time, we each got tired of soda, so we just drank plain water. The Coke plant had an artesian well that drew water from a very deep, clean source. It flowed just like a regular water faucet. We'd get our water by cupping our hands under it. Gene quit after school started. I don't know what he did then, but I was the only one working that night shift. It kept me busy. I worked at that third job until I finally had to quit in December 1952 because of eye problems I'll soon describe.

I now look at my first three jobs fondly. Gene was a good friend. He was not a person who liked school. He graduated from high school, though he was not a scholar. As he excelled at doing any kind of manual work, it was not surprising to find he joined the Seabees, learning construction methods. After he got out of the Seabees, he became a construction manager for Kaufman & Broad out in California making mansions out in the hoity-toity neighborhoods and/or communities. And these were the million-dollar homes when most houses were going for $30,000 to $40,000. I understand that he got extremely rich as a construction manager there. I understand also that he probably made more money than anybody else in our graduating class, which was kind of ironic, and kind of nice for me to remember him by.

AN INCONSEQUENTIAL DECISION

My background in eventually becoming an engineer was "interesting" at times and very painful at others. This is a story of pain. And it involved one of those inconsequential prior decisions I wrote about earlier.

I stayed overnight at my friend Dougie Funnel's house. The next day, we played with other kids in an abandoned house that had been moved temporarily to a vacant lot next door to Doug's. I was nine years old. We found a box of "what looked like" spent .22-caliber bullet casings in the attic. The box read, "dynamite caps," which we ignored. Deciding to try "wood burning" using the casings as a hot metal tip on a wood stick, we heated the casing with a match. One exploded. I permanently lost sight in my right eye and my left eye was badly damaged. I was totally blind for several months.

The accident happened in March 1945. I missed the remainder of the school year. By the beginning of the next school year in September, I was able to see well enough with my left eye that I resumed school, going on to the fifth grade. However, in the ensuing two years, my sight again deteriorated. Eye specialists in St. Paul, Minnesota found that my "bad eye" was negatively affecting my "good eye" and needed to be removed.

After the operation, I was fitted with a plastic artificial eye. In ensuing years of grade school, junior high, and senior high, I kept up with my classmates – vision in my left eye was nearly normal. But I periodically had eye infections. In my senior year, I had a particularly severe eye infection which was exacerbated by a misdiagnosis from and incompetent treatment by a local doctor. I went to St. Paul to see eye specialists again. They immediately hospitalized me and started a series of treatments, including heat packs, triple typhoid injections (to induce high fevers that they thought would burn out the infection), and steroid pills. I was on the verge of recovery when I suffered a detached retina in my remaining eye. The poor status of medical knowledge at that time did not permit these civilian doctors to know steroids' bad effects – specifically causing retinal detachments. Penicillin was not available to the public yet, though it had been used to treat GIs in World War II. Most antibiotic drugs, currently used to treat severe eye infections, had not been discovered by the 1950s.

My cousin-in-law Kenny Hassler worked in the State Capitol building in St. Paul and knew a number of legislators. He was able to get one of them to sponsor a special bill that paid to transfer me as a charity patient to University of Minnesota Hospitals for the latest treatment options. A Dr. Hines, who was a retina specialist at The Mayo Clinic in Rochester, MN, came to do the retina reattachment operation, assisted by one of the U of M Hospital's ophthalmology residents. After injecting me with local Novocain anesthetic, he removed my eye from my head. I could look at myself without using a mirror! I told the doctors of my discomfiture in seeing myself this way. They then covered the iris so I could not see.

In 1952, retina reattachment consisted of "poking" a needle a controlled distance into the sclera (white of the eye) and discharging an electrical spark. This was done many hundreds of times over the detachment area. The rationale was that the resulting formation of scar tissue would secure the retina to the back of the eye. After reattaching muscles that control eye movement (those which had been cut to take my eye out of its socket), my eye was put back into my head. I was forced to lie totally motionless for the ensuing month, my head held still using several sandbags to prevent even fidgeting. I could not move my head at all for fear detachment would reoccur. The first three days were pure hell! I had what I now characterize as a "thousand concurrent migraines." The quality of the rest of my life was literally hanging in balance at that time. Somehow, I was able to keep still during this critical period. It took every bit of will power I possessed, and I now suspect help from above.

After six weeks in bed, I was allowed to move. A few weeks later, I was allowed to get out of bed. I could not walk. My body had forgotten, so I had to relearn to walk!

During this terrible time, I had many friends come to visit and help me study and keep up somewhat with my schoolmates. Being in my senior year, I desperately wanted to graduate with them. Dr. Don Martin, my sister Edy's brother-in-law, was going through medical school at the time. In spite of a hectic and demanding schedule, he spent considerable parts of his free time reading to me. I especially owe him the greatest gratitude.

A FELLOW AT THE DOOR

Following my three months in the hospital, I returned to high school, staying with my sister Irene and brother-in-law Reino and their three kids. I'm very grateful to them for taking me in, Reino especially. I had moved in with them at the beginning of my senior year since my dad and new stepmother Irene (whom Dad had married after Mom died) had moved to California the day after he retired. I hadn't wanted to go with my Dad since I would have had a new school situation to get used to – another one of those "life-defining decisions!"

I was probably a little-bit-better-than-average student. I didn't try especially hard, and I never took schoolwork home. I did okay. I graduated seventh in my class of approximately 150. After graduation, I was at a total loss as to what I would be able to do with my life. Miss Beakner, our high school guidance counselor, suggested that I take up accounting. I now thank God I didn't! But the search for an alternative was still a doozy. I had hoped to go to engineering school, but I had no money. My savings had been used to pay for the first hospital stay in St. Paul (though hospital rooms cost only $14 per day).

Sometime during the summer of 1953, a fellow appeared at my sister's door asking about me. He was from the State of Minnesota "Aid to Disabled Persons" department. He said they had heard about my situation and indicated that I could take some tests in St. Paul to see if I qualified for their program. If I were accepted, I would be able to go to any college in-state under a state scholarship. So, I went down to St. Paul and took a bunch of tests, including the Minnesota Multiphasic (which showed that I was very defensive), and was accepted upon their finding that my vision was only 20/300 in my remaining eye. I was legally blind!

I did not want to go to the local community college for the first two years of engineering school as others from my high school did, as I had heard they did not have a strong curriculum. (Although my friend Gomer did go to Itasca

Junior college in Coleraine, MN for the first two years and turned into a terrific engineer. He effectively managed the engineering department at White Sands, NM for NASA late in his career.) For me, Carleton College in Northfield, MN was an option – they had a scholastic reputation that rivaled any Ivy League school. I visited Carleton with help from a local family whose son, Frank King, was also considering Carleton. Both of us decided against going there in spite of its reputation for excellence and the fact that its student to teacher ratio was only about eight to one. If we had gone there, we would have had an almost tutorial education! But it was a "rich boys," hoity-toity school – I knew instinctively that I would not fit in there.

Finally, I decided to go to UMD (University of Minnesota, Duluth Branch), which was a newly formed campus in the state university system. Duluth was only eighty miles from "home" and would permit relatively easy travel back and forth, yet it would allow some independence for the first time in my life. And so, I headed off to school.

HIGHER EDUCATION

DAD'S LESSONS

Concerning the first quarter of attending college, I have never had a bigger shock in my life! I had been one of the smartest kids in high school, but now I had to compete with many fellows who were much smarter, having come from far larger schools in the Duluth and general northern Minnesota area. With my poor sight, I had to read my textbooks using a rectangular magnifying glass lens three or four times. It had a handle attached to hold it. (I still have this after 65 years.) I have to credit my Dad with my getting through the first year when 75% of the engineering students "flunked out." He had tried to teach and instill in me three things while I was growing up:

1) Be honest with yourself. You will be able then to be honest with others and thereby lead an easier life! He had mostly succeeded with this lesson, though I admit to several missteps in my life. One incident involved my going to the local store (when I was seven or eight) to get some groceries

for Mom. A friend accompanied me. I guess I was trying to impress him with my generosity, so I stole a five-cent candy bar to give to him on the way home. I had put it in the shopping bag Mom had sent along. Ida Miner, the store owner's wife, found the candy bar, told me I had not paid for it and would have to "put it back." I was terribly embarrassed in front of my friend. To this day, I think of this incident if I am tempted to do something wrong. In a second incident, when I was still young, I lied to Dad about a piece of broken plaster on an unfinished upstairs banister! "I didn't do it!" Well, I did do it. This plaster had been sticking up above the roughly finished top surface for several years. Its very existence bothered my sense of "rightness." I took a hammer to knock it off and smooth it down. Unfortunately, I took a bit more than I should have – leaving a chip out of the plaster below the top of the banister. Dad covered the chip with molding he installed later. It was another incident learned the hard way!

2) Dad also taught me how to wipe my butt! You are to use five sheets folded over twice… I still follow his directions 75 years later. This taught me conservation. Do not waste! And the most important lesson:

3) Never be afraid of hard work! This tenet continues to be the single, most important directive in my life. I found I could compete with far smarter people, simply by working harder and longer at solving a problem than other people would commit to doing.

PRE-ENGINEERING

I did well at Duluth in most courses. I loved and excelled in physics and chemistry. Chemistry was easy in the first course. We had something like 100 engineers in our inorganic class freshman year, but by the time we got into our second year, there were maybe 50 left. A whole bunch of nurses took that first course with us, and at the end of it, all the engineers got As while all nurses got Ds. So, when we took organic chemistry from the same instructor, he said, "I guarantee, none of you engineers..." – and there were only 20 engineers left – "I guarantee that none of you are going to get As." I took that as a challenge. I spent as much time on organic chemistry as I did all my other courses, including differential equations, physics, and drafting, which was also difficult for me, as I couldn't see. (Back then, it was using a T-square and a drafting board and trying to get lines precisely down.) I had to work, but I got my A!

Despite this victory in organic chemistry, I almost flunked typing (which was forced on me by the state overseer). My teacher gave me the benefit of the doubt when I got 19.5 words per minute (WPM) in the final test as one needed 20 WPM to get a D. It was the only D that I got in college. I treasure it more than some better grades I subsequently got in other coursework.

THE "BIG U"

Most of us who had made it through our pre-engineering at UMD went on to the "Big U" at Minneapolis in the fall of 1955. Again, I was totally out of my element, but so were the other guys with whom I had gone to school at Duluth. We "UMD-ers" learned quickly we had to stick together!

Reading the indoctrination instructions, we were told to report for class assignments at 8:00 AM, and so we did! All the other guys (girls were non-existent in engineering in those days) knew the real system and showed up at 3:00 AM for course selection. Normally, one takes classwork in the mornings and labs in the afternoon. We from Duluth were forced to do the opposite since all of the regular classes were filled. It was another of those trivial life-changing moments. We were able to work together as a support group and it turned out that we were given the best instructors – full professors! Some early classes were taught by "less than capable teaching assistants!" Most of us breezed through the final exams while "early birds" struggled until their test times were "up" and they were forced to turn in incomplete work. And I remember at the end of that quarter, all of us from Duluth got As in fluid mechanics while the rest of them barely made it through. Our instructor, Ruben Olsen, had been a Navy submariner and sprinkled his lectures with harrowing tales of under-sea life. He was the very best fluids instructor we could have had. Our stress analysis instructor, last name Vitovec, had been a Czech engineer conscripted by the Nazis during WWII to design the ME-109 fighter. Our classes could not have been more interesting! So, it worked out. And that's the way things have happened in my life – they work out. This initial experience stayed with the "Duluth" group throughout our college years. We were much more supportive of each other while most other students were forced to "go it alone" while competing with each other.

FINANCIAL TROUBLE

After my third year, my sight was again evaluated. The state examiner determined that I was no longer eligible for state aid – I could see well enough that I could read normally. Lack of their financial support posed a real problem. I had only been able to save money for one school quarter. Fortunately, I had a great undergraduate advisor – Roger Eichhorn, who found me a scholarship from the "Wm. F. Morse Foundation" – five hundred dollars! It was enough for another quarter of school.

I've had a friend, Gomer, since we were 12 and I went to his birthday party. We became chums because we were both interested in model airplanes and not that interested in girls. We used to go out to the airport on our bikes five or six miles a lot, especially during summer, and try to get rides with the people who had gotten their private licenses with the GI Bill. (They were working on commercial licenses and wanted passengers, so it kind of fit together!) Our love of airplanes held us as buddies. Gomer had done his pre-engineering at IJC (Itasca Junior College) for the first two years in Coleraine, six miles east of Grand Rapids. During my third year, when I went down to Minneapolis, Gomer had stayed behind and taken a year off to get some money together for further schooling. I had been alone going into my third year, but during my fourth year, he joined me at Minneapolis. We shared a dorm room throughout the remainder of college. I was in mechanical engineering; he was in aero.

Gomer still had a weekend job with the US Post Office (PO) in our hometown of Grand Rapids, MN and drove home every weekend, a distance of almost 200 miles. I was able to get a job at the Blandin Paper Co. working as a paper tester on the early Sunday morning shift. Gomer worked for the PO Saturdays and studied Sunday mornings. I studied Saturdays. Roger Eichorn found me a second job as research assistant in the Heat Transfer Lab of the Mechanical Engineering Department. I was working 30 hours a week in the lab (paid $1.09/hr for 20 hours) and six hours each Sunday ($20). With work and my scholarship, I had more than enough money to get through my fourth year! Just for reference, state aid had paid $800, $1,000, and $1,200 for books, tuition, and board and room for my first three years of college: a total of $3,000! I paid with money earned (and scholarship) for the last three years: another $3,000. A total of $6,000!

TV TROUBLE

As soon as I got off work at noon on Sunday, Gomer and I would head to the "Twin Cities," making it back in time for "Maverick" – which was our favorite, and the only, TV program we allowed ourselves to watch. Sometime during that first year, Gomer said, “I’ve got an old TV I can get to work; why don’t we bring it down here? We don’t have to stand at the back watching Maverick. We can watch in the comfort of our dorm room!” So, we did. That lasted one quarter. Both of our grades dropped one full point, so we took the television back to Grand Rapids and we started studying again. Thankfully, our grades recovered.

MASTER’S

Normally, Minnesota had a five-year term for an undergraduate Bachelor of Engineering program. However, if your grades were high enough, and you had a recommendation (from Roger Eichhorn), you could “skip” your fifth year and get both an undergraduate and master’s degree at the same time when you finished your graduate program. I did well studying heat transfer and thermodynamics and had a 2.85 GPA (3=A), and so, near the end of my fourth year, I was asked if I would be interested in going to graduate school during my fifth and sixth years instead of continuing on with regular courses. I took that option. I elected to do a thesis program (instead of more intensive coursework) for a master’s program. Dr. Eckert, who was the head of the Heat Transfer group at Minnesota, offered me a job as a teaching assistant in his graduate heat transfer radiation course. I also worked in the lab as a research assistant doing experimental work for Eckert and Irvine on a triangular duct heat transfer experiment. It was supposed to be 20 hours a week, but you had to work 40 hours in order to get the work done. So, I worked a minimum of 40 hours per week in addition to doing a full scholastic program. It was an extremely difficult time. That said, I was making $2.50/hr for 20 hours per week. I was flush with money... until I bought a used car during my last year at school!

"BAD HABITS"

Gomer and I had a "bad habit" of "letting off steam" by going periodically to Lake Street in South Minneapolis where the used car lots were located. We would pester the salesmen – looking but never buying! On one such excursion, a particularly good salesman got back at us. Gomer fell in love with a two-tone blue '55 Super 88 Oldsmobile and I saw a coral and cream '56 Olds 88 I liked. We got the two cars, each getting a $25 discount. My savings were wiped out. I was suddenly $1,200 in debt. Throughout the remainder of graduate school, I had a choice in budgeting money: I could either buy one stein of beer per month or a tube of toothpaste. Guess which choice won. (My teeth went bad.)

Gomer had little trouble with his Olds. Mine was a different story! Soon after I got it, the transmission 2nd gear stopped working. I took it to Malkerson's Downtown New Car & Repair Facility. They wanted $300 to fix the transmission. I said no, went out onto their sales floor, and started vocally complaining that the owner, Malkerson, a regent of the university, was cheating students. I soon got a manager coming to me saying, "HUSH! We'll discuss this in my office." I settled with him, getting my transmission fixed for $25. On my last trip home to Grand Rapids before going on to California, the engine started to "clack." My brother-in-law Reino found it was a broken exhaust valve spring. He readily fixed it! Later, in California, I found that Malkerson had put undersized old tires (black walls made to look new) on the car. Also, the vinyl seat covers hid old dirty cloth seats that showed great age. I found that the car had had its odometer reset from a high mileage down to 35,000 miles. I shied away thereafter from buying used cars. A lone exception to this rule was an old, cheap Chevy pickup that served me well for many years.

ECKERT'S EXPERIMENT

I remember a "brush" with mercury poisoning in grad school when I worked in the heat transfer lab. Common practice when making thermocouple junctions was to twist the wires together, then connect both wires to a 12-volt battery, connect the other battery terminal to a bowl of mercury, and then momentarily dip the twisted pair into the mercury. A flash would occur – a welded junction would be formed. When the hazard was learned, this practice was prohibited. However, mercury fumes lingered in all the heat transfer labs. Each had cork floors. Over prior years, mercury thermometers had been broken, the fluid leaking into the cork, and this hazard was not recognized until after I left school. But I had inadvertently minimized my exposure while working at my job for Prof. Eckert, running his heated triangular duct experiment.

The lab was abysmally hot during the day; a fan did little to ease daytime discomfort. So, I worked in the evenings. It was still not good enough. The lab next door was scrapping a home furnace that had been used in an experiment. I asked for and was given the "squirrel cage" blower and motor combination. Multi-pane windows (8" x 10") covered the east wall completely. I removed one pane, built a stand for the unit, adapted a transition duct between the fan and windowpane, then sealed the duct at the window. I fashioned a slide-in, shut-off valve for the air duct as well as an outlet that I could direct at my station in front of Eckert's experiment control panel. I had cooler fresh air flowing over me! It was my first engineered facility! Not much to look at, but it made lab life bearable, and, apparently, literally more habitable.

THESIS

My thesis involved determining friction factors (for laminar and turbulent flows) over a wide range of Reynolds numbers for several isosceles triangles (apex angles of 10, 20, 30, 40, 50, 60 degrees). Laminar results matched theoretical expectations. Turbulent flow results showed a smooth curve that transitioned from a low number into the Blasius constant for round pipes.

My grades were not as good in grad school. I did OK in heat transfer courses, but advanced thermodynamics and advanced calculus were a mystery to me. I squeaked by with a 2.00 GPA ("B"), which was the absolute minimum required to graduate. My thesis advisor, Dr. Tom Irvine, told me in the late spring of 1959 that he would be leaving the university in late August. I had to finish my thesis before he left or start over with a new thesis subject and a new advisor! I worked eighteen-hour days to finish it. I could not hold down a job – there simply was not enough time in a day. My brother Bing lent me $300 to tide me over during the summer of 1959. I had all of $10 left at the end of that summer, which I "blew" on a filet mignon dinner for my girlfriend and myself at her uncle's restaurant. I suspect we were subsidized since the bill was exactly 10 bucks!

Finishing all of my planned experimental work, I thought I had a week's "leeway." Irvine then informed me I had to redo one of my experimental test series to "verify and corroborate" my data. Each one of the test series had taken exactly a week! Once again, I did it by working my butt off, literally day and night. I had my thesis typed and took my final oral exam at the last hour, late in the afternoon of the day Irvine left the university for a job in North Carolina. Defending my thesis was easy – "I had it cold." But I flubbed a simple math question posed by the math professor who attended my oral exam – my nerves were frazzled at that point. He must have taken pity and passed me anyway. I got my bachelor's and master's degrees later that year by mail – I did not attend graduation since I was already in Southern California.

ONWARD

Leaving the university, I went home to pack as much "stuff" as I could get into the Oldsmobile. I also took my nephew Kenny Jones home to Pueblo, CO so he could finish high school. He did not want to leave Minnesota, where he had enjoyed the summer being a carefree 16-year-old boy! Kenny drove while I slept. I had driven us out of Minnesota. Kenny started dozing off on some road in Iowa. Fortunately for us, Iowa had raised "lips" on the side of the paved roadway, so when the car veered to the side, I felt this lip vibrate the car, and woke up – which saved our lives, thank God. We got to Colorado after a night and day driving, with a short nap on that access road in a cornfield in Iowa. The Olds developed a bad tire from a misaligned front end on the way to Pueblo, but Kenny's dad Len paid for a new tire and got the front end aligned for me.

I left for Gridley, CA in the early afternoon to see my folks before I started work at Rocketdyne in Los Angeles. While driving through the Rocky Mountains that night on old highway US 50, I nearly got run off a cliff by a truck driver coming down on my side of the road. Shaken by this incident, I found the next roadside café that was open at three in the morning, got some coffee, and talked with the waiter. He asked me where I was going – "California – Los Angeles!" He said, "I just left there – it was too crowded for me!" That was in late August 1959… I would say the same thing in the fall of 1973!

DAD'S FOOTSTEPS

I made it over the Sierra Nevada mountains through side roads and the sleepy little town of Grass Valley (Google later had its headquarters there) into Gridley. I stayed a day with Dad and Irene. Dad had changed considerably in the six years since he left Minnesota. The "easy life of retirement" had not treated him well – his muscles had turned to flab! Remember, Dad had retired from the paper mill the day after he turned 65 (Sept. 15, 1952) after working there since the mid-1930s. He had had a very physically difficult job most of that time – loading big logs onto a conveyor chain that took them up to the paper mill from the river where they had been stored as floaters. He had handled approximately 400 cords of wood a day, which probably amounted to 600 or more tons by weight. He had worked six or seven days per week, 10-12 hours per day throughout WWII. Strenuous work had given him a physique like Charles Atlas – he had had arms as large as another man's legs. Weighing 280 pounds, I doubt he once had an ounce of fat on his body.

His whole life had been one of hard physical labor, starting when he was a young boy. Recall one of his favorite stories about how his father had made him work "13 hours a day behind the plow" when he was on the family farm in Maple Ridge (60 miles north of Minneapolis). Beyond that, as a young man, he had been a lumberjack in the camps throughout northern Minnesota. Getting up at 4:00 AM, lumberjacks worked from "sunup to sundown" every day of the week during winters, no matter how cold it became. In his retirement, he seemed to be "tired out!" I felt sorry for him in a way. You can see why he had taught me to "never be afraid of hard work."

Because of eye problems, I was limited to mental labor – even at the young age of 23. I would not follow my father's footsteps! I had to do, with hard mental labor, whatever I could to make up for not being as smart as some of the other engineers. Throughout my career, most of my bosses appreciated the fact that I would never leave an assignment unfinished – I worked until the work was done, usually on time and within budget. I learned that lesson well from my Dad!

After visiting with Dad and Irene for the day, I headed south to LA where I first contended with freeway traffic. I lasted four miles on the Hollywood Freeway. It turned out that I got off the freeway at the correct exit by pure luck. I only had a couple miles of city streets to get to Gomer's apartment house and was waiting there when he came home from work with his roommate. Gomer took me over to Rocketdyne so I could find out where to go on September 1, which was a Friday, for an orientation in the main building at 6633 Canoga Avenue in Canoga Park. And so, on September 1, 1959, I started work at Rocketdyne, a Division of North American Aviation, in Canoga Park, California.

COMPUTERS

BEFORE COMPUTERS

I'll start with a "lack of computers." There were none available for engineering students at the University of Minnesota while I was in graduate school (1957-1959). I was working for a master's degree in Mechanical Engineering with a major in heat transfer and a minor in mathematics. All of the various heat transfer courses were "heavily weighted" in the use of differential equations and my math courses were slanted toward the theoretical solution of calculus problems – usually related to a derivation of "existence theorems." I could not grasp that "a possibility of existence of a solution to a problem" was important to establish before one obtained the solution itself! I did not do well in my theoretical calculus and differential equation courses. There were no "cookbook recipes" for solving differential equations. The usual method was to guess a solution and test it to see whether your guess satisfied the original differential equation. Try as I might, guessing a solution was not my forte.

I squeaked by in getting a master's degree from doing a decent job in heat transfer courses and laboratory work. My thesis involved measuring and correlating fluid friction factors in various isosceles-shaped triangular ducts. Dr. Eckert, who was then the head of heat transfer studies within the Mechanical Engineering Department, was good at deriving pertinent differential equations and managed to get that knack across to most of his students – myself included. It was just that solving these differential equations eluded me. There were few existing methods for "machine solution" of differential equations, and those that were available were tedious at best. And, as I said, they weren't yet available to us in university.

ROGER'S LESSON

Roger Schmidt was a fellow graduate student who shared an office with several of us on the fourth floor of the old Mechanical Engineering building, which had three floors… I guess our office had been an afterthought. The "fourth floor" was a large, black-tar-covered roof with a little cubicle up on the top maybe 12-foot square by 10- to 12-foot ceiling height that held four desks with little room to walk between them. It had a few windows that would not open and life was miserable up there. In the summer, the tar nearly melted, it was hotter than blazes, and there was very little (if no) ventilation. The heat was unbearable and the humidity was stifling. We used a walkway from the stairway to the fourth floor to avoid stepping through the tar on our way over to the cube room.

I learned to swear from Roger that summer more than I had from my dad. While my dad only espoused a couple profane epithets on occasion, Roger was replete with many different swear words. And Eckert had given him a project worth using them all.

While I worked on my master's degree thesis, Roger hacked away at a computational project for Dr. Eckert to earn money so he could continue with his master's degree. The US Air Force had contracted with Dr. Eckert to solve a complex heat transfer problem that involved warhead support structure on the Atlas missile. They wanted to determine whether the corrugated structure on the top of the missile would be sufficiently strong enough to withstand ascending to its apogee en route to Russia (regarding altitudes, speeds, heat transfer conditions, etc.) while carrying a warhead. Heat transfer on this corrugated structure was not known, so Dr. Eckert derived the governing differential equation based on the Navier-Stokes equation. Navier-Stokes could occupy the whole front blackboard of a classroom until Eckert would do his magic and start throwing away terms. Roger was tasked to carry out the actual numerical solution to the infinite series solution of the equation that Eckert had derived. The chosen solution method was called "Method of Isoclines," in which slopes representing first derivatives of the computational solution are plotted in rows on a two-dimensional graphical grid. To evaluate an equation with the Method of Isoclines, you have to calculate hundreds, if not thousands, of particular derivatives at particular points of the x-axis and function axis, or where the derivative is displayed. Thousands of slopes are needed because the method relies upon an individual eyeing a graph and picking the most logical "path of the derivative function" from an initial value point. And so, to do this, you pick different x values, do a string of derivatives along that x-axis, and then move over a bit and do it again. And you keep doing this until you get out far enough that you think you might've come to a point where you can get a solution. After that, you look at all the derivatives on a graph and try to follow (what should look like) the line that the function maps out. And then *that* function is the one that you have to evaluate. Evaluating this subsequent graphical integration would then solve the problem.

Considering the fact that he only had an old "Marchant" mechanical calculator, which could add, subtract, multiply, and divide (I don't recall if his could do square roots or not) to do the work, and that the mathematics involved a long series of algebraic terms for each solution point, evaluating each calculated slope took Roger significant time. On top of that, his Marchant calculator was hand-cranked instead of some newer electric motor-driven ones (which were commercially available, just not at the "U"). He was not only hot and miserable like the rest of us in our "hellhole in the sky" office environment, but he was worn out by the physical effort involved in hand cranking this old mechanical calculator every day, all day. Roger did so much cranking that summer that his right arm became stronger than his left. Cranking on the machine and out a steady course of invectives the whole day through. But I learned more from Roger than assorted profanities.

Near the end of the summer, he was almost finished with his project. Another of our fellow graduate students, Skip Hansen, dropped by to see us while he was registering for fall quarter. He had spent the previous year programming computers for the Sperry Univac Corporation in St. Paul. He asked Roger what he was doing, and Roger told him, and Skip said, "Hmm… give me the formula and I'll run it over on our computer. I'll have a stack of cards for you in the morning." And the next day, sure enough, there was a stack of punched cards on Roger's desk with results verifying the solution that he had worked on all summer, proving that the structure was stable and adequate for its mission. As I remember, Roger was both furious and relieved at finding Skip had corroborated his work of the entire summer with one night's effort. So, boy, that set in my mind: **I was going to learn computing**. No two ifs, ands, or buts about it. I didn't know what computer programming entailed, but I would learn it at the very first chance I got when I started working. This proved even more valuable than my new ability to swear in a variety of languages and fashions! Much of my design work and data reduction throughout my career has utilized computers with substantial labor savings. But first, I had to learn to program!

THE NIGHTMARE OF PROGRAMMING

My first actual brush with computers came when I was assigned the task of evaluating various spacecraft radiator designs. Rocketdyne was assisting Atomics International (AI – a sister company within North American Aviation Corporation) with their attempts to gain a foothold in atomic energy in space. AI had programmers who built computer models of various parts of each system that usually featured liquid metal as thermodynamic working fluid. I "began programming" by "plugging in numbers" in these existing programs to see what would happen in each scenario we envisioned. I found it was not satisfying work, mostly because all of my input was totally arbitrary. It had no basic meaning to me. I understood nothing beyond "you have to do it this way or it won't work!" I didn't even know what computer language was used. I had no concept of "programming" yet. Later, I was asked to use an existing generalized heat transfer program called "TAP" (Thermal Analysis Program) to evaluate some complex heat transfer problems. Supposedly, this program could do "anything involved with heat transfer." I had an even worse time with TAP. Again, input was totally arbitrary. But, at least I knew it was written in FORTRAN (FORmula TRANslation). Though the bulk of the program was hidden within a common stack of punched cards, I simply added the "FORTRAN deck" to the end of the stack of cards I had generated. I still didn't know why one "put a minus sign in space 42 on card 54" other than the fact the program would not run without it.

My early programming experiences were also hampered by the fact that I worked at Santa Susana on top of a mountain to the west of the San Fernando Valley. We had no telephone or other direct link with computers located in the San Fernando Valley at the main Rocketdyne facility. A courier would take stacks of punch cards, boxed and placed in mailbags, to the computing center at specific times each day. You raced getting your work done to make a scheduled mail run. Much of the time, until the computer mail returned, you had nothing to do. If you had made an error, your "deck of cards" came back either without running, or a slab of folded paper came back representing a "core dump" that contained thousands of lines of a dozen or more columns of simple number sequences, which meant something – if you knew machine language. Unless you knew what a particular number sequence meant to the computer, nothing made sense. I usually had many pages of garbage to rummage through to find my error unless I could wrangle help from someone who knew the system and understood the language. I despaired that I would never be able to accomplish anything as a programmer nor gain that elusive and unimaginable power of doing a summer's worth of work overnight. Another "problem" evident in my attempt to program: the main computers were operated by what I have termed a "priest and priestess" culture – people who had absolute control over your computing destiny. They could hold your work on any pretext for any length of time or put you ahead in the lineup of jobs to be done at their discretion, whim, and fancy. I never got "in good" with any of them to enjoy a priority status as some other programmers had done.

Salvation came when Rocketdyne management decided to employ computer services provided by the General Electric Company, which had several mainframe computers that were located in downtown Los Angeles. These computers were operated in a "time-share" mode. In this mode of operation, a large computer acts like a larger number of smaller and slower computers that run concurrently. This operating method is obtained by having the total computing time on the large computer sliced into small intervals. Simultaneous jobs from different users were interleaved into these small time slots. One accessed a time-sharing computer over dedicated phone lines using teletypewriter machines running at a speed of 300 baud (bits per second). They were spectacularly slow compared with today's "ordinary" modem speed of megabits per second and fiber-optic speeds of gigabits per second some thousands time faster yet, but they matched well with shared timing of the large computers of that era. One never knew that he didn't have a whole computer to himself! And, teletypewriters used punched paper tapes to store and input programs instead of decks of punched cards like our mainframes used. Each Teletype machine had a tape reader and punch so one could keep control over his own programs – and his own destiny! And the teletypes printed programs on paper scrolls so one could read later what was written and reintroduce a program into the computer using the local teletypewriter at a later time.

I finally was able to learn FORTRAN source code programming after a lot of self-teaching and practice.

Early FORTRAN programming was difficult to master, primarily because of rigid formatting rules. You had to line up rows and columns of code exactly according to stringent rules. Later, FORTRAN permitted "free formatting," which meant that the rigid structure was very much relaxed, and programming solutions to problems became much easier and faster. While at Rocketdyne, I only used FORTRAN language programs. I attempted to use other languages such as APL and COBOL, but I never became proficient with them.

MY FIRST MACHINES

When I left Rocketdyne and took a job with Argonne National Lab's Engineering Division, I thought most fellow engineers would know programming. I was wrong. Many of the engineers in the Engineering Division at Argonne knew nothing except how to operate slide rules. Worse yet, management operated in the slide-rule age and resisted all efforts to change to computational methods, even those promising much greater productivity. I tried for two years to get time-share computers into the division before I was successful. Then, to get people started, I taught an introductory course in BASIC language computing. Eventually, the division got a number of portable machines that could be moved to different desks and connected to existing office phones using modems that had rubber cups for the ear and mouth pieces. But there was still a problem: the mainframe computer to which portables were connected was still controlled by the same "priesthood" I had experienced at Rocketdyne. All programming work was accessed from within the mainframe's archives. One could not operate independently. Also, operating rules were changed arbitrarily from time to time, so one never knew if an old program would operate anymore – especially if a period of time had elapsed between usages. Beyond that, the secretaries at Argonne had special word processor machines that were some bastard brand and design that wasn't compatible with anything, and so anything you gave them had to go through conversion programs to get into the system, and it was a pain in the butt. It was better than having to retype a whole report half a dozen times to get rid of mistakes and always winding up with more mistakes when you finally ship the thing out the door loaded up with Wite-Out (those were the days), but there had to be a better way!

Microcomputers became available commercially in the early 1980s. Tandy Radio Shack came out with a single-cabinet machine that had 64 kilobytes of memory, two 130-kilobyte floppy disk drives (four-and-a-half inch things that were slower than hell), and a built-in screen and keyboard. It featured a built-in BASIC language interpretive compiler that occupied half of the available memory. Thus, about 32 kilobytes of memory were available for any program. One could write code in "English" and the computer would translate this code into the machine language it could understand and process. Compilation, which was done every time a program ran, was slow but bearable. The Tandy Radio Shack microcomputer was around $4,000. All one needed besides this computer was a printer, and Dot matrix printers were the current answer to printout needs. But money was always dear as far as this sort of thing at Argonne…it was quite freely given in terms of salaries, but when it came to equipment, it was a different color money. I wangled, cajoled, and campaigned for one of these machines for another two years. Finally, my division director relented, and I got "my own" machine. It was glorious – I could easily do 10 times as much work as the next engineer who was still using a slide rule, and I could usually beat out those using the corrupted time-share portables. But there was one problem…after staring at the monitor for a few hours, one literally went blind. The grayscale screen was fuzzy and hazy, and the pixels were so big that it hurt my eyes. I was limited to working a couple morning hours and another couple hours in the afternoon each day. Then a friend, Jerry McDaniel, offered a potential solution.

Jerry wanted me to buy a new machine called a "Televideo." We would each get a 25-dollar discount if we both bought one! (It was shades of my used car days!) I had been working a second job as a consultant for the National Bureau of Standards (NBS), who administered a program for the Department of Energy (DOE) evaluating energy-related inventions, and I had saved up enough money to buy the $2,700 computer and an excellent Qume printer (another $2,000)! The Qume was a daisy wheel printer, which meant that you could change out the font by quickly changing out the daisy wheel, and I could easily get those from the secretaries at Argonne, as they had spares. The Televideo had 64 kilobytes of memory, two 140-kilobyte floppy drives, and a built-in high-resolution green screen with fairly small pixels! I could watch it *all day* without eye strain! It featured a CPM processor (a predecessor to MS-DOS), running at the unbelievable speed of two megahertz while running any programming language (since none were stored within the machine). I used the BASIC language which came on a disk with the machine, at first.

I soon realized that 64 kilobytes of RAM was pretty pathetic. It became unbearably slow in short order, so I tried PL-1 (a modern variant of FORTRAN), which was a much faster compiled language. Compiling a program requires running the machine twice: once to convert English into machine language, and then again to obtain answers. Compiling PL-1 was abysmally slow. It sometimes took half an hour switching chunks of code back and forth between floppy disks and computer memory. I bought a one-megabyte extended memory board for another $1,000 as well as a coprocessor computer chip for an additional $750. I could now compile in seconds. I had the fastest PC at Argonne. I thought I was in Fat City!

At that point, a new compiled programming language called "Turbo Pascal" was introduced for PC use. I bought a personal copy and installed it on the Televideo. It could be run in a semi-compiled mode or straight compiled mode. In the semi-compiled mode, it had a self-debugging feature which rapidly cleaned up syntax errors! Once a program ran, it could be switched over to compiled mode for faster operation. I started to program exclusively in Turbo Pascal with WordStar as my word processor.

IBM came out with their first PC and revolutionized the industry by introducing a common architecture for all their machines. Prior to this, each manufacturer made its machine sufficiently different so that its code would not work in other brand machines. Now, all of the manufacturers made "clones" which mimicked IBM and its new MS-DOS operating system. All new IBM-type machines could talk with each other! Shortly after that, IBM introduced a faster Intel 286-based machine. My Televideo was now slow in comparison. I had been using it for both Argonne work and for my consulting work for NBS. I needed a faster machine.

Once more, I campaigned for a faster machine on Argonne's dime. Toward the end of a fiscal year, my immediate boss, Ken Kuczen, said he had $10,000 I could spend if I could get the paperwork done and the items procured before the end of it – September 30. I personally "walked" the paperwork through procurement and got a Japanese computer (NEC) and a 19-inch color monitor for $7,000. It had an Intel 286/287-chip set (it had an Intel 286 processor; I added a 287 math coprocessor), a 40-megabyte capacity hard drive with two 180-kilobyte floppy disk drives, and ran MS-DOS. The monitor was "crisp and beautiful!" I think it had 1080 lines of pixels. I was in heaven. Once again, I had the fastest and best machine at work.

Argonne then adopted a policy of not allowing personnel to use company equipment for personal matters. I had given the Televideo to a friend, so I needed my own machine again. I opted for a Toshiba portable, which weighed 14 pounds! Today it would be classified as "luggable!" It had a 10-megabyte hard drive and basically the same setup as my NEC (286/287-chip set). It had an orange screen, which also was very easy to read, although the orange color was strange to view at first. After adding a coprocessor to speed math calculations, extra memory, and a portable printer, I had approximately $7,500 invested, all paid with earnings from NBS. I kept my Toshiba at Argonne, often running two simultaneous machines in compiled Turbo Pascal to further speed calculations. It doubled what I could otherwise do in a given time. I still used the "old but high-quality" Qume daisy wheel printer for output.

Intel introduced a 386-chip set, which I ignored. However, when they got the 486-chip set running at 39 megahertz and hard drives that were ranging up to 100 megabytes memory, I "just had to get" another machine for myself. It still had large floppy drives, but they had 240-kilobytes capacity. I kept the 486-based machine at home to consult on NBS work. Eventually, this machine seemed slow, so I ordered a new Pentium machine running at 300 megahertz with a 6-gigabyte hard drive and a two-and-a-half inch, hard-sided 1.4-megabyte "floppy drive." Windows 95 was the new operating system from Microsoft that replaced its old MS-DOS. I bought a super nice, 17-inch Sony high-resolution color monitor to go with this "state-of-the-art" system. As I had retired from Argonne, this machine stayed at home with the old Qume printer. Consulting for NBS had ended.

I subsequently moved to Houston where a consulting job in uranium processing developed. I bought a 1.9-gigahertz Pentium V machine with 40-gigabyte hard drive-storage capacity and a laser printer. I no longer have this machine, which cost approximately $3,500 in total – connected via DSL to the internet.

CURRENT MACHINES

This story was largely written on a Lenovo desktop running under Windows 10, using an AMD 6 processor running at 2.9 gigahertz, 500-gigabyte hard drive, CD/DVD read/write drive, three USB slots for plugging in flash memory cards, a mouse, and a printer – all for $1,200. Earlier iterations were written 14 years ago on a Toshiba portable with a 10-gigabyte hard drive. By the time I upgraded its capability with a coprocessor, I had invested $3,000. Today, I use a much better Windows 10 machine. It is 10 times faster, has a 500-gigabyte hard drive, and cost half that of my portable machine.

In the space of twenty-five years, personal computer speeds have increased more than a thousand-fold and available hard drive memory by about the same factor. Cost has dropped an order of magnitude: if one accounts for inflation, another order of magnitude is taken off cost. I purchased flash memory for $10/gigabyte – compare that with the $1,000 I paid for a single megabyte of memory in

1985. A "high-end" personal computer today compares in processing power and speed to the largest mainframe computers of two decades ago. In using my old Televideo to solve a particular problem, I used to let it run overnight at Argonne. It would have an answer by noon the next day. Just for fun, I ran the same problem on my newest machine using the same parameters – it took but seconds to run and get the answer. Such is progress in available computing power. We now have mainframe-equivalent systems which used to occupy whole large, air-conditioned rooms sitting on our desks. And, they don't cost an equivalent of $6,000/hour to run!

Programming has advanced at an equal pace. New languages abound. I have written only in Turbo Pascal for some years. It is a compiled language with built-in "error checking" capability! Syntax errors are found automatically. You still need to know your physics to get the correct equations into the program for solution, but an ordinary PC can now solve systems of nonlinear algebraic or even differential equations simultaneously. My old Televideo could handle 50 such equations at a time.

Howard Geyer, who worked for me at Argonne, developed a systems analysis program that could literally design a complete nuclear or fossil fuel-fired steam/electric power station in minutes. It was versatile enough to solve many types of static or dynamic systems. Nothing like it was/is commercially available. Time marches on! My friend Gomer's son-in-law was working on computer chips for home computers that are yet another thousand times faster than existing machines. Where will it end? I certainly don't know. Moreover, I really don't care. I have had my run. I now understand how the "Old Fogey" complex works. I'm in it for the duration!

A NICE DAY FOR AN AIRPLANE RIDE

It was the early 1980s when IBM came out with a PC. There was a rogue manager at IBM. He was down in Boca Raton in Florida and he had decided that his group was going to design a small computer. And so, he came up with the PC. There are many details about the story that I don't think many people know.

At the time, I got a free computer magazine called *PC World* (or *PC* Something). It had all sorts of technical articles in it, lots of advertising, and, just in front of the last outside page of the magazine, there was always an article by Penn of Penn & Teller. Penn was the fat, chubby guy; Teller was the little, skinny guy who never spoke. Before Penn was the comedic star we know him as today, he was actually a computer guy.

Penn had several passions in life. One was Uma Thurman, and if he hadn't written his article about Uma and how he was going crazy over trying to get in touch with her, he would write some pretty decent stories about what was going on in the computing world.

One of the stories he wrote was how Microsoft Corporation and MS-DOS got started. Whether or not it's true, I don't know.

At the time that IBM was setting up this Personal Computer (PC) division, they had to get an operating system. The extant one was CPM, so they went out to Monterey, California where the fellow who had basically developed the CPM system and had control over it lived. He was to meet them by appointment. But apparently, it was a markedly nice day in Monterey, and this CPM guy had an airplane. He says, "I'm going to go flying." So, he dissed the IBM people, didn't bother to show up for the meeting.

You didn't treat people from IBM like that. You see, IBM was king of the world at that time in big computers, and these people who had started their PC branch had that same philosophy, so IBM PC said, "We're going to find someone else." They went to Seattle, where they found Bill Gates.

Bill Gates and Paul Allen apparently had started a computer software business – I don't know if they called it Microsoft yet, but I understand that Bill Gates had $25,000 from his parents and had bought out a little place called Seattle Computer. He had a new operating system based on a Unix operating system, I believe. Unix had been designed for medium-sized computers.

IBM showed up at his door and Bill Gates was peaches and ice cream. Anything they wanted, "For sure, we'll do." IBM went back home well-satisfied, and Microsoft had its start. The two got together and the rest is history, except for this: whoever at IBM was managing this new PC place made a critical decision that influenced the whole small computer world. And that is, he was going to have open architecture for his machines. Any other manufacturer could copy it.

The practice had been that every company had a different architecture and needed a different CPM to run it. And it was a holy mess trying to work from one machine to a different brand machine in running programs. When IBM had an open architecture, they also fostered a common Microsoft language, the MS-DOS. And the two of those then set the world on fire because anybody could clone the IBM PC without a problem. It was all open to the public. PC clones appeared all over. Everybody was making IBM clones: various Japanese companies – Toshiba, NEC – and then some from other countries. Soon there were plenty of other machines you could buy, but basically, they looked and acted like an IBM PC. They were just cheaper.

PC computers really changed the world for me and for many other engineers. I looked at it as a world changer, but with a very limited perspective regarding only engineering calculations and word processing. I had no idea that there would be a myriad of other uses for home and business computers. If I had known, I probably would've made a decision different from what I did.

IN HINDSIGHT

At that time, I told my first wife Ellen, who was playing in the stock market, to take $10,000 of the money I had earned as a consultant, go to a stockbroker, and buy Microsoft stock. But she never thought too much of my intellect. She had been Phi Beta Kappa junior year in college and considered herself far superior intelligence-wise to me. I didn't know anything in depth about financial things, so I didn't do it myself. Years later, I found out that $10,000 initial investment would've been worth about $7 million. It kept splitting and gaining value. Que sera, sera... The computer revolution has taken hold, and now everybody's got one or two of them.

MICROSOFT AND APPLE

Of course, there's another parallel story, and that's Apple. There was a massive fight between Apple and Microsoft for a long time in the courts about the graphic interface. Now, I can only tell my understanding – I might be wrong. But my understanding is that Apple basically took it from PARC (Palo Alto Research Center), a division of Xerox. PARC had developed the mouse interface when Apple came along and somehow acquired it. I think Steve Jobs was a kind of individual much like Bill Gates. They were both titans and grabbers. They didn't have too many morals as to how they got programming material.

Apple and Microsoft were fighting to keep rights to graphic interface in the courts. The courts finally decided Microsoft could have Windows interface. So Apple had its Macintosh and Microsoft had its Windows. There, the central story began. It hasn't ended yet. I don't know if it ever will.

ROCKETDYNE

MY FIRST JOB

I had an inauspicious beginning at Rocketdyne. I reported to the main plant at 6633 Canoga Avenue, Canoga Park, CA for orientation on Friday, September 1, 1959. The first day was filled with indoctrination sessions and filling out paperwork. By good fortune, I was assigned to the Research Department. I was asked by one of the other young "engineers to be," "how did you manage to get into Research?" Other inductees were astonished that I had landed this "plumb" job! I did not know at the time that Research was considered within the company to be the "cream of the cream of the crop" of choice assignments. I only knew that I finally had a job! But I had no concept what "this job" would become over the next 14 plus years I stayed with Rocketdyne. I quickly found out that I didn't know much of value to the company yet. I had a lot to prove to myself and others along the way. I survived the first year, although Bob Levine (three levels above me) wanted to get rid of me by strongly suggesting "I would fit in better elsewhere."

THE WRONG THING TO SAY

The following Monday, September 4, I drove up the mountain and started my job at Santa Susana. I reported in at the guard gate. A secretary was called to show me the way to my new boss's office, and I was admitted into Area 1. Paul Combs and Terry Lamberris, two experienced rocket engineers who had been at Rocketdyne a few years, were told to show me around the Research Division and other facilities at Santa Susana Field Laboratory. Several buildings were Research facilities. PRA (Propulsion Research Area) and another test area called CHTL (Combustion and Heat Transfer Lab) were the two main places where Research people did various small-scale experiments.

Paul and Terry showed me the new F-1 engine that was to power the first stage of the Saturn V vehicle that would take men to the moon. They took me over to Area 2 where the F-1 was mounted on the Alpha test stand, and we looked at the F-1 engine that had just fired five minutes earlier. I was told to climb up inside it on a 12-foot stepladder with a flashlight to look at the injector. And so, I did. Cooling water and fuel were still dripping off the injector.

Well, the F-1 engine has a three-foot diameter throat, so it was fairly easy getting up inside the combustion chamber, which has a 42-inch inside diameter. This chamber was probably about three or four foot long. I was able to get near the injector and inspect it quite thoroughly, but I couldn't understand what was happening to it. Burn areas were scattered all over its face! There were thousands of holes (roughly a quarter-inch diameter) that were spaced very closely together all over the injector face. The injector was basically a stainless steel plate covering a multitude of fuel and oxidizer feed passages. It featured a large number of circumferential rings that had been pre-drilled and welded into grooves in the injector plate. I could not understand how any kind of hot gas flow around and behind these holes could raise the stainless steel to temperatures where it would burn. Stainless steel has a relatively low conductivity. But, to go from several thousand degrees Fahrenheit to cryogenic temperatures, or even a few hundred degrees in the space of an eighth of an inch, was unimaginable. How could combustion gas get behind the little, bitsy spaces between injected streams of either liquid oxygen or kerosene and cause burning?

When I climbed down from inside the engine, I was asked, "What do you think?" I said, "It beats the hell out of me." That was the *wrong thing* to say. In later years, I learned that when one was in this kind of situation, you'd say, "I'll think about it and I will let you know." That would have been an acceptable response. Well, my guess is that Paul and Terry went back and talked to the big boss, Bob Levine, and said, "This guy doesn't know anything and is worthless, get rid of him." Levine tried to convince me to leave Rocketdyne. He couldn't fire me. Problem was, I had what was called "super seniority." The US government had a policy that said a company can't fire a new hire for a year. In that time, I proved my worth.

Later, somebody came up with the simple suggestion of changing those injector rings to a silver-laden copper called Narloy. The increased conductivity solved the problem, so they no longer had an injector burning issue. Another problem remained, however: combustion instability in the engine that ripped the whole test stand apart!

SEAWORLD

One of the first things that I had to do at Rocketdyne was go over to Pasadena, gather a group of scientists who were attending a conference at JPL, and take them to SeaWorld. It was off the Palos Verde peninsula quite a distance from Pasadena, probably 40-50 miles. I drove to a car rental place in Pasadena, arriving early to pick up an eight-passenger van. There was no van available there. I started hollering loud and clear that you damn better well get an eight-passenger van right now, right here, or you are going to have problems with one of the major corporations in this area! After a little wait, I got the correct size van, picked up my group of scientists on time at their hotel and took them to SeaWorld.

They acted like a bunch of kids at the circus, scattering themselves around the place to see the different exhibits. Fortunately, I had given each a time and place to congregate before going back to Pasadena. They could take it all in, looking at the dolphins, orcas, sea lions and sharks, and whatever else SeaWorld had in the outside and inside tanks.

The scientists were all happy. We spent a good part of the day there, until I brought them back to drop them off at JPL. I drove home, glad that the day was over and that I had done well as a shepherd of scientists.

I heard the next day, Levine had said, "At least we found something that he could do." I found Levine could be pretty snide; I never liked him, he never liked me. Fortunately, I had Tom Coultas and Bob Lawhead, who were managers between us.

SHOCK-ABSORPTION CHARACTERISTICS OF A SPONGE

I started on a "real" job where I was under supervision of a senior engineer in Research. I was helping Ed Rabin study the shockwave absorption characteristics of a sponge. It was an ordinary kitchen sponge, colored yellow. It was one of those sponges that starts out paper thin, but when you add water, expands, and stays expanded upon drying again. We cut out a section from this sponge, fit it into the end of a tube that we were bouncing shockwaves in and out of. We had an acoustic driver with which we could produce any kind of acoustic wave including shocks. We measured the waves in and the waves out. We tried using digital recording to figure out what the difference was and never could see any difference! So that experiment was a total bust. But it did prepare me for a future program, which I'll get into presently.

POTASSIUM LOOP

Coultas and I worked on a couple loops; they were supposed to be precursors to space power systems. One was a potassium loop. And for some reason, he picked me to come down with him at all hours of the day and night to run this potassium loop with him. It was one of these rules where you had to have two people because it could be dangerous. The potassium could eat through welds, and you would get squirts of potassium metal coming out. You damn well better not be in front of it, because it would cut you in two! And so, the rule was: You always had to have two people.

We'd be there up 'til midnight, on some nights, trying to get this potassium loop to run. And potassium had this capability of taking oxygen off the side walls of the tubing instead of the chrome or whatever oxide was on the sidewall. It would turn into potassium oxide that would flow through the system until it plugged the system up, and then we'd have to unplug it. And that usually meant finding the plug and heating it with an acetylene torch until you melted the plug without melting the tube, or else cutting that section of tube out and replacing it, etc. And it was a pure folly. Nothing ever came of the potassium loop, even though it had the potential of being a Rankine cycle-type space power system.

MERCURY LOOP

Similarly, we got a program for a mercury loop. It was a smaller scale setup. Coultas designed the test section which, ultimately, was a pathetic little thing. The difference there was that mercury was known to be horribly toxic as a vapor. And so, a special test cell was prepared. It had distinct epoxy paints that would seal against any kind of liquid. This was on the floor, ceiling, and walls. The entrance wall was a rubberized curtain that would not absorb anything, and it hung down into a water-filled trough, so the bottom and the top were sealed, and the ends were sealed. And when you went in there, you wore a Scott air pack with not demand air, but forced air, and you wore a complete rubberized suit that sealed you off from the mercury. And it was one hell of a thing to wear that suit. I did it a couple times and said, "Enough!"

That program went nowhere. But mercury had been a candidate as a working fluid for a space power system. So that was the end of the mercury, too.

NAK - A SODIUM-POTASSIUM MIXTURE

Nobody knew if liquid supply lines caused instability. One of the questions was: Are there pressure waves that run up and down the supply lines that feed the fuel and the oxidizer to the engine and can have the combustion characteristics changed? I obtained what's called "NAK," a sodium-potassium mixture that is liquid at ordinary temperatures. I made a shock tube using NAK as a flowing fluid. And I could flow this NAK through different piping elements like orifices and pipe bands and then measure the shockwave going into this element and coming out of this element and, again, ship this data over to Freddy Traub and have him ship it down to the people in mathematics to analyze.

Well, I had to have a very good shockwave. So, I devised a big hammer that swung down from a given height, then whacked a piston located on one end of the shock tube. The piston had a very thin lead ring that kind of gave it a little bit of a "give" so that it didn't bounce. A shock would be formed, a very steep slope shockwave that had a well-defined front. It was basically what the mathematicians call an impulse function. You get a step-up shape in pressure that lasts for a while before it drops off, giving you enough time to analyze what's going on during the time of that shock. And so, I looked at that and shipped off the data, and nothing came back. Well… something came back.

I found out that shockwaves propagate through orifices that are bigger than ¼ diameter, almost without change. When you get down below ¼ diameter, you start losing shock strength. And that was the distinction. Well, it meant nothing because nobody put orifices in flow lines to feed the engines that were anywhere near that big. So that was kind of a total bust program too. But at least we found that out.

TRICHLORETHYLENE

The next program was a fairly good one. Somebody wanted to map the mixture ratio distribution in the F-1 engine for the fuel and oxidizer across the chamber from the injector down a ways. Well, there's no way they could do it inside the engine. Nobody had invented computer tomography yet. And so, I think Coultas came up with the idea of having inert fluids that would mimic oxygen and fuel in a correct density ratio. I used water and trichlorethylene. Now, back then, trichlorethylene was a common solvent that was used to clean *everything*. And so, there was no real thought about the dangers as a cancer agent. And so, I had a tank of trichlorethylene that I dyed blue. And I had a water supply that I could change the pressure on and change the flowrates. I could pressurize this tank equivalently. I had the machinists "machine up" segments of the injectors on the F-1. You see, the rings were either doublets (that means impinging two jets) or triplets, where three jets would impinge and sequences that repeated it. So, I didn't need very many of these things repeated in order to show what the whole injector face would do. And so, I patiently squirted trichlorethylene and water simultaneously through these elements, and I could have crossflows that would mimic what the crossflows in that particular part of the injector would be. I mimicked everything as faithfully as I could. I had a transparent tray that had a bunch of tall compartments that I collected the spray in. The spray would come down and it wouldn't splash out if I didn't keep the spray on too long. And I could measure quite accurately with a Vernier caliper what the height ratios were.

Taking all this data, I plotted mixture-ratio distributions for the F-1. And guess what? I came up with the simple fact that the F-1 was a lousy mixer. Down within a foot of the injector face, the mixing was still only about 60% complete.

The question was: What is going to be done about it? And the answer was: Nothing.

And the reason was, it didn't make a damn bit of difference because, at that mixture ratio, the F-1 was having the same specific impulse as if it had very good mixing. It's just in the chemistry in that if you have a lower molecular weight fluid, it increases specific impulse. If you have a corresponding lower temperature, specific impulse decreases. The two compensated, so it made no difference over a wide variation of mixture ratio. Thus, nothing was ever done to improve mixing to get increased performance. The mighty F-1 had bigger problems!

It might be of interest to note: the orange flame tail on the Saturn V rocket after it lifted away from the launch pad was due to microscopic, unburned carbon particles radiating energy in the visible spectrum. As this carbon burns in the enveloping atmosphere, carbon monoxide and dioxide gases are formed. These gases radiate in the infrared spectrum, not visible to humans.

F-1 TEST STANDS

The F-1 engine had been tested at a million-pounds thrust at Santa Susana, but the engines were going to be run at a million-and-a-half-pounds thrust in a Saturn vehicle. In fact, you run it a little bit higher than that – 1,650,000 – just right at the beginning to get the vehicle boosting. But it meant that they had to build new test stands. So, they built several new test stands out at Edwards Air Force Base in the Mojave

Desert. These test stands were big steel structures with hefty tanks. Everything else on them was large scale and necessary. Once completed, they pushed a button and everything on the test stand disappeared.

Well, they didn't want that to happen, but they rebuilt the test stand, pushed the button again. Another engine and the test stand disappeared.

There was some combustion instability that developed very quickly. When you have three tons of propellant per second going through this engine, you have three tons of high explosive that can go off at once. And that was enough to take everything down to the concrete. So, something had to be done. Coultas was given the job of finding out what was happening in the F-1.

Coultas acquired a group of engineers to work for him exclusive to this program. It was a big one. Paul Combs was the major contributor in the group. Terry Lamberris had quit and gone to work for Pratt Whitney. Coultas started looking visually at high-pressure combustion mimicking the injector patterns in the F-1 in a transparent-walled chamber. It had three- to four-inch-thick Plexiglas reinforced to hold up pressure and they could look at it with high-speed cameras. They could touch off squids to mimic initiating an instability. They worked on that, and I didn't have anything to do with that part of it. $350 million later, the problem was solved!

Coultas solved it by installing veins on the injector face that split the injector into little compartments. I don't know how many, but the veins stuck out about six inches, and they were cooled adequately. Coultas determined that the cause for instability was the fact that kerosene's critical pressure was lower than the pressure they were operating at in the engine. When kerosene was squirted into the engine, it started out as a fairly cool liquid. (It was heated up in cooling the engine somewhat, but it was still fairly cool; it was still a liquid.) But as it got heated up in the combustion zone, it went through a period of changing into a gas without going through a phase change because it was above the critical pressure. There is no surface tension holding droplets together, so when these droplets got out into the stream far enough, any kind of a wave would shatter them from being a certain size into itsy-bitsy nothing size, increasing the area tremendously, increasing the combustion rate tremendously, and causing a detonation.

So, if you did all of this in a protected space, the kerosene was essentially already mixed in a very small size with the oxygen, and any kind of variation then beyond was inconsequential, and the engine stayed stable. Only took 350 million bucks to show that. I have to think most of that money was spent rebuilding test stands at Edwards. The F-1 engine became a certified man-rated engine for the Saturn V vehicle.

NORTH AMERICAN SWATCHA PATENT

After a few years, I found myself always involved in assorted small studies at Rocketdyne. I usually had several projects going at once. First one I'll mention is this: I had to go down to North American Aviation headquarters at Downey (near

LAX airport). NAA people were talking with Union Carbide regarding a patent that North American had called the "Swatcha patent," which involved high-pressure water jet cutting. Union Carbide wanted to use it in wood sawmill operations and come up with a way of cutting wood using a much thinner slicing method than saw blades to minimize "kerf" or wasted wood. I was invited to go up to Duncan, Oklahoma to Halliburton. Halliburton was a small company in Duncan that made high-pressure oil well mud pumps. The building, housing executive and engineering offices, was maybe 100 feet wide, a couple hundred feet long, and three stories high. We had a meeting with the Halliburton President and some senior staff. We agreed to go outside to observe a mud pump cut wood.

There was a lot of noise, lots of spray mist, but wood would not cut. The 20,000-PSI water jet was directed down to the wood piece. After penetrating a short distance, it turned a 90-degree corner and went out sideways. The experiment was a failure. I returned to Rocketdyne where I tried to think: "What can one do to make water solid enough that it will cut wood?" I tried all sorts of thermodynamic cooling schemes. I never did come up with anything workable.

Somebody else up in Seattle I think said, "Well, you know, you got this high-pressure water squirting at a few thousand feet a second. Why can't we add some itsy-bitsy pieces of sand in a secondary chamber and have it sweep these little itsy-bitsy pieces of sand along with it, and see what that does?" Those people were able to cut nuclear reactor vessels' six-inch-thick stainless steel with this thing!

And it was all done with water and sand. You didn't have to have a flame to cut through that steel. You could cut these reactor vessels up into chunks and get rid of them and handle stuff readily with this. And so, I don't know what happened as far as a Swatcha patent, but I had nothing to do with the solution. Too bad.

HYPERSONIC AIRCRAFT

I was called again to go down to the North American headquarters regarding a hypersonic aircraft. That time, I got to talk with a North American vice president named Bill Cann who showed me around the offices, and I got to sit down in the chair Dutch Kindleburger had sat in when he ran North American Aviation when they were producing the P-51 fighter during World War II. I thought that was quite an experience!

Mr. Northrop of Northrop Aviation was in on this meeting, and we were talking about what could be done with regard to building a hypersonic aircraft that would go Mach 10 at 110,000-120,000 feet and stay cool enough that it wouldn't burn up. It would have payload capability and long range. Somebody had come up with a concept that looked like a pregnant duck. The concept had a long nose that reverse tapered back on the sides, top, and bottom to the duck belly. And then it had a transition that looked like half of a linear rocket engine that ended at a tapered tail. If you injected hydrogen near the front end, by the time the hydrogen fuel got mixed with air and heated up to burn, it would be going around the corner and it would produce thrust. Basically, it was a literal aerodynamic enclosure because of expected shock structure on one side. On the other side, it would be pushing against the aircraft. It could go Mach 10. You had to initially get it moving at supersonic speed to get it to work, but that was a separate problem. It could have used a booster rocket stage to do that or supersonic inlet jet engines, but we didn't have anything to do with that task.

The interesting aspect of the problem presented to us was the fact that while the craft had plenty of engine power and plenty of fuel for a long-duration, high-speed run, it couldn't be cooled over the vast area that was exposed to aerodynamic heating. Structural cooling was going to be a problem. What do you do about it?

This was the beginning of the Space Shuttle era. Lockheed had come up with a super shuttle insulation, which was extra lightweight ceramic foam that could stand a couple thousand degrees Fahrenheit easily. I picked it up in one hand, held a blowtorch on a different side until it glowed white hot, and immediately touched the hot side. I felt no pain, no heat effect whatsoever. This material had no heat capacity. It was amazing stuff. However, it had its problems. In spite of its low density, there would be so much on the airplane that the extra weight would keep the aircraft grounded. Also, the material was very frangible; it broke easily.

I invented a concept I called the "hairy airplane." Instead of foam, I would use strands of ceramic fibers that were very fine. Many layers of these fibers would be laid down against the surface to be insulated. It would be like a high-nap rug or the skin of an animal, like an otter skin. It would lay along the wing or the other surface, and there would be numerous layers, and these many layers would act as multiple radiation shields. Conduction along the fiber axes would be minimal. The only stress would be tensile along the fiber axis. See, I looked at the problem from a heat transfer standpoint. Radiation from fiber to fiber would be the only transfer medium. Convection between fibers would be suppressed by packing density. But what was the radiation?

Radiation is ordinarily a fourth power function of temperature. It turns out that the equivalent conductivity is a third power function of temperature, so in steady state, foam would have to be thick enough so that the temperature would degrade enough even though it was a third-power function. A lot of the foam would be running really hot, and only a little bit of this foam would be running cooler down near the aircraft surface. Foam would require a super low expansion coefficient to survive service under these conditions. Fibers have no thermal stress buildup. I couldn't find any ceramic fiber to use, so I used really fine, stainless steel wire. I made up a test section and a test stand I could run it in. I had made up another test stand where I could generate an impulse function of high-temperature gas and I could get up to about 1200°F, and I could run a couple pounds a second.

I also had a two-inch valve that would open in less than a millisecond. Less than a thousandth of a second! How did I do it? I had a double diaphragm – two-inches diameter (they're called "toilet seat diaphragms"), so they didn't shred.

What I did was I pressurized the heater part of this where I had a pebble bed that would have a whole bunch of material in it heated up to 1200°F. The gas going through it would go from ambient up to 1200°F within this heater, and it had enough heat left that it would operate for a few seconds at the maximum temperature. It would be pressurized up to below the pressure of the double-versed diaphragm. I would run the middle chamber between the two at half of the pressure and then I would run the main heater section at full pressure. So, say, if I had 600 PSI in the main chamber, I could run 300 PSI in this middle chamber, and each of the burst diaphragms were rated at, say, 400 PSI. So, neither versed diaphragm would blow because they had 100 PSI to go. But if I bled out the pressure in this middle chamber into a closed tank, it had a small volume, so it went from 400 down to nothing. And it didn't take much gas to fill up that little tank. All I had to do was dump that pressure in the middle chamber. The first diaphragm would blow, the second one would blow in a fraction of a millisecond, and away they would go, and I'd get an impulse function – a mathematically equivalent function that I could analyze. I could look at an analytic solution to an impulse flow and compare it to what I got.

So, doing that, I saw that even the limited amount of material I put in would act as an effective radiation shield. Now, I could also analyze what would happen with this third power business and still come up with a rug or an otter skin-type arrangement that would last for the duration of the flight. And it would be less weight by far than what the foam was. So, I proposed it.

Nothing ever happened, but sometime later, the shuttle dropped a bunch of its foam and went to a blanket of these fibers. They would put a quilted blanket on the craft. So, they used a quilted blanket instead of my hairy airplane idea. And I felt somewhat justified, but also pissed off that somebody took my idea. But such is life.

SUPERCYCLONE

Coultas wanted me to look at a secret, classified paper that described a nuclear rocket experiment. Someone had posited, "We could build a nuclear rocket using small pebbles of nuclear material, have hydrogen injected tangentially in the rocket chamber that would spin the pebbles around, and act like a pebble bed. You'd have excellent heat transfer, which can be calculated. Extremely hot hydrogen would exit through the throat and provide high specific impulse for thrust." Well, it didn't work.

The reason was that these pebbles rolled around, ground against each other, making fine dust. It's called "elutriation." Fine dust got blown out of the rocket engine so the nuclear fuel load, eventually, was lost. The engine wouldn't work anymore. That program was abandoned. However, it got me thinking about cyclone devices. It took me 20 years, but I finally came up with a way to have a cyclone system work better than any other dust/gas device. I call it a "supercyclone."

Now, most people know what a cyclone is. It's a device that sits on the outside of a silo on a farm. It's got a cylindrical top and a conical bottom. Corn or other grain falls out the bottom, while air that is used to transport grain goes out the top of the cyclone. The silo is filled with grain falling out the bottom of the cyclone. Corn is big. Cyclones on farms are inefficient, but they're workable because they can separate corn from air. In a cyclone that needs to separate fine particles, the situation is entirely different. You must have what's called coupled torque. In other words, you've got to spin it with two opposing sets of jet streams. A company called Siemen's developed a cyclone separator. A description of their cyclone is published in *Chemical Engineers' Handbook*. Siemens had a row of nozzles pointing tangentially inward along one side and another row diametrically opposite pointing inward in the opposite direction. They obtained a stable spinning gas flow field that had large particles go out the bottom and gas flow out the top. It worked, sort of. It worked better than the corn one would. But it had a cutoff size that was still too large. "Cutoff" is the size of particles that go through the device without capture. Theory tells us that larger particles are swept outward by centrifugal forces and eventually wind up dropping out the device's bottom. The Siemens device had radial inflow of gas associated with its tangential downward gas flows. With small particles, Stokes' drag dominates particle forces and overcomes centrifugal force. So what do you do? You must arrange for a radial outflow of gas over most of the cylindrical part of the cyclone. Stokes drag will act in concert with centrifugal force

After two decades trying to analyze the system, I wrote a computer program that showed how to satisfy the above-stated conditions. I developed a way of computing the angular distribution of each of these lines of tangential injectors where injection angle increased as you went from the top to the bottom where the solids exit and the top where the gas flows out. By tailoring the downward component of the injection angle along the length of the cylindrical section, a radial outward flow of gases exists along the cylindrical part of the device. Down near the bottom is another matter, but down there, you've got a chance to capture the particles again.

While at Rocketdyne, I suspected that one could use von Kármán's integral boundary layer theory and Schlichting's Turbulent wall Shear Stress theory to predict how particles could be separated from the fluid flowing in a cyclone. In conjunction with mass flow and area balances, which were determined using a binary chop methodology, I was able to solve these formulas and obtain constraints in the system at each injection station.

Jim Bailey's binary chop was the key to obtaining a solution to the set of equations that allowed me to design my supercyclone separator. A computer evaluated flow areas and mass vector distributions needed to obtain radial outflow of core gas such that Stokes' drag assisted centrifugal force in trapping smaller particles in transport to the solids outlet.

In review, the supercyclone design was based on the principle that the centrifugal force in spinning fluid inside the cyclone would tend to migrate larger particles out to the outer wall. However, in standard cyclones, Stokes' drag predominates with smaller particles and would drag them against the radial outflow of larger particles acted on by centrifugal forces. Smaller particles follow radial in-flowing gas. Small particles consequently go out the top of the separator with the gas. Thus, something had to be done to ensure that the Stokes' drag acted in concert with the centrifugal force field to deposit smaller particles in the outer region. There, they could drop down with gas flow and gravity to the bottom to be discharged. Now, down at the bottom, the gas flow would (necessarily) go inward, but as long as the trapped particles at the bottom went through the centrifugal force field assisted by Stokes' drag toward the outside for the entire length of the device, they could be recirculated until they were recaptured. At that point, an exceedingly small percentage of particle mass would go out with the gas.

Further details on my supercyclone can be found in the Inventions chapter.

SPACE SHUTTLE ENGINE INJECTOR TESTING

Another test program to be run by Harry Dodson (of large engines group) was for a heat exchanger designed to heat relatively high flowrates of hydrogen gas at high pressure to relatively high temperatures. He was to mimic the high and low temperature cycling in the Space Shuttle main engine injector. Shuttle engine injectors were subjected first to low temperatures from cryogenic liquid hydrogen flow and then subsequent high-temperature gases coming from partially pre-combusted propellants in the startup cycle.

The Space Shuttle main engine used two-stage combustion for high performance. In this two-stage process, a small amount of hydrogen is burned with a lot of oxygen to produce oxygen-rich hot gas at high pressure, 1500°F. This gas operates one of the turbo-pumps that pressurizes propellant. Similarly, a large flow of hydrogen is burned in a small flow of oxygen in a second pre-burner to heat hydrogen to similar conditions and operate a second propellant pump. Because the injector had to last through a thousand heating/cooling cycles, some way had to be found to prove the engine injector could endure this amount of thermal cycling at the stresses involved.

I designed a tube-type, counter-flow heat exchanger that alternated hot hydrogen gas flow in the heating part of the cycle with liquid nitrogen flow to the engine injector mimicking the cooling portion of the cycle. It had a thermal combustion rating of 100 megawatts and fit within an envelope three by five foot width by six foot height. Internal combustor and heat exchanger flow areas were two by four foot. To supply hydrogen gas to the burn zone, interestingly enough, I actually used standard natural gas burners from commercial swimming pool heaters…at over 100 times their rated capacity. I did not know if they would stand up to that service load, so I pretested one unit by itself. I painted stripes of special heat-sensitive paint that fused into a brown glass at varying temperatures. In that way, I found the temperature I expected them to operate at before I committed to the design. I tested one unit (of 24), having identical expected flowrate of hydrogen with a high-speed fan blowing air parallel to the ground. It produced a hot "wind" 150 feet away. You could not see the flame, but you felt the hot air flow and radiation.

The hydrogen gas to be burned was obtained from the high-pressure gas that would have been dumped overboard and flared. Instead of wasting this fuel, I captured it in a high-pressure tank and used a pressure regulator to supply the fuel burners with a regulated, constant flow of hydrogen from the otherwise pulsed-input flowrate and variable source pressure. The hydrogen flow in the burner section had to be staged. Half flow was introduced first from burners manifolded from one side of the combustion chamber until a stable flame was detected, and then the second half of the hydrogen flow was introduced from those burners manifolded on the other side of the combustor. This avoided a detonable hydrogen mixture accumulating during initial flow transients. Combustion air was supplied by two squirrel cage blowers of a capacity that matched hydrogen flow for correct combustion stoichiometry. A sophisticated set of interlocked sensors and controls were used to ensure required combustion chemistry.

"Proof of design" testing of the Shuttle main engine injector lasted over a time period of three days for a successful 1,000 cycles. This program was accomplished within a relatively short time period since I had designed the unit with a few-minute cycle time. I rejected the suggested storage heater design others had proposed because it would have required many hours to regenerate between tests.

However, I didn't run the test program because I had already left the company.

STORAGE HEATERS FOR HIGH HEAT LOAD GAS FLOWS

Several years into working, I ran into some old friends from graduate school, Floyd Larsen and Roger Schmidt, at a conference at the University of Maryland in Silver Spring. I gave a paper at the conference on my high-temperature vacuum insulation for the Viking mission to Mars. They were presenting papers also. Roger's was on Mie Scatter Theory, which has to do with why different pigments have different colors because of their scattering characteristics of light that comes incident to a surface: i.e.: iron oxide paint is red and titanium oxide paint is white. Roger was always very smart analytically. I have no idea what Mie Scatter Theory is or why it works, so Roger's paper didn't do me a damn bit of good any time in my life, but Floyd's did!

Floyd's work at Fluidyne Corporation in Minneapolis involved energy storage heaters. The company designed storage heaters used in making steel. Open-hearth steel plants preheat the air before it goes into the blast furnace and thereby get a higher gas temperature that flows across the iron ore and melts it. He described to me, in detail, design criteria he used in sizing heaters. In essence, Floyd got me started designing storage heaters.

I went back to Rocketdyne. Using George Dusinberre's book on finite difference methods that Harland Burge introduced to me, I could do a better job than Floyd! With this type of computer analysis, I could design any kind of storage heater that anyone might want. Why do you want storage heaters? They provide a means to input a small amount of heating energy over a long time period and then discharge this energy at a much higher rate over a short time period. I became known as the storage heater guy in Rocketdyne Research.

I used his advice and extended his analysis using numerical computer techniques to predict performance and permit my designing more complicated efficient units for research applications. Sometimes a storage heater was the only way one could get megawatts of thermal energy output for a short duration while inputting kilowatts over a much longer period of time. We used them for rocket propellant conditioning and as heat sources for high-temperature gas flow.

Taking other people's initial thoughts and extending them with additional analytic considerations to other difficult design problems became "My Hallmark" throughout my career. I owe a lot to Roger and Floyd: one, for getting me started in computing, and the other, for giving me a tool that I used throughout my career.

JOHN WRUBLE'S AIR AUGMENTATION TESTS

I helped John Wruble, an engineer at Rocketdyne, by designing an energy storage heater for his study of air-augmented rockets. He needed a hot air source that would blow air in parallel with a simulated rocket exhaust with the gases mixing at ambient atmospheric pressure. Several megawatts of power equivalent were needed for short durations (half-a-minute per test). As usual with most research programs of the era, "money was tight." I analyzed the problem, determined what might be an acceptable design, and set out to find suitable "free material" to build the hardware. Atomics International had accumulated a great "boneyard" of surplus materials. We found an outer stainless steel pipe casing and what was purported to be 400 series stainless steel tubing that we would use to pack inside the pipe as heat storage media. A couple pipe flanges, stainless steel plates, and some welding later, John had his air heater.

He bought standard electric heater elements, strapped them to the outside of the pipe, and wrapped the whole unit with fiberglass insulation. He was ready to test.

After several successful tests, in which he operated the unit at 1200°F, he decided to go to lunch. He had just finished a test which had depleted the core energy, so he had to do a reheat. Thinking he would be back from lunch in time to control the temperature as usual, he turned the heating power above the nominal value "to ensure the unit would be ready" when he returned. He was delayed, however, so when he returned from lunch, the unit's core temperature was near 1400°F. So, he thought, "I'll just blow a short blast of air through it and cool it down to the correct test temperature." When he did this, flames shot out of the exhaust port. This behavior was not expected! Obviously, something was wrong. The heater seemed to be burning up! So, the fire department was called.

Firemen seem to have one solution to fight fire: lots of water. When water was sprayed on the smoldering heater, it erupted like a volcano. They quickly realized it was best to just let the fire burn out by itself. After the unit cooled, I took a sample of slag to the machine shop, held it against a grinding wheel, and looked at the sparks. Zirconium metal was indicated – *not* 400 series stainless steel. Zirconium has an approximate ignition temperature in air of 1350°F. And it really likes to continue to burn in water! John had to go the full ASME (American Society of Mechanical Engineers) code route when he had his replacement heater built. It cost his program over $7,000 instead of being free like the first unit I had made for him. All material was certified as in compliance with the design. The pressure rating was specified and testing was ordered.

Even though the unit operated at atmospheric pressure, it could not be foreseen that another application would not operate this heater at some higher pressure. I did this second design for John as well, and, once again, for free!

A STEP FUNCTION SUPPLY - HIGH-TEMPERATURE & PRESSURE GAS

I had a small high-pressure air heater built for one of my test programs. It could heat several pounds of gas per second from ambient to 1200°F for a time period of a few seconds. It provided approximately 800 kW thermal energy output for input power of two kilowatts over an interval of 15 minutes. We had procured a small Air Force contract to study hot gas ignition of solid propellant rocket motors. Funding was very tight again, so testing had to have minimal cost. I developed small models of the solid rockets that matched configurations of large solid rocket motor grains, used thin copper sheeting to simulate shapes of internal surfaces, and installed fine wire thermocouples on the copper sheet back surfaces away from the gas flow. I used a transient response analysis to predict how the transient temperature data would translate into heat transfer coefficients and generalized heat transfer correlations. This analysis required that the hot air flow start instantaneously. It represented a simultaneous step function in both temperature and flowrate.

I designed a special valve that could hold back the hot gas yet open within a fraction of a millisecond. I did this with a double burst diaphragm valve that had an intermediate pressure between diaphragms of half the system pressure. Each of the diaphragms was rated for two-thirds system pressure. The upstream diaphragm was broken by releasing the intermediate air pocketed between the two diaphragms into a closed tank. Once the downstream diaphragm experienced full pressure, it also ruptured. The diaphragms featured a design that captured diaphragm fragments to preclude plugging downstream air passages. The program was successful, correlating heat transfer in both head end and aft end ignition system designs for each of the several solid rocket motor internal propellant web configurations.

A second contract was awarded to us, and was also successful, extending results to other newer solid rocket motor configurations.

Film cooling, where a lower temperature fluid is interposed between a hot fluid and a surface to reduce heat transfer to that surface, had been studied extensively for steady flow conditions. Film cooling in applications that have rapidly accelerating flows had not been studied, especially in transonic gas flow regions. One suspects that film cooling would be less effective at maintaining lower surface temperature in accelerating flow because the high Reynolds number turbulent mixing would enhance diffusion of hot gas into coolant. Appropriate heat transfer correlations were needed. Using apparatus of similar design to that described above, accelerating flows were established, flowrates were measured, and heat transfer correlations were developed from the transient thermal data in a highly successful program.

A paper was published in the *International Journal of Heat and Mass Transfer* (1968) giving theoretical derivations, which were supported by extensive experimental data.

A ROCKET'S RED GLARE

My apology to Francis Scott Key: '*the rocket's red glare, the bombs bursting in air…*' Well, I did blow up Harley Burge's rocket engine.

I was called into Coultas' office early one afternoon. He told me I would be testing Burge's rocket engine later that afternoon. I protested, "I have a mid-term test in Laplace Transforms tonight." "When?" "7:00 PM." "You'll have plenty of time; the test runs at 5:00 PM on Bravo stand in

Area 2. Go now, talk to Lew the lead mechanic. He'll show you the rig. All you have to do is tell the console operator to push the start button," he said. "Sure!!" I agreed skeptically.

It was not a simple system. Harland Burge, under contract with NASA, had devised a new cooling concept for rocket engines with potential to make them lighter weight. But, on this day, he was not available to be "test engineer!" A thin inner core shaped with sheet metal, having the correct contours for directing hot gas flow, was mounted inside an outer shell. The outer shell had spray nozzles situated in a pattern that ensured complete coverage of the inner shell when spraying coolant. The inner shell was molybdenum. The outer shell was stainless steel. Coolant was liquid metal – lithium. Harley had spent considerable time developing the spray elements. They looked like Mexican sombreros, having holes in the dome.

In Burge's design, liquid metal would be recirculated using a pump and heat would be dissipated into an external heat exchanger. However, a pressurized supply tank with another "catch tank" was used instead of a pump-type circulation system to simplify the plumbing. The idea was to keep the shell operable at high temperatures yet contain the high-pressure rocket exhaust. Preliminary experiments using single nozzles showed great promise in handling expected heat loads. A heated tank held the lithium prior to testing. A dump tank would collect the lithium draining from the engine. A homemade magnetic flowmeter was to measure lithium flowrate. It consisted of a permanent magnet mounted crosswise to the tube carrying lithium. Flowing liquid lithium generates a voltage potential cross wise to both the magnetic field and flow direction. Wires welded to the tube at these diagonally opposite locations carried the generated signal to recorders. In theory, it was a neat package, but there's always a fly in the bowl of Jell-O.

I had the console operator pressurize the lithium tank to start coolant flow. We did not get expected voltage, but got a lower voltage, indicating a lower than required flowrate. I had lithium tank pressure increased. This took more time. Tank volume was finite. A few moments of indecision passed. I told the console operator to light off the engine. It used hypergolic propellants. Opening valves ran the engine. Approximately three seconds after engine ignition, a massive fireball erupted from the test stand with a subsequent explosion I assume was the collection tank of lithium burning! There was no way to fight the fire. We had to allow it to burn itself out. Everything in the test stand was ruined. I do not know the cost of repairs, but it had been a quarter-of-a-million-dollar experiment. After the fire died out, I had to catch a ride to Area 1 where my vehicle was parked with two NASA observers…no words were spoken on that ride. I went to class incapable of putting more than my name on the test booklet and flunked that mid-term test handily. I got no sleep that night!

The next morning, I went to work thinking it would be my last day. When I got to my office, Harley Burge was there… smiling. The test, as it turned out, was a complete success! If it had not worked, the engine would have burned immediately. And periodic test cell rebuilds were expected! I was not fired but was something of a hero for at least 10 minutes that day.

And, as a postscript, I "aced" the final exam in my Laplace Transform course and got a B as a final grade!

Harley went on to head TRW's successful Saturn V lunar command module variable thrust orbital insertion and lunar orbit "escape" rocket engine development and testing program.

GE VULCAN 20 MM GATLING GUN

The General Electric Company was experiencing overheating problems in its 20 mm "Gatling gun" weapon system used on US fighter jet aircraft in the late 1960s. After firing a certain number of rounds from a barrel and chambering another unfired round, this round would "cook-off." That is, it would fire without intention due to heat from the hot gun barrel igniting the gunpowder! Further, barrels were getting too hot to maintain shape and accuracy. Inside, barrel surfaces were being scarfed away by later projectiles, thus eroding the gun barrel at an unacceptable rate. GE Company wanted Rocketdyne's Research Division to find a way to cool gun barrels to eliminate cook-off and minimize barrel heating. I was assigned the project.

I started by reading a compendium of gun internal ballistics of all descriptions related to projectile velocity, heat transfer to internal surfaces, and a host of other factors. Literally hundreds of millions of dollars had been spent up to date to increase gun performance and gun life. Yet, no information was available describing how powder burned in the breech chamber or what heat transfer correlation might describe heat transfer throughout the barrel length. GE could not correlate measured projectile position/time data with measured pressure data. According to what was available in GE's studies, Newton's third law relating force with mass and acceleration seemed to be off by about 25%. Did one doubt Sir Isaac, or was something unaccounted for in GE's calculations? I decided I would build a transparent section of the breech of an equivalent 20 mm gun to see how gunpowder burned and answer these questions.

I designed my gun with four-inch-thick opposing 12-inch-long quartz windows mounted in a massive iron structure one-and-a-half feet square by two-and-a-half feet long. The quartz windows were potted in rubber, protected from direct combustion by thin Lexan plastic sheets glued to the hot gas side. The two-piece projectile was rectangular in cross section to match an equivalent circular area of a 20 mm projectile. The total length of my projectile was calculated to match actual projectile weight. A Teflon sheet seal was positioned between the two sections, which were snugly bolted together. Projectile sections were apportioned so expected acceleration would provide a seal pressure greater than breech pressure at any given position (until the Teflon was used up). The excess pressure on the seal resulted from acceleration forces. This sealing action was significant. It permitted adequate sealing without excessive friction affecting projectile acceleration. This seal arrangement worked well!

High-pressure, fast-response, 100,000-PSI-capacity Kistler pressure gauges were mounted along the barrel to show transient pressures. Three special "Fastex" high-speed motion picture cameras (14,000 frames per second, 16 mm, 400 feet of film in each camera) were set up to view the gun windows at various positions. Each was set with differing aperture settings in hopes that at least one would capture the correct exposure. The actual powder charge from a 20 mm shell casing was poured into the breech chamber. It was time to test the gun.

One round was fired. Both of the quartz windows shattered, but the windows shattered far enough behind the projectile that a clear view of burning powder could be seen in one camera's frame sequence. This camera's sequence of 15 frames (out of the 400 feet) showed unburned powder was pushed along behind the projectile by the burning accelerating gas. Since the initial powder charge in a 20 mm shell weighs 25% of the projectile, our data thus proved Newton's Third Law was upheld! Seeing the burning powder charge gave insight into the scale of combustion and its effect on convective and radiant heat transfer rates. Analyzing the combined turbulent convection and intense radiation to determine an expected heat flux distribution gave enough insight to permit development of computer models depicting transient "saw tooth" gun barrel heating of internal surfaces. Analysis results fit nicely together with experimental data!

Ultimately, however, these results were discouraging in the sense that they showed it is impossible to externally cool a gun barrel that is continuously fired. Peak heat flux approaches one megawatt per square inch during the brief period of time when the burning charge passes a given barrel position. At this high heat flux level, it was possible to show that predicted heating matched recorded heating in this single test firing. The only rational alternative approach in lieu of steady cooling is to block heat transfer to the inner barrel surface in some way. An ablative material applied to the barrel ahead of the burning charge might be a possible way to solve the problem. However, bullet design would be severely impacted. Incorporating ablative material into the shell case would take up precious space that is now allocated to the powder charge or projectile. The military's current approach is to limit the number of shells fired in a burst. Placing this type of restriction by imposing a non-firing interval between bursts allows external cooling to limit barrel temperatures. This might be the only practical approach to solving cook-off and barrel erosion and overheating problems. However, I would hate to be a pilot who has to wait for his barrel to cool before he can shoot back at an enemy!

American and foreign military switched from arming planes with guns to arming planes with air-to-air missiles in the last part of the 1960s. Pilots could shoot these missiles at each other, never having seen their enemy. A final note on this subject: The Armed Forces of the US seem to have a pre-established contractor cadre with whom they will do business. Anyone could respond to a request for proposal. It appeared to be impossible to break into this "old boy's network." We at Rocketdyne Research Department tried valiantly to get into new research areas without success. We were limited to working for NASA and those military groups that had been established for rocket research.

The 20 mm Vulcan cannon is still used on some military aircraft. An example is the "Warthog" ground interdiction plane that flies low and slow. It sprays bullets in a fashion that renders accuracy a non-issue.

Curiously enough, while researching *Moiety of a Gingerbread Man*, author Larry Carlson devised a solution to the original problem that could be implemented to substantially reduce internal barrel heating, should anyone be interested…

THIS IS THE US NAVY

While I was at Rocketdyne, most of our work was with NASA or the Air Force, but once in a while the Navy came around with a request for a proposal. It usually came into research, and then research came to Coultas, and then Coultas came to me.

On one such occasion, the Navy wanted to test jet fighters at -50°F – getting them up and running after soaking at that low temperature for some period of time. But they didn't want to go to the North Pole to do it. In other words, they wanted to stay comfortable in southern California while accurately simulating Arctic conditions. The first facility would be at Point Mugu!

A second facility was envisioned for testing hypersonic (Mach 10) scramjet engine missiles that burned boron fuel. Boron fuels are very toxic, so the facility was to be located on San Nicolas Island, which is 90 miles off the coast of Southern California. Because this island had been a bombing test range during WWII, it was off limits to the public.

POINT MUGU COLD START/RUN JET PLANE TEST FACILITY

The Navy had a hangar at Point Mugu in Port Hueneme/Oxnard (up the coast from LA about 25-30 miles), that could be kept at -50°F and house a complete aircraft like an F86. This was back in the 1960s. Long soaks at low temperatures were an easy problem for them to solve. Firing up a jet engine that was gulping 300 pounds of -50°F air per second was not! It would suck out all of the cold air within the test facility in a few seconds and rapidly gulp and heat incoming replacement air! Not only would you have to duct the hot exhaust gases out without heating up the building, but also, you'd have to do something to the air you were sucking in so that you didn't heat the building up that way. So, you had to supply a flowrate of several-hundred-pounds-per-second 50°F-below air to feed the engine through ignition and while it ran in order to see what its operating characteristics would be like under cold conditions. Test durations were slated to be several minutes long to simulate the time it usually takes to get airborne under the proposed cold conditions.

At the time, I was working for Grant Hosack along with two engineers from Point Mugu who had a hard time living with their names: Tinklepa and Pokernicky. We thought about the problem together, but it was usually up to me to do all the design work. I came up with a plan: the jet engine would suck in air from outside, but part of the ingested air would be in combination with a spray of liquid air, which would allow us to manipulate the overall air temperature as needed. A jet airplane could then be started within the cold-soak cell and run for the few minutes that represented "time to attain 'takeoff.'" The hot engine exhaust would be isolated and dumped outside the test cell.

Now, the problem, at the time, was that the people who made liquid air didn't keep it as liquid air – they had fractionating towers. These fractionating towers yielded liquid nitrogen, liquid oxygen, liquid neon, and liquid argon, etc. This meant that we would have to recombine nitrogen and oxygen ourselves to make liquid air, which meant having several tanks of cryogenic liquids instead of just one. Having had cryogenic experience, I then devised a system wherein liquid oxygen, liquid nitrogen, and ambient air would be mixed in the correct proportions to achieve the required temperature within a very brief time using pumps, valves and tanks that were common fare at Rocketdyne. In this way, we could properly mimic the conditions of, say, Fairbanks or Nome, Alaska. But, in the end, the extra tankage and the added complexity increased expenses.

When the Navy found out what this facility would cost, they suddenly lost interest and, ultimately, decided to do cold start testing in Northern Alaska during the winter.

SAN NICOLAS ISLAND HYPERSONIC WIND TUNNEL

In another aborted proposal attempt, also in the '60s, Grant Hosack and I developed an air supply for a hypothetical hypersonic missile test facility to be instated on San Nicolas Island. (As I mentioned, it was imperative that a remote location be available to accommodate the highly toxic boron propellant.) These Mach 10, borane-fueled air-breather missile tests would require significantly specific operating conditions.

Specific simulation altitudes and missile speeds were classified, but a thermodynamic calculation of initial temperature (1900°F) and pressure (300 PSI) was shown to be necessary to expand the air to test cell conditions. Grant was an aerodynamicist, and from his hypersonic shock calculations, he determined that in order to have a missile look like it was going through undisturbed air, we would need to test within a square-shaped cross section measuring 20 feet on each side. Mach 10 flow in a 20 x 20-foot cross section operating at many thousands of feet altitude and low absolute pressure (1/50 of an atmosphere) resulted in a flowrate of 50,000 pounds of hot air per second. That's an awful lot of air – that's 25 tons per second! As it expanded, this hot air cooled to required test conditions.

The question was: How can you supply air that looks like it's cooled down, flowing at low pressure, at high speed, and high flowrate? And the answer was: You'd better start out at a higher pressure and a higher temperature in some kind of a burner.

I developed a conceptual design to supply this facility with its required air from cryogenic storage tanks using fast-operating valves and multiple large combustion chambers. My design required seven to nine large injectors and chambers mounted on the sides of an "accumulation" plenum chamber in parallel flows. The plenum exhausted through a large expansion nozzle into the test cell. At this time, the F-1 engine Rocketdyne built for Saturn V was the largest liquid-fueled engine made. Its injector was limited to a 48-inch external diameter by available milling machines. We faced a similar limitation for mating flanges. The plan was to use a pre-chamber mounted at the end flange of each side unit. This pre-chamber had the actual combustion function. It would burn hydrogen or methane with oxygen, depending on whether the system could tolerate carbon combustion products in the vitiated air. Total thermal energy generated to achieve required outlet flow parameters would be provided. Side ring injectors with impinging jets mixed fluids. The Dickerson-Arbit mixing model would be used to ensure uniform flow through a huge axial nozzle into the test cabin. Another two smaller Atlas booster rocket engines would be used as inducers to evacuate the test chamber, thereby allowing hypersonic expansion to be established at the beginning of the test. Once test cabin flow was established, dynamic pressure could be regained in a subsequent diffuser section for air flow disposal into the surrounding atmosphere without help from the booster rocket engines.

We would supply liquid oxygen, liquid nitrogen, and liquid hydrogen or methane fuel, then operate the system at appropriate flowrates to achieve pressure corresponding to expansion requirements. Again, you'd have to use both liquid oxygen and liquid nitrogen because nobody sold liquid air. It couldn't be perfectly clean air as there was no way you could supply enough energy to heat and pressurize clean air at this level of power. Many thousands of megawatts of motive and thermal energy were needed.

We were confident that our design could provide all of the necessary conditions. So, we wrote and submitted the proposal. We recommended a preliminary subscale build that would permit development testing and verification of operational capability using a single module.

Again, the Navy declined when they found they would have expenses exceeding hundreds of millions of dollars. But my story doesn't end here.

Grant and I decided that we'd get something out of the work, so we wrote a paper. I subsequently attended a symposium sponsored by the Western States Combustion Institute at the University of California, San Diego (La Jolla) and presented this work, shocking many attending university professors by the design's total scale and audacity. They were nearly stupefied – it was unbelievable! Next up was Professor Forman Williams. His model was a cribbage board with a farmer match stuck in each hole. He lit one end and watched the flame progression from one end to the other, then said, "This is how you model forest fires." The highly acclaimed conference head, Tony Oppenheim (professor emeritus of combustion studies/heat transfer/chemistry, UC Berkley), got up after Foreman's presentation and said, "Well, I think we have seen the extremes of combustion modeling and design today! The largest and the smallest in our repertoire..." That always gives me a chuckle – it was a "no deal" with the Navy, but it was pretty entertaining to a distinguished college crowd.

HYDROGEN PEROXIDE DECOMPOSITION GAS GENERATOR

A couple more projects deserve reporting considering their uniqueness. A Rocketdyne contract required a hydrogen peroxide decomposition gas generator with quite a large capacity gas-generation rate compared with existing units. Hydrogen peroxide is quite unstable above a certain concentration level. Silver is an effective catalyst used to initiate decomposition. However, once any of the H2O2 starts to decompose, it generates a large amount of thermal energy which promotes remaining liquid peroxide to decompose violently in an uncontrolled detonation. The engineers previously assigned to the project saw many versions of their test hardware blow up and disappear.

I looked at the problem analytically in terms of controlling the initial heat-release rate and subsequent energy transfer into the remaining hydrogen peroxide. With this analysis backing my concept, I was able to design a structure that recycled some thermal energy from the hot exit gas back to the head end of the unit in a very controlled manner. I kept the subsequent reaction controlled by limiting the amount of liquid at any given position in contact with this "energy backflow." Thus, none could accumulate and explode. All hydrogen peroxide reacted by the time it reached the outlet. I demonstrated stable decomposition at flowrates which exceeded 10 times that previously attained by any other designer, and thereby satisfied all contract terms.

WATER COOLED NUCLEAR REACTORS

One of the senior engineers at Atomics International (AI) developed a hydrogen gas removal system for water cooled nuclear reactors, which can experience a "LOCA" (loss of cooling accident). Water cooled nuclear reactors typically generate a small amount of hydrogen and oxygen from water decomposition due to nuclear radiation. Normally, these gases are recombined within the cooling system so none accumulate over time. However, if a reactor shell is breached, these gases discharge into secondary containment.

Water cooled reactors were designed with several safety features. One of these protection schemes was to spray copious quantities of water throughout secondary containment in the event of loss of reactor coolant. This water spray was intended to cool the reactor shell to prevent a meltdown. However, it was found that decay heating raised shell temperatures above the point where nucleate boiling from water spray would adequately cool the shell surface. When shell temperatures exceed a certain level, adequate nucleate boiling transitions to film boiling. Film boiling is a far less effective cooling mechanism. (Notice water droplets dancing on a hot skillet.) Reactor shell breach occurs after a relatively short time elapses following reactor cooling loss. A substantial secondary containment shell is provided in all US reactor systems to prevent release of radioactive material to the public. The following narrative relates how spray cooling in secondary confinement is an effective deterrent to the release of hazardous nuclear material to surrounding public areas.

Only a small percent of water coolant that traverses an operating reactor traditionally splits into hydrogen and oxygen from nuclear radiation. But, with a reactor breach, hydrogen gas can accumulate within the secondary containment shell until it reaches a detonable concentration. If hydrogen gas accumulation is not limited, a hydrogen explosion could occur with breach of secondary containment. Subsequent spread of radioactive debris in the surrounding countryside would follow. This scenario is completely unacceptable.

AI had developed several methods to get rid of hydrogen gas within secondary containment at concentration levels which are too low to burn or detonate. One involved using a catalytic reaction chamber. The other used a high-temperature counterflow "oven" that reacted air with hydrogen at lower concentrations than are ordinarily combustible. They were trying to sell these systems to nuclear power plant owners. However, they needed to know what the existing water spray system's effect on hydrogen burning or detonation would be as part of their sales background material.

I set up a 50-foot-long shock tube made of 15-inch diameter, schedule 40 carbon steel pipe and having an attached six-inch diameter, six-foot long driver section. These sections of pipe were separated by a thin Mylar diaphragm for each test. A series of water spray heads were mounted on radial "spuds" that pointed the sprays along the pipe axis. Air and hydrogen gases of various volume ratios were mixed and introduced into the spray section in a series of tests. Detonable hydrogen-air mixtures were always used in the driver section. A spark plug located at the head end of the driver pipe ignited the stoichiometric driver gas mixture. Detonations were achieved within the driver pipe within six inches of the spark plug, so a strong detonation wave propagated into the test section in each test. High transient response rate pressure transducers were located at five locations spaced equally along the spray pipe.

On command, water was turned on to the spray heads, recorders were activated, and the spark plug was pulsed. A strong detonation (approximately 600 PSI) ruptured the Mylar diaphragm and traveled through the water spray region. I found that detonations were suppressed within a short distance in the spray pipe (several pipe diameters) at any concentration of hydrogen and air (including detonable mixtures). However, the hydrogen would continue to burn around and within the spray field for ignitable or detonable mixtures. A small pressure "bump" would occur throughout the large pipe for a few seconds until the water spray cooled combustion gases back to ambient. The magnitude of the pressure bump depended upon the initial mixture ratio in the large pipe. Larger hydrogen concentrations produced larger pressure bumps that never exceeded five PSI. A report (AI-73-29) describes the program and displays results.

After the scheduled test series was completed, I ran a test without using water spray in the large pipe, having a hydrogen and air mixture ratio at the detonation limit (19% by volume H2). There was a loud *BANG* that could be heard in the blockhouse 150 feet away from the test area. Motion pictures of the test assembly showed the whole test assembly "jumped into the air" about two feet when the detonation occurred! The spray head radial pipe spuds (one-inch schedule 80 stainless steel) were all bent, albeit at various angles. The amazing thing was that the spud closest to the detonation source was bent the most – in an *opposite* direction to the original detonation wave. I could not understand this phenomenon until I realized that the shockwave hit the ellipsoidal end cap of the large pipe, was then amplified by a "lens effect," and reflected back along the pipe axis as a complex wave traveling opposite to its original direction. I could only guess that this wave had a much larger pressure front along the pipe axis than the originating wave. The pressure transducers never saw that part of the wave since they were located in the pipe wall.

AI had no success in selling their hydrogen reduction systems. With water spray systems already provided in secondary containment, a new hydrogen accommodation (reduction) system wasn't needed!

Later, the Atomics International engineer, Jim Hendricks, and I were invited to attend a board meeting of the Northeast Utilities Safety Commission in Boston. I presented a paper we had written about experiment design and results. I emphasized two facts: 1) The spray must be available within secondary containment following a LOCA. This meant that electrical power to water pumps supplying this flow must be available regardless of the status of the main power lines leading out from the distribution system. Emergency power lines should have separate cable trays bringing in pump power. 2) In view of the fact that the experiment showed such radical deleterious effects on robust experiment equipment, detonable hydrogen concentrations with no water spray must never be allowed to happen. A suggestion was given to purposely ignite hydrogen within secondary containment following a LOCA whenever H2 concentration level reached five percent volume. This practice was to continue until the reactor cooled to the point it no longer produced H2 gas by dissociating water.

THREE MILE ISLAND

When Three Mile Island happened, the operators kept track of hydrogen concentration within secondary containment. Over a period of time, it increased to become a burnable mixture (above five percent by volume H2). They purposely ignited the mixture, resulting in a slight pressure “bump” of a few PSI over ambient. The secondary containment shell held the bump pressure handily – it was designed for much larger pressure differences (approximately 65 PSI). The public was never put in any kind of jeopardy, in spite of all of the media reporting to the contrary.

However, in spite of this successful handling of a potential threat, the American public rejected nuclear power for the next 30 years. Only recently has nuclear power become a viable power option in solving our energy crisis. Once again, Carlson's Second Law holds true: "Never underestimate the stupidity of the American public." I might add: "That goes double for the news media!" The American public listens to the media, whose personnel basically know how to read a teleprompter or write prose that reads well. Content is something else.

Contrast what happened in Japan and Russia when they had their nuclear disasters with our Three Mile Island experience. The following relates my "take" on each of these two truly hideous accidents.

FUKUSHIMA DAIICHI NUCLEAR DISASTER

Japan had four water cooled nuclear reactors located in their Fukushima Daiichi Prefecture on one of their northern islands. They were at only a slight elevation above sea level near the seashore, supposedly to economically provide cooling water for the standard Rankine cycle power generation system. Diesel electric generators were provided to supply emergency power to allegedly secondary containment spray system pumps. Clean water was stored in cisterns below reactor buildings. If the Japanese had followed US designs, spray systems would have been located within secondary containment. The design of these four reactor systems was essentially different from that at Three Mile Island. In both cases, spray cooling emergency pump power could have been close at hand. I do not know this for a fact. But the biggest difference was that the Three Mile Island region would never be hit by a tsunami. Tsunamis with wave heights of 65 feet could be expected at Fukushima.

During the 2011 "Fukushima Daiichi nuclear disaster," one of Fukushima's reactors was on "cold shutdown" for maintenance. Nothing happened to it. Secondary containment withstood the tsunami forces without failure. The three other reactors were operating. I understand that their secondary containment structures also withstood the tsunami wave. However, the diesel generators located at sea level did not withstand seawater immersion. Emergency pumping power to spray pumps, if they even had them, would have been lost in all three operating reactor systems. A LOCA occurred in each operating reactor; consequently, hydrogen was released into secondary containment. News reports said Unit 1 and 3 containment buildings suffered catastrophic damage (i.e.: were "blown to pieces") as detonable concentrations of hydrogen were reached and ignited. Unit 2 had a different outcome. Unit 2's secondary containment had been vented to release high-pressure gases. A high spike in radiation levels was noted at a remote sensor and recorder site located a distance from the reactor buildings before the hydrogen detonations occurred in Units 1 and 3. Thus, all three units contributed to radiation release to surrounding populated areas. According to various internet sources, 135,000 people were evacuated within a 30-kilometer area.

It was reported that the Japanese government has spent over $200 billion (equivalent) on cleanup. Japanese officials stated they expect cleanup efforts will continue for another 40 years. An unknown person was reputed to have said this incident occurred because Tokyo Electric Company did not want to spend extra money to locate emergency generators at high elevations, nor put in tsunami-proof enclosures with adequately supported air supply systems and exhaust gas stacks. I do not know if they had awareness of the cited paper I presented to Northeast Utilities prior to construction. Streaming videos in 2020 (Curiosity Stream) show air views of rectangular concrete reactor buildings that looked to be intact. However, videos of interior floor spaces show much debris scattered about. Since widespread contamination of outlying areas was reported by news media, containment by secondary buildings must have been breached in the reported explosions. I cannot see why Japanese designers chose rectangular buildings for ultimate containment. Flat walls and roofs cannot withstand nearly as much overpressure as cylindrical walls and hemispherical caps that are reinforced for tensile loads.

CHERNOBYL

Chernobyl was a monumental disaster even compared with Fukushima. Hundreds or thousands died immediately from radiation exposure when men were sent into the area to combat spreading cataclysm. How many more will die from delayed exposure? We will probably never know. The Russians are close-lipped about the incident. So, what exactly happened? You have to know how the Chernobyl reactor was built to understand what transpired.

It was known before the incident that Russian reactors were made with huge cubes of carbon in blocks serving as moderator, just as Fermi's first Chicago Pile had been built. However, inside these carbon blocks, many canisters of uranium fuel were positioned. Also, many hundreds (if not thousands) of U-tube-shaped steel steam generators were positioned throughout the carbon mass. Hot, high-pressure water was probably supplied from manifolds. When water turned to steam at high pressure, it was collected in other manifolds to be delivered to steam turbines. Multiple control rods were also positioned within the reactor to absorb neutrons and limit reactivity levels.

BBC TV relayed that control rods were lifted, a lateral reactor core shift occurred, and control rods could no longer be dropped all the way to effectively shut down the reactor. Carbon temperatures soared, metal containers inside the core melted or burst. Steam lines ruptured, sending hot steam into hotter carbon. At 1500°F and above, carbon and water form gases methane and hydrogen. Trapped inside the metal containment building, a detonable gas cloud formed above the reactor. This metal building had no overpressure containment capability. It was several-hundred-feet wide, possibly a hundred-feet high. A detonable cloud of gas that large would have shredded the metal building and torn apart any equipment inside.

The radioactive cloud from Chernobyl reached the Scandinavian countries hundreds of miles away. The BBC reported the worst was yet to happen unless something could be done to drain water trapped under the molten reactor core that was melting its way downward. If there had been a steam explosion that blew the molten reactor core skyward, the tragedy would have been many hundreds of times worse than the initial blast.

Coal miners from the Urals were brought in to dig out the area under the reactor so water could be drained and concrete set in place to stop the core from melting down through the earth. All of these men died from immediate massive radiation exposure. Helicopter pilots dropping concrete onto the reactor suffered high radiation exposure and death even though they were over the reactor for seconds each time they dropped a load.

The huge sarcophagus that was erected around the reactor failed after 50 years. It has been superseded by an even larger one that is supposed to last hundreds of years. Lethal radiation at Chernobyl will be around for another hundred thousand years. Russian engineers claimed before the incident that their design was superior to American designs. Chernobyl amply proved otherwise. I could never understand their claim. A system that had hundreds of welds inside a hot carbon body subject to weld failure or just leaking was a surefire way to get a water-gas reaction, which, as we learned in high school chemistry, would produce copious quantities of hydrogen and methane ripe for explosion.

These two real disasters and a supposed one at Three Mile Island have set nerves of the world's populace on edge. Who could trust nuclear power companies to provide safe power when faced with the possibility of such a huge disaster happening in one's own backyard? I hope to relate how the nuclear power industry got started in the US. Other "free-thought" countries followed US design lead, adapted designs as they saw fit, and proceeded with a nuclear power commitment.

I intend to finish this discussion with hope that new technologies can mitigate waste disposal problems from water cooled reactor fuel disposal. I will state my understanding of new systems that might supply nuclear power to localities safely and at high efficiency.

ORIGINS AND DISPOSAL

How did water cooled reactors get started? Engineers at Argonne National Labs made the very first power-producing reactor system. It was housed in a steel-shell secondary containment building on Argonne's site 30 miles southwest of Chicago's loop. My boss, Ken Kuczen, was one of the engineers on the project. The system generated only enough electric power to light a half dozen 150-watt bulbs. Various companies and the US Navy copied the design, upgrading power levels.

Admiral Hyman Rickover pushed the Navy into building nuclear-powered submarines. Surface ships, such as aircraft carriers, were also fitted with nuclear reactors. Rickover set up a training site in Idaho for submariners to learn how to operate reactors in submarines. These operators eventually left the Navy and got jobs in industry operating commercial-power-generating reactors. They could meld well in this new industry because builders had used Navy design data to build commercially. I do not favor water cooled reactors. President Jimmy Carter purportedly said, "Rickover was the greatest engineer who ever lived." I disagree. He is in no small way responsible for the situation in which we now find ourselves involved.

A bit more background is needed at this point: fuel used in reactors is beneficiated (processed to higher concentration of fissile material) to get fissile concentrations (U235) of 20% compared with natural uranium, having 0.7% U235 isotope. Water cooled reactors typically burn up two or three percent of the fissile material before dumping it from the reactor. This procedure is done to avoid breaching fuel cladding that would otherwise release fission gases and nasty solids into the water cooling. Spent fuel rod assemblies are stored in water-filled "swimming pools" to absorb decay heat and shield from radiation. Harmful radiation levels persist for *one hundred thousand years*. That's a "wonderful" legacy to leave for the few thousand generations of folks who will follow us. I blame Hyman!

Hyman reportedly said, "If our oceans were made of sodium, some damn fool would want to use water cooled nuclear reactors." This supposed logic was to counter use of sodium-cooled fast reactors for sub and ship propulsion power. A submarine, Seawolf, was built with fast-reactor propulsion power. It had a smaller hull, went faster, had better fuel usage, etc. Then it had a small sodium leak that (I understand) was easily fixed. However, Rickover used this "problem" as an excuse to gut the Seawolf, install a smaller water-cooled unit, and watch it fade from glory.

Argonne developed a small fast reactor that generated minimal electric power in the early 1950s. It was located in Idaho. A second Experimental Breeder Reactor (EBR-II) later went online as well, also in the mid-1950s in Idaho. It was used to do fundamental research on reactor physics and safety issues throughout its nearly 40-year life while generating 20 megawatts of electric power with an availability of 95%. DOE shut it down in 1994. I'll write extensively of my involvement with EBR-II in the later ANL sections. I will also tell my view of future developments in nuclear power I see as necessary if we are to get stable electric power at gigawatt levels for future generations. Of course, what really happens in the future depends totally on perspicacity and the vision of politicians in power.

Argonne developed a process to recover usable fuel from spent fuel assemblies from either water cooled or fast reactors. This process was called "electro-winning." My friend, Jim Bailey, was the engineer who did the development work and testing. This fuel recovery process involved electrolysis of spent fuel in chopped-up pieces of fuel assemblies. A spongy mass of usable fuel accumulates on one electrode. It can be further processed into new fuel that is encased in new, stainless steel tubing. Highly radioactive decomposition products of the fission process are encased in molten glass. Chunks of solidified glass are deposited in nuclear waste disposal facilities. The important thing to remember is: This waste decays to a harmless level in one hundred years. People could and can safely hold it after this relatively short period of time. Argonne had a facility called HFEF (Hot Fuel Examination Facility) which was located immediately near EBR-II. Spent fuel assemblies were regularly transferred from the reactor to HFEF for examination. All work was accomplished using remote manipulators. HFEF had three-foot-thick borated glass windows to directly view work in progress. It also had remote-controlled cameras that could focus in detail on work as required. That said, HFEF was shut down in 1994 along with EBR-II.

There is no rational reason to store waste nuclear fuel from any kind of reactor for 100,000 years. Some political solution must be forced on electric utilities to amortize waste-disposal costs on a current-cost basis. It makes no sense to burden future generations with these costs, which can only get higher.

Electric power is usually generated in blocks of 1,000 megawatts. There is an economy of scale in this way. However, power transmission over long distances results in resistance losses as high as 10-15%. Having smaller power generation units located near where power is consumed makes a lot of sense. Only intermediate voltages are needed with short transmission lines. High voltages have severe inherent safety problems.

New modular 50-megawatt power generation units are envisioned where one could be transported by a single truck from a manufacturing plant to a selected location, offloaded, and plugged into a local utility grid. One of the new envisioned power generation systems uses a molten-salt-cooled reactor supplying high-temperature energy to a supercritical carbon-dioxide closed Brayton cycle. This cycle promises thermodynamic efficiencies of 50%. Waste heat can be dumped into the atmosphere using air blast heat exchangers. Even higher energy utilization rates can be found where the electric power generation is located near an industry in need of process heating. Several of these systems are in development at present. (A note of explanation: jet planes use an open Brayton cycle where air is ingested and compressed; fuel is burned with hot gas exiting through a turbine, which spins the compressor. Jet engines produce huge amounts of horsepower for their size. In a closed Brayton cycle, heat is added at one point after compression, work is done in a turbine, and the working gas is cooled and recirculated to the inlet of the compressor. High mechanical power levels can be obtained using compact high-rotation speed equipment.)

I AM NOT AN ANALYST

I've always had a hard time solving differential equations, though I could formulate them. Professor E.R.G. Eckert had taught us well for any given fluid dynamics/heat transfer problem at U of M. We could take the Navier-Stokes Equation and derive most any required differential equation from this generalized theorem. Nevertheless, I still couldn't crack the code. I had taken six courses of calculus during undergrad and graduate school and even more later in night school. I had a decent understanding of what Newton and Leibnitz had invented. Their calculus allowed someone to find out what happened to a dependent variable in an ordinary differential equation as an independent variable changed. Partial differential equations represented multi-dimensional systems where many variables could change, thus affecting dependent variables. I understood the reasoning behind all this analysis. The situation was that the easy problems had been solved by the geniuses of years gone by. Only tough ones remained.

I see no logical reason to teach calculus to high school students. It should be left to math majors in college. I never used it in my working career. The usual technique for solving a calculus problem was to guess a solution, differentiate your guess, and see if it matched the starting equation. I was a lousy "guesser." My "breakthrough" in doing such analysis came when I learned to transform differential equations into corresponding "finite difference equations."

Harley Burge shared a text written by one of his professors at Penn State, G. M. Dusinberre, titled *Heat Transfer Calculations by Finite Differences*. This book changed my professional life. Difference equations represent differential equations (which use infinitesimally small steps) by using larger, "finite" steps in changing independent variables to proceed along a solution path. A larger step might introduce a stability problem in solving the equation. However, one can keep the mathematical solution stable by merely limiting step size according to criteria developed by Dusinberre. The stability criterion permits a difference solution to follow the analytic solution quite closely. By reducing step size even further than the maximum size allowed, subsequent iterations can show how accurately the analytic solution is being followed. With computers, one can redo calculation sequences with ease.

On my last day at U of M, Tom Irvine (my master's thesis advisor) had told me, "You're a good experimentalist, but never try to do analysis." I had accepted that view of myself. Tom Coultas, however, would never accept my protests that "I am not an analyst." He became my mentor and insisted I take all the night schooling my schedule would allow during the first 10 years I worked at Rocketdyne. He and another supervisor, Bob Seader, had faith in me I lacked in myself. I had another "breakthrough" in doing analysis when a colleague at Argonne (Jim Bailey) taught me how to solve transcendental equations. A transcendental equation is one where you have to know the answer to get the answer! Yes, there are such problems. The solution technique is to throw away all values of the unknown in a known interval that do not permit a match of the chosen value with the assumed value. Sounds difficult. It isn't, just hard to explain.

Coultas had an abiding principle as a supervisor: "You can make any mistake once, but beware of making the same mistake again." I made mistakes many times, but not the same one twice!

Many years later, while I was in Moscow, Russia, I saw what the reverse philosophy could do to inhibit output from talented professional people. They were not allowed to make any mistakes whatsoever at any time. Consequently, they did little, if any, work! These bright engineers knew they would get regular raises and advancements if they "merely showed up for work" – and so they did!

BELL'S LUNAR ASCENT ENGINE

There were not many engineers in Rocketdyne's Research Department (total of 200) who programmed computers – maybe a dozen or so. Coultas asked me to assist Carl Oberg in solving an infinite series solution to an equation he had derived. Rocketdyne had been tasked by NASA to "fix" a combustion instability problem in the lunar ascent rocket engine made by the Bell Aerospace Corporation. Bell's lunar ascent engine was going to lift astronauts off the moon. It was the only thing between them and spending the rest of their lives there. If the ascent engine did what was happening at Bell's test lab – burn the combustion chamber out in half the time it was supposed to run, astronauts would go splat back on the moon!

The ascent engine was known as a "screamer." It had a combustion instability that increased the chamber heat transfer rate to such a large extent, the uncooled carbon composite would burn through, and the engine would self-destruct long before its expected mission life. In other words, the astronauts would never make it back from the surface of the moon to the command module.

NASA had the idea that the engine injector was somehow at fault. They had Bell get the injector to Rocketdyne and Rocketdyne brought it to Tom Coultas.

Coultas had a reputation for solving Apollo's F-1 engine instability problem. He looked at it and said, "Well, we've got to know what's going on." He assigned the problem to Carl Oberg, who was a brilliant chemical engineer, and also a very sharp mathematician. Oberg did a "Green's Function" solution (a fourth order integral equation, had an infinite series solution of algebraic terms) to determine the predominant mode of instability in the engine. But once he had the mathematical solution, he didn't know what to do with it! Hand calculations to evaluate an infinite series of terms is not a task that could be anticipated with any thought of future happiness (a la Roger Schmidt). It was a problem made for a computer!

Carl couldn't program. I could. So, Coultas gave me this task. I used a time-share computer that gave me complete control of its use. I could readily make program changes at a moment's notice. I did not have to rely on couriers and wasted transit times to get computer runs done. My findings? Oberg's infinite series solution did not converge. The computer spewed out gibberish. There was a mistake somewhere, either in my program or in Oberg's solution. I could find no mistake on my part, so I informed Carl of the problem. After several days waiting, I asked Carl if he had found his mistake. No, he had not, though he "had checked his work a thousand times." I took the job to find his mistake myself. I had Green's Functions in college with little understanding, but something happened to me in my "work environment!" I understood what Oberg had done! I found his error, a simple substitution of a plus sign for a minus sign. HIS SOLUTION STOPPED GIVING GARBAGE!

I didn't know where to truncate the infinite series, so I set up the program to "eject" an answer after evaluating a few million terms and then continue calculating for another few million terms before finding a "final answer." I could then compare the two answers to see if they agreed within a tolerable small difference. The two answers were close, so the series converged.

With the sign changed and the program's rational answer, Carl and I were ecstatic. We told Coultas. Coultas was happy. He had machinists mill little (almost imperceptible) Helmholtz resonator cavities spaced at intervals around the rim of the injector where it mated with the chamber. Helmholtz resonators can be designed to operate at a certain frequency. They soak up that energy.

On a whim, Coultas had a mechanic go to Ace Hardware and buy some ordinary red enamel and green enamel paint, a little can of each. He had the mechanic paint the fuel lines red and the oxidizer lines green. Rocketdyne shipped the modified injector back to Bell Aerospace, they tested it, and it was stable. NASA was happy.

The Ascent engine was installed in Apollo 11 and Armstrong and Aldrin lifted off the moon. In the movie *The Right Stuff,* Neil Armstrong reputedly turns to Buzz Aldrin saying, "It's a smooth ride." Well, what the public doesn't know is that "it's a smooth ride" meant that they knew that the engine was stable and that they didn't have to worry about it burning up the chamber and them going SPLAT! Now you know the background – the astronauts had obviously heard about the engine's stability problem before it was fixed. But, there is, as Paul Harvey comments, still "the rest of the story."

Bell Aerospace could not see what had been done to modify their engine injector aside from the red and green paint.

20 or 30 years after I had worked on this project with Oberg, I worked at Argonne Labs in Chicago and became friends with a former Bell rocket engineer, Scott Smith. He said, "Larry, you don't know how much consternation this paint caused us! We analyzed that red and green paint seven ways to Sunday to try and find out what magical properties it had to stabilize that engine!" Because apparently, they could not detect those Helmholtz resonator cavities on the external rim of the injector, or they didn't look closely enough because of the paint. And so, they lived with this red and green herring that Coultas had provided them. That's the rest of the story, as it would be told by Paul Harvey on the radio.

There is a subsequent part of this story as it pertains to me. Coultas had quirks, and one of his quirks was that he'd often use the back of an old envelope that had room to scribble on and the stub of a pencil that was so short, you could no longer sharpen it, to do his calculations in order to save company money! He did calculations *in his head*. Later, in retirement, Coultas told me he had hand calculated the approximate instability frequency that had to be absorbed in the Bell engine good enough that he had already sent this injector to the machine shop before Oberg and I finished our assignment. It was probably done by the time we got done with our analysis! Oberg and I knew nothing about his doing that at the time. But I believe Coultas, because he didn't tell lies. He was very honest. At least the solution Oberg found and I programmed corroborated Coultas' estimate. (I would probably say it was an estimate, not just a guess.) So, it kind of burst my balloon and bruised my ego when my wife Deann and I visited Coultas and his wife Joyce at their home in Winchester, Illinois and he told his version of events, but this edition makes a better story!

DISSOLVING HYDROGEN FOR THE NAVY

Bobby Dickerson was a coworker and friend at Rocketdyne. I considered him the smartest engineer in the department. He had an innate ability to analyze problems and provide theoretical solutions. Unfortunately, he usually wasn't able to implement a theoretical solution to make some working hardware. Luckily, I excelled at making hardware. Therefore, I made sure I kept abreast of what Bobby Dickerson was doing most of the time. I would ask him pointedly, "What's happening with you?" He had no guile and would tell me.

One time, Bobby had been given a problem which involved dissolving hydrogen in water. Nuclear submarines electrolyze water to make oxygen to replenish their limited air supply, thereby allowing them to operate for extended periods underwater. Hydrogen is a waste product they want to dispose of without outside detection. The question was:

"Will the hydrogen dissolve in saltwater before it reaches the ocean's surface?"

Bobby approached the problem by noting the depth at which the submarines operated as well as the size of the bubbles released. He calculated the solution rates as the bubbles ascended using a Henry's Law constant for a dilute solution of hydrogen gas in water with bubble dynamics equations he found in a Russian text, *Physicochemical Hydrodynamics* by Veniamin Levich. He found that, below a certain depth in the ocean and below a critical size, bubbles would dissolve nicely before reaching the surface. The Navy then knew how to release hydrogen without detection.

I extended his analysis to a problem of dissolving air in water at relatively shallow depths where atmospheric pressure is a significant portion of the total pressure (as it influences the process). I later used a finite difference computer analysis to design sewage aeration machines of various configurations and, later still, adapted the analysis to predict air solution rates for the Searle Company in its production of NutraSweet. Gas solution in a liquid is an important process in many commercial industries.

A FIXED-POSITION ELUSIVE SONOBUOY

During the first 10 years, Rocketdyne was a veritable playground. Work was fun – albeit very strenuous and challenging! There were many odd but interesting projects on which I worked. I remember one in which the US Navy wanted a sonobuoy that would have the ability to pop up and down on command between a submerged position at some specific depth and the sea surface. Of course, it wound up in Research, and I wound up doing it. (Coultas threw everything at me he could.)

The original sonobuoys, chucked out of Navy P-3 Orion airplanes into the water, floated on the surface. They were supposed to detect Russian submarines lurking on the east (or even west) coast of the United States via underwater sound waves. If anything came near, we would know. The Russians countered this by having their trawlers come by and sweep up the sonobuoys shortly after they were dropped into the water. A "pop down sonobuoy," on the other hand, would automatically dive down below the area swept by nets when an enemy trawler approached, and when they went away (hopefully dispirited), the sonobuoy would pop up to the surface again to transmit its information to American listening posts.

I worked out the scheme that furnished hydrogen gas for floatation of the antenna unit. This antenna unit was attached by an umbilical cord to a main unit which housed the hydrophones and was anchored to the sea floor. Hydrogen gas was automatically supplied in a plastic bubble by the chemical reaction of seawater with lithium metal. Water was admitted to the floatation chamber at the correct level whenever pressure was reduced by action of a latching valve, which opened to discharge hydrogen from the float. The correct pressure differential of "new hydrogen gas" that subsequently inflated the float was obtained using a short "pigtail" of tubing that dangled from the float unit to establish a pressure head. It worked in conjunction with the latching valve to admit seawater to the reaction chamber. When the float was full of gas, the hydrogen displaced water from the reaction chamber and pigtail tube, isolating the lithium from further reaction. You'd have dozens of cycles of this before you'd run out of lithium.

Another engineer came up with the design of the electric solenoid-action latching valve. With the latching feature, the unit needed only sporadic bursts of electrical power for control, which made it very electric-power efficient. All you needed was a momentary pulse of electric power, so you didn't have to power this valve all the time. That was a really neat feature on his part.

We designed the complete unit, which worked to specification. We didn't have 100 feet (in accordance with ocean depth) for testing, so I set up a tube that was 20- or 30-feet high and tested the unit thoroughly there. You'd push a button, and the solenoid would push the plunger over to one end, locking. You pushed it again, and it would move to the other end, locking. After some dozen cycles, I said, "Okay, we proved the thing works. Let's send a proposal out to the Navy."

The proposal was rejected because the senator of the northeastern town who built the old sonobuoy systems prevailed upon the US Navy. He didn't want the company to go under and all these people to go without jobs, so that was the overriding factor. Further, it cost more than the Navy was willing to spend. Instead, the US Navy bought thousands of one-shot sonobuoys that were swept up by Soviet trawlers in constant cold war games at sea. I've often wondered what the Russians did with all tens of thousands of useless electronic circuit boards. This was another case of the government "buying cheap" to save money.

COMPOUND A TORPEDO PROPULSION

We had another Navy proposal come to Research. The Navy wanted someone to develop a torpedo with peculiar operational characteristics. The idea was that you'd be able to let the torpedo out of the submarine to loiter independently at a slow speed for up to 24 hours as it searched for Russian submarines. It would have hydrophone sensors to detect and identify foreign vessels. Once it found a candidate target, it would go into a high-speed mode, developing approximately 700 horsepower. I believe it was meant to achieve 60+ mph and hone in with 30,000-yard sprint capability. Altogether, these requirements meant that this torpedo must have much more propulsion energy available than existing torpedoes.

Previously in WWII, torpedoes burned high-proof alcohol with hydrogen peroxide oxidizer to generate steam which ran a turbine that turned a propeller. Speed and range through the water were more limited. This proposal was complex and demanding. Once again, I proposed use of a mixed halogen oxidizer a fellow engineer at Rocketdyne developed. It was called Compound A. I can disclose that it's presently known to be chlorine pentafluoride – one chlorine atom and five fluorine atoms.

When chlorine pentafluoride became available, it was a natural candidate for use in this torpedo. Using Compound A with lithium would garner 8,000 BTUs per pound of reactants. The ordinarily used alcohol and peroxide yielded 2,000 BTUs per pound of reactant. A factor of four in energy availability combined with the fact that Compound A and lithium were dense meant that you could use the reaction of Compound A inside of a lithium tank to tailor your reactions to avoid changing the center of gravity in the torpedo. Two Compound A tanks, one on either side of the lithium tank, could balance out your torpedo, keeping a constant center of gravity. GE had developed the motor, which used an efficient Stirling cycle. Our torpedo design looked like it could do the job that the Navy wanted. We submitted the proposal. We didn't get the contract.

I found out years later that Fluidyne Corp. had also submitted a proposal to the Navy for this torpedo. They proposed using sulfur hexafluoride with lithium as an energy source, and the Navy bought it. Fluidyne got the contract, even though sulfur hexafluoride would only generate 6,000 BTUs per pound instead of 8,000, a definite decrease in capability. But the Navy apparently was happier using sulfur hexafluoride than they were using Compound A.

I've never heard of anything being built (to the point of being operational) using these reactants in this new torpedo, nor of its consequent hunter/killer capability, but again, the

Navy was the Navy, and so many things in the Navy you just can't understand, because it's the Navy.

DIGITAL WAVEFORM ANALYSIS

Another curious project at Rocketdyne involved determining operating characteristics of solid-propellant rocket booster engines. I built two shock tube tunnels for these studies. In one, I burned solid propellant sample slices while bouncing high-amplitude shock waves off the burning surface. We were trying to determine a "complex impedance function" of the shockwave form by measuring the shape of the wave coming onto the surface and again after it left the surface. By digitizing these waveforms and analyzing differences, we hoped to find out what caused combustion instability in solid-propellant rockets.

We never did find the impedance function, but we had the smartest mathematicians around working on the project for us. They were using advanced digital methods to analyze waveforms! In effect, they were leading a digital revolution in sound recording and sound reconstruction! The impedance question became moot when another researcher proposed using aluminum powder to enhance solid rocket propulsion performance. The aluminum powder did very little to enhance performance, but it solved instability problems completely! (Sometimes, one just gets lucky!) Now you know why there is always a "big white cloud" when a space probe takes off from the Kennedy Space Center. It's the "gazillion fine aluminum oxide particles" that are formed by combustion of aluminum powder contained in the solid propellant.

With the second shock tube, I hoped to determine the complex number transfer functions of shock waves traveling through pipes and fittings (elbows and orifices) that are part of liquid rocket propellant supply systems. At the time, no one knew how much effect the upstream piping had on combustion instability. There were only general guidelines to follow designing propellant supply systems. I set up a liquid-metal-filled tube that had very high frequency response pressure transducers affixed along its axis. With this apparatus, I showed shock waves propagated with little attenuation through most piping systems. One really had to work hard to prevent shock propagation upstream into tanks and propellant supply systems. This work reinforced an "adage" of rocketry: "You must have a significant pressure drop across the injector to isolate a supply system from transient pressure pulses generated by combustion instability dynamics." It felt good to show why this fact was true. It had only been known before by inference from trial-and-error testing of actual liquid propellant rocket systems.

SHOCKWAVES AND SOLID PROPELLANT COMBUSTION

We were interested in what happened as far as shockwaves influencing solid propellant combustion. I went down to the combustion lab, and I set up an experiment in one of the test stands where I could have a square, stainless tube that was rated for 1,000 PSI. And I could run it at several hundred PSI, which was about the pressure level that solid motors ran. I also had a splitter vane at the far end that formed two separate channels. On one side of the splitter, I could ignite a piece of solid propellant. This solid propellant either had a burning surface that was facing the wave coming in or it could be sideways to the wave. Additionally, I had fast-response pressure transducers that were located along each side of the separate channels. I had mounted a plain, flat steel end on the other side that served as a reference reflection surface. I ruptured a mylar diaphragm that would send a steep fronted shock wave of about 3-4 PSI pressure difference down the tube. I would shock the solid propellant as it was burning, and I would try to measure the incoming wave both on the burning propellant side and on the plain side that had nothing except the flat steel end wall. I would measure the wave coming in and out and I would send this digital data across the street to Freddie Traub who had a high-speed, large digital-tape-recording facility. He could pick up microsecond-type variations.

In spite of having the best recording equipment and clean, crisp, clear signals, we could never find anything that suggested a difference between reference and test signals. Still, we sent our digital data to mathematicians at another facility to try to glean some significance from our data. None was ever found. But I came to a conclusion.

I deduced that whatever was happening in solid rockets did not have anything to do with little pieces of propellant area. Whether it was sitting sideways to the hot gas flow, whether a shock was going sideways, or a disturbance was going sideways, or whether it was going head on, little things meant nothing. It was *the whole motor grain* that had to be the problem. And the problem was that every solid propellant motor back in that early era, (the early '60s), blew up at some point during its burn time. It didn't matter what the initial grain configuration was, or any of the operating parameters being changed – they blew up! And nobody knew why or how to fix them.

They had an expression, "We would put everything in there but the kitchen sink." They had what they call "resonant rods" that they would dangle in the combustion zone, and these were supposed to break up the pressure waves and prevent the solid motor from going unstable. Never worked as planned. The resonant rods would burn out and get spewed out the back end and that would be that! And I don't know if they ever put a kitchen sink in there or not, but I wouldn't doubt it.

So, someone suggested at some point that we substitute aluminum powder for some of the rubberized fuel. Basically, solid propellants are a mixture of an oxidizer (that started out as potassium chlorate and then it became ammonium perchlorate) with a rubber-based fuel. And so, they added aluminum into this mix, stirred it all together, let it cure, and you got a solid propellant they could make motors out of. The reasoning was that aluminum has a fantastically high heat of combustion: 300,000 calories per gram mole, which is far more than that of rubber. Typical feel is probably 1/15 or 1/20 of that. So, the expectation was that they would get increased impulse. Back then, liquids, specifically kerosene and oxygen, could get 250-some seconds of impulse and solids would get a little less.

They added the aluminum. They didn't get any higher impulse, but it stabilized those engines. My guess is that the little particles of aluminum oxide were spewed out the back end in huge clouds of white smoke. That's what you see when you see one of the solid propellant engine firings at the Cape lifting off as auxiliary boosters on some core vehicle, billowing clouds of white smoke: aluminum oxide particles. A dense cloud getting spewed out acts as gas flow resistance to pressure waves moving through. After that time, solids were stable. The problem was solved, and nobody worried about a small difference in impulse.

LET'S HAVE RAIN AND NO SMOG ON TUESDAYS

I know the title of this section is kind of cute, but there's a reason I made it that way. At some point in time, somebody at Rocketdyne said we should get a technical group together that did brainstorming and came up with new ideas on how to use Rocketdyne technology. I was nominated for this group. When you were nominated, it was not optional, so you did it. This group would meet once a month. It was led by one of the supervisors in Research chemistry. His name was Jack Silverman.

Jack and I never got along. He was, to me, a condescending S.O.B. and let everybody know that he was superior and would run the show. Well, before one of the meetings, I wrote a white paper on this subject that had to be submitted before the meeting. I was introduced to the group by Jack who said, "Larry's got this idea on generating rainfall in the San Fernando Valley and getting rid of smog. You might talk to us about it, Larry." So I did.

My idea was this: Rocketdyne had developed a lot of new technology over the preceding years that not only involved rocket engines but also auxiliary new equipment such as large pumps and turbines. For example: people don't know, but the Boeing hydrofoil that operated in Puget sound was driven by Rocketdyne pumps like those used in jet boats, except they're much bigger. I saw one of the pumps used in the Boeing hydrofoil. It was only eight or nine inches in diameter and three-foot long. It took 3,000 horsepower. A much larger water pump was on the drawing board. It was three-feet in diameter and 12-feet long. It would pump 60,000 gallons per minute with a pressure head of 1,000 PSI. Its power requirement matched that of a current GE jet engine being used to supply peaking electric power.

I used these numbers for a design basis to design a system that would supply huge quantities of water for a duration of a few hours at any one time to induce rainfall in the San Fernando Valley of Los Angeles. What would this system look like?

In the western end of the San Fernando Valley, there is a dry lakebed called Chatsworth Reservoir. Los Angeles never filled it with water because it would have just evaporated over time. The lakebed was approximately 80 acres in size and could have a depth of 10 feet of water. Fresh water was obtained from the Owens River for use in the San Fernando Valley. It was continuously piped through a large conduit. Chatsworth Reservoir could have been the water terminus and a source for outflows. A number of Rocketdyne pump/GE gas turbine combinations could pump water at high flowrates up the mountainsides at the west end of the valley where westerly winds prevail. Pumped water would gain 1,000 foot elevation yet have plenty of pressure head left over to distribute water to banks of nozzles that would form fine mists. Air thus treated would be cooled and tend to flow down the mountainside. By balancing the amount of water and knowing air velocities, one could get cooled supersaturated air that would be heated by sunlight, rise to higher elevations, cool by expansion, and condense water to rain downstream in the middle and eastern ends of the valley. I had spoken with our Rocketdyne meteorologists before I wrote the white paper and got their agreement to proceed.

At the end of my talk, Jack Silverman said, "You sure have big ideas, Larry, do you have any more?" I couldn't let that pass. Knowing he was Jewish, I said, "I want to air condition Israel." That comment did little to patch up our enmity.

THE NEW ROAD TO SUZIE

When I started work at Rocketdyne, I had to travel up the hill to the Santa Susana Field Laboratory, or "Suzie," as we lovingly called it! Rocketdyne had two facilities. The main engine production plant was down in Canoga Park and was bordered by Van Owen on the North, Victory Boulevard on the South, Canoga Avenue on the East. I don't know where it ended on the West, but it was a large acreage, probably 160 acres, in Canoga Park and 20,000-30,000 acres on top of the "hill." It was big! The engine testing facilities and the main research facilities were located on top of the mountain. A small amount of Research office space was kept in the Van Owen building north of the main engine plant. Mountains in Southern California near Los Angeles are not that high; they're really large hills. The San Fernando Valley has an elevation of 900 ft. The Santa Susana Field Laboratory was at 1,900 ft.

When my wife and I bought a house, we chose a location midway between the two facilities. I had about 4.5 miles to go to work at either place. Compared with most Los Angeles drivers, I had an easy commute to and from work. And of that, I'd say a mile and a half was on flat land in the valley on Valley Circle Drive and Roscoe Boulevard.

The road "up the mountain" was tortuous, filled with many switchbacks. There were places on the side of the road where the bank dropped immediately for hundreds of feet at a steep angle. There were no guard rails. The old two-lane road that existed when I started work was abysmal. The macadam paving was worn out with many potholes that seemed to never get filled. Hairpin turns of 180 degrees were positioned at hazardous places. Centerline paint had long ago worn off. And the top of the mountain was subject to dense fog – really, it was at a common cloud elevation. There were several thousand people who worked "on the hill." If a large truck was ahead of you, going or coming, you could expect a tedious trip. No room was available anywhere to pass. In short…it was not a good drive every day.

At some point, after I had been working many months, NASA decided that it was going to test the second stage of the Saturn V rocket using actual hardware, all engines, and flight tankage. The three J-2 rocket engines burned liquid hydrogen with liquid oxygen for about 150 seconds. Tankage was too large to transit the old road. It had to be widened considerably and re-paved with new base material and thicker macadam. So, we got a brand-new road, paid for by NASA.

It was beautiful! It was much wider, though still two lanes. Lanes were well demarcated by a very visible wide orange stripe. We didn't need to drive in the wrong lane anymore. Though, we did have one problem that remained: if you worked late at night, the fog would roll in so thick that you could not see the orange center stripe. Even with the new road, there were patches that had steep hillsides that went down hundreds of feet at a very steep angle. I talked to the head supervisor, Bob Lawhead, who had the road maintenance people put orange reflectors on the center stripe at ten-foot intervals along the whole thing. Lawhead was great in the way he'd get things done for his people. After that, you could go down the road at night, following the sparkling reflectors all the way down to the bottom. Usually, near the bottom of the hill, fog would clear out. Then we could drive safely throughout the valley.

Although we had a nice new road, someone voiced concern, asking, “What would happen if a hydrogen tank burst or had a leak?” Well, as with most everything, the problem came to Tom Coultas to evaluate. And Coultas came to me and said, “Figure out what would happen, Larry.” So, I did.

I lived less than three miles away as the crow flies from this potentially huge gaseous explosion. I decided to look at the problem as a “worst-case scenario possible.” That’s how you do these problems: you start with what you know has happened in the past and extrapolate effects. For example, a tank of propane gas exploded in a small southern town, wiping out everything within a half mile. Nothing remained of any house except for the cement block foundations. With 450,000 pounds (225 tons) of hydrogen mixed with oxygen; you could have an explosion equivalent to an atom bomb. Gas explosions in air do not act like high explosives. A blast from a high explosive falls off exponentially with distance. Fuel explosions in air die off linearly with distance. They start with a smaller blast pressure, but this pressure wave persists longer with distance. If a gas detonation starts with a few-hundred-pounds-per-square-inch pressure wave, it can still have a five PSI pressure front at a mile or more. That is strong enough to smash any standing structure. You never know how hydrogen will react. It takes almost no energy to set it off. Its ignition energy is as low as 10^{-8} ergs.

The one example that we’d had at Rocketdyne (that I was aware of) was John McCarthy running hydrogen cooling tests in a facility at Santa Susana. He had the test area rigged with a number of flares to ignite any hydrogen so it wouldn't accumulate if a test section burst. And as happened, the cooling tube burst. He had very fast-acting valves that shut hydrogen flow off on both the inlet and outlet. He figured that he had 1/10 of a pound of hydrogen escape. It did not ignite inside the test facility. It went up through a vented roof and detonated above the facility. The vented roof was thin sheet aluminum, which had no strength whatsoever. But the test area walls were quarter-inch steel plates. I went to look for myself. The quarter-inch steel plates were shrink-wrapped around large "dome loaders," as we called them. They were big hemispheres that were made of steel several inches thick, two feet in diameter. And to have a piece of quarter-inch steel shrink-wrapped around that device was impressive. That was what happened with 1/10 of a pound of hydrogen detonating.

We, as a group of combustion experts at Rocketdyne, had investigated our intentionally having fuel air explosives as weapons. So, we had background in that area of research at that point. What it came down to is that if you mix fuel with air at its optimum stoichiometry (an exact mixture is needed to burn completely), you can readily get a detonation. So, as a result of my evaluation, I told Coultas, "You'd better not have NASA test the Saturn vehicle here. It's too dangerous. Find someplace that's remote." So, after giving us a brand-new road, NASA moved their test facilities for both the F-1 engine clusters and J-2 engine clusters using flight hardware to the remote Stennis Operations in Mississippi. I don't know if they ever had a problem down there, but we could sleep at night in the San Fernando Valley. You could imagine what would have happened if there had been a problem. It would have completely shut down the whole engine test program!

As it was, I can add one thing: the little kids in our neighborhood would tell their parents, “The Reds are coming, the Reds are coming!” The kids would look up in the sky at night and see the rocket’s red glow from flames bouncing off the clouds. You could hear the rocket rumble; it scared them. Just seeing the red glare and hearing the noise was enough to get kids worried.

THE STAN TYKARSKY TRAGEDY

By March 1965, my boss Tom Coultas was forever giving me “little jobs” that needed to be done right now. After five years on the job doing mostly experimental work, I acquired Stan Tykarsky as my own technician. We’d done several complex experimental projects and worked well together. Tom had obtained a “whole” 50 hours of time for the two of us to do a job testing a commercial brazing torch head using methane and oxygen instead of acetylene and oxygen, but at 10 times design-rated heat generation rate. Would the torch head survive?

Multiple high-pressure bottle sets mounted on skids, for both gaseous methane and oxygen, were available from “stores” at Rocketdyne’s Santa Susana facility. I could use a test stand that was gutted of previous test equipment. Space alongside this test stand to place skids was available. However, recently, a liquid oxygen tank had been set up on the stand with a "blast shield" in place between the tank and the test area. This blast shield consisted of submarine wire mesh (quarter-inch diameter stranded wire on one-inch square spacing). The shield, eight-foot high by 15-foot wide, was anchored to stout steel posts on each side of the test stand. The posts were set in concrete. I was the first engineer to use the new oxygen supply system, which was rated at 3,200 PSI operation.

Gaseous nitrogen was available for pressurization. Venturi flow controls were installed in each system. With venturi control, inlet pressure could be set. Downstream of a sonic or cavitating venturi, flowrate is not affected over a wide range of downstream flow resistance. I planned to run each supply system at 300 PSIG (pound-force per square inch gauge). Downstream tubing size, lengths, and valves were sized to have low pressure drop. I had a small counterflow heat exchanger mounted in the liquid oxygen (LOX) flow to gasify it.

Stan installed piping and wired valve controls. Rocketdyne ran a 400-ton-per-day LOX plant at Santa Susana. Our lab had a one-ton capacity LOX buggy that could be towed behind our pickup truck. We would only be using a few hundred pounds of LOX (including tank cooldown), but since we paid merely $12/ton, we could get extra.

Stan got the LOX, filled our LOX tank, opened the manual pre-valve for the methane. I set up an oxy-acetylene torch in front to the side of the test article and sparked it to be used as an igniter. I put the whole test area on RED LIGHT. A red-light condition means NO ONE goes outside a blockhouse except responsible engineer and a buddy. I was responsible engineer, Stan my buddy. I pressurized the tank to 300 PSIG with gaseous nitrogen. I had visual sighting of all the test hardware. I set all valve controls to ON. Nothing happened. No burst of blue flame as expected from the test article. No orange flame from methane. If only it was flowing.

I thought Stan must have miswired the valves. We went out to investigate. I had Stan stay behind the blast shield for protection and I went out to the test article. I never got the chance to test that the solenoid valves were wired correctly. I was standing alongside the test stand when the LOX tank exploded. The blast wave threw me through the air about 15 feet. I landed on a soft sand bank, knocked out for a few seconds. My hard hat was cracked.

When I awoke, I went to see Stan. Others came out of the blockhouse. Stan lay on the asphalt. All his clothes were burned off him, even his tennis shoes. 100% of his skin was burned to a crisp. Two ambulances were called, taking each of us to a local hospital. Stan died later that evening. We all attended his wake and funeral.

One of my fellow engineers remarked, “I could have told you you’d have trouble with that tank.” I hated him ever after. Another, a friend – John McCarthy, told me, “Larry, this will be a turning point in your life. You can let it destroy you, or you can use it to become a better engineer.” I chose the latter, though it was not an easy time for months.

I was a pariah among some acquaintances. Tom Coultas also took responsibility for the accident. I took long walks with him at Santa Susana, both of us crying. State of California investigators determined that the tank had been made from titanium, not the 400 series stainless steel as had been told to Harley Burge, who got it as surplus from the Apollo program. Titanium is a "capricious" metal. It doesn't have a stable oxide coating. On Apollo, it was used for storing high-pressure helium gas. I was told later that both the gaseous oxygen and helium tanks "looked alike."

I have wondered if Apollo 13 had a titanium tank for its gaseous oxygen on Command Module. NASA has stated it believed the fire started by an O2 pressure transducer overheating. I hypothesized that the transducer was connected to the tank by a stainless steel tube. Stainless steel doesn't burn in gaseous oxygen unless it is heated to a very high temperature. A pressure transducer is not provided with much electrical operating power. However, Gomer, who worked on the Apollo missions, later corrected me. He noted that a spark is not needed to ignite something in oxygen.

My good friend Gomer also told a couple stories of his own harrowing experiences in running tests of Apollo hardware at Johnson Space Center's large vacuum tank in Houston. He related these stories to me in our email correspondences, following my divulging my story to him. His testing included Command Module and LEM hardware. I share his stories to show he knew far more about these systems than I did.

Below is a sampling from our email correspondence. My questions: "Did Apollo have liquid O2 tanks," and, "if so, what insulation was used?"

Date: Wed, 10 Jun 2020
From: Gomer
To: Larry Carlson

Did Apollo have liquid O2 tanks?

Below is what I copied from wiki:

Electrical power was produced by three fuel cells, each measuring 44 inches (1.1m) tall by 22 inches (0.56 m) in diameter and weighing 245 pounds (111 kg). These combined hydrogen and oxygen to generate electrical power, and produced drinkable water as a byproduct. The cells were fed by two hemispherical-cylindrical 31.75-inch (0.806 m) diameter tanks, each holding 29 pounds (13 kg) of liquid hydrogen, and two spherical 26-inch (0.66 ½ m) diameter tanks, each holding 326 pounds (148 ½ kg) of liquid oxygen (which also supplied the environmental control system).

If so what insulation was used.

I don't know - just looked like standard mylar foil on the outside. We did not fill with cryos for vac testing. The tanks also had stirrers inside so it wasn't just liquid/gas. A spark does not need an organic to ignite in pure Oxygen.

We used a lot of Freon for substitute liquids for anything liquid in the Apollo systems like rocket fuel and oxidizer etc. Crew & fuel cells got supplies thru quick disconnect fittings.

I laughed when I saw the fuel cells weighed 245 pounds. One night I saw one of the techs get pissed. Day shift had removed a fuel cell we installed the night before for some reason and it was sitting on the floor about 20 ft below the bay it belonged in. We had used the proper bracket that held a hand cranked winch to lift the fuel cell and swing it into the bay. Naturally that had been removed after we got the three cells in place. Putting on and taking off the winch was a pain in the butt. There was a removable "handle" on top of the cell that the cable attached to. Danged if the tech didn't grab the handle and carry the fuel cell up to the bay and set it in place. I was impressed even when I didn't know they weighed that much. He was a real macho looking dude. Same guy later went out to Downey for a trip when we were doing the block 2 checkouts there. Met a high dollar babe that liked his looks. Flew back to Houston with him and they rented a car and parked where they could see his house. Called his wife to come get him at the airport which was in Webster in those days (we used to ride Twin Otters up to the airport). When wife was well on her way, guy went in the house, got what he wanted, back out to the car and disappeared off to California with the woman. Probably as hired stud. Wife related story to friends. I guess I could fill a non tech book with a lot of stories.

Don't know if I ever told you my one scary experience. We were rigging to test one of the Shuttle payload bay radiators that fit inside the door but could be also moved like 1/2 way out to radiate from both sides. I had found a couple lengths of 4 inch Aluminum beam and had a tech weld them together to make the length needed to reach

> out to center of the door. Then a counter weight on other side of pivot. Dammed weld broke and about a 5 ft section of the beam came swinging down in an arc of cable. I dove about the same time my hard hat went flying off my head and the end of the beam with a rough weld sailed by. Just close enough that when I ran my fingers thru my hair they got bloody. Even scared the shit out of the techs. To me just another example that I have a primo Guardian Angel! Fortunately, none of the test article got damaged. Replaced the weld with a couple of bolted on plates and system worked fine. I agree, we paid our dues for this retirement.

Gomer never wrote a book of his own, though he had enough stories worth telling to do it. He had often remarked how it was really something that two poor kids from northern Minnesota got the chance to contribute greatly to the US Space Program. I include this part of his story to illustrate I was not alone in having memorable times in the US space race program. Gomer, by himself, found a design flaw in a Cassini propellant supply that would have left the spacecraft without maneuvering propulsion as it came up to Saturn.

All of this said and done, my career eventually got back on track, and I was accepted once again by most coworkers. In tandem with John Wruble's air augmentation test mishap, my policy became: Get all my work checked independently.

GEORGE SUTTON

When I was in grad school in October of 1957, I took a course in rockets by Professor Perry Blackshear. I thought it would be an easy class, maybe an easy way to get an A and boost my grade point average, and I was interested in rockets. Sputnik happened right during the middle of the curriculum, so the interest in space was extra high. I think there were 25 or so engineers enrolled in the course.

Dr. Perry's classes were engaging, and I thought, "This is going to be a good subject for me," until he threw us a curve in the middle of the program: the lecturer wanted everyone to do a trajectory analysis. That means start with a rocket on earth and follow it up until it gets into orbit, calculating all of the different variables that are needed to determine what this trajectory will be and whether a given vehicle is up to the task. (I can't remember if he specified vehicle characteristics.) That meant probably 50 hours of intense work to do the problem! And all we had back then were slide rules; no one had a computer. So, you'd have to step along as you went up into the trajectory, calculate everything with a slide rule, keep track of it in a great big table of answers, and likely just keep going until you ran out of fuel. Whether you got into orbit or not, I would have no idea. Anyhow, I decided right then and there that I was not going to do it because I did not have the time to waste; and that's how I saw it. So, I audited the remaining part of the course and thereby never got a grade. I've not regretted my decision.

The textbook Perry Blackshear used was the second edition of *Rocket Propulsion Elements* written by a fellow by the name of George Sutton. Sutton had done a decent job back in the early '50s. The book featured assorted pictures of various jet engines and rocket engines of various ilks alongside descriptions. One of the featured missiles was the German V2 rocket that had bombarded England. The book showed a trajectory for that rocket, which started out with I think 50,000 pounds of thrust and got up to 60,000 pounds of thrust as it approached its apogee. As I remember, this was a very simple engine, a "milk-can-shaped design." The Germans were burning fairly pure alcohol – probably ethanol – with oxygen. Alcohol does not have a remarkably high flame temperature compared with other hydrocarbons because you've got that OH radical in the alcohol molecule that says, basically, that you've already burned part of it up. Carbon vanes were partially immersed in the rocket exhaust, and with those vanes, they could steer the V2 rocket itself. And that's how they got it pointed at London. Guidance systems in those days were not exceptionally good, so the V2 did not have a very precise landing point; they sort of aimed it and hoped they had the right trajectory and distance controls set in for it to fall on London. Some did, some didn't. Sutton illustrated this scenario well.

I had been at Rocketdyne for a number of years when Coultas introduced me to George.

George Sutton, at that time, was a vice president of Rocketdyne in charge of looking for any place where applications of Rocketdyne technology could be sold.

Rocketdyne Research had no restriction in its areas of study. One time, in this pursuit, I followed George on a trip to Arizona to look into copper mine operations. Why copper mines? It turned out that these mines had problems we could help solve.

COPPER MINES

George and I went down into a mine in Superior, Arizona that had been excavated for many, many years. The copper ore had originally been discovered on the surface, but people had gradually mined it so that, by the time we came along, the mine was many thousands of feet underground. The vein ran at about a 45° angle to the surface. A cage powered by a pulley system raised out and lowered workers down deep into the mine. This had been done at some intermediate stage when they were still below the copper seam. After they had mined down to that level, they dug lateral tunnels out a ways, dug another vertical shaft, and installed another cage with a power system that went down even deeper. The mine had a stepped feature to allow ore to reach the surface.

George and I went down to the 4,500-foot depth where miners were actively digging ore. It was hot and it was humid – 100% relative humidity at 120°F. Everyone wore rubberized suits that encased your entire body. These suits, deemed necessary by mine management, intensified one's discomfort.

This mine had 300,000 horsepower for compressors and high-pressure fans to ventilate the mine and to provide high-pressure air for powering equipment down below. All equipment was air operated other than lighting. They couldn't afford to have electric sparks. Jackhammers used most of the high-pressure air. The interesting thing is: if you start with 90 PSI air at the surface, by the time it gets down 4,500 feet, you've got 150 PSI just because of the weight of the air. They had to actually regulate the pressure down at the work sites. Periodically, they set up blockages so that they could move ventilation air around from the surface to particular parts of the mine where they were working. They had to do this for several reasons: one was that the 100% humidity was atrocious. They got rid of the water that drained from worked surfaces by blowing dry desert air into the mine! When the desert air came out again at the surface, it was saturated. They did not have to pump liquid water from the mine. Another was that huge quantities of ventilation air would purge the mine, preventing accumulation of methane gas. (Yes, metal ore mines can have methane problems too.)

George Sutton and I got dressed in mining suits, donned mining boots, helmets, and lamps. We started off with a guide to go down into the mine. It took a while for us to ride a train from the first iron cage to a second iron cage that went down further, and then another train to go near where men were working. We had to crawl through the final passage where work was in progress. My God, it was sweltering. I could not imagine people working under those conditions.

When a miner put in an eight-hour shift, he spent the better part of an hour getting dressed and waiting for the cage, then another hour getting to where he was going to be working. The same two hours were spent at the end of his shift getting back to the surface, changing clothes, and cleaning up to go home. Based on that estimate, I guessed mine management might get four hours of work out of each person each day. And since the conditions were so horrible (rubber suits, rubber boots, heavy equipment, heat, and humidity), men would be slow working in this environment.

The idea I had was portable air conditioners at the work face. The mine had five-horsepower air motors and plenty of high-pressure air. They could run a little air motor, drive a freon system like one from a car, use the compressor and heat exchangers, and blow cold air into the workspace. The miners would be working with more comfort and might dig more ore. That's what we tried to sell management. They weren't interested. I don't know why. We spent a day in Superior, and I remember, at the end of the day, we were taken to a little "literal hole in the wall" Mexican restaurant. I had the best beef burrito I've ever had in my life, along with a bottle of "XX" beer. That beer tasted great after exposure to that mine.

On the second day, we went to another mine in a nearby town. It had a totally different setup. They had gotten down with their trains well below the ore mass. All they had to do was chip away or dynamite to knock the overhead ore loose and let it fall down into work areas. There, they could drag scoops along to get the ore over into a train and haul it out. It was a completely different situation...but it was still hot deep in the mine! Though it was similarly miserable, they were far more efficient in removing ore. The downside was that ore at this mine was nowhere near as rich in copper as the ore at Superior.

Nonetheless, both places made money, and that was all they were interested in. Again, we had nothing to sell them. Our copper mining adventure was for naught.

HIGH-RISE FIRES

I kept in contact with George Sutton for some time, and, down the road, he invited me to go to downtown Los Angeles with him to talk to the fire chief's office about possibly exploring a new way to fight fires in high-rise buildings.

I had, at some point, come up with an alternative. You'd have a jet engine, and burn jet fuel. You'd have depleted air – the oxygen content would be less than normal, maybe equivalent to 8,000-12,000 feet. It would be breathable – if you could cool it down. The idea was to spray water into the depleted oxygen air flow in a mist, creating fairly cool air with depleted oxygen that you could pour into a building. If you were extinguishing a building with internal elevator shafts or stairwells, or you could get this air routed around the facility in some other way, you could, in essence, flood a whole building with this mixture and put out the fire. We presented this concept to the LA fire chief. He immediately rejected the idea.

He said, "We cannot afford to do anything different from what we do now. If we were to use your method and something were to happen where someone was killed, we would have liabilities. We have no liabilities now because everything we do has precedent." George and I were not able to sell the idea. And it was all because of "political considerations."

OIL TANKERS

George and I didn't give up; we also went to see an insurance company. It insured big oil tankers. Now, back in that era (the late '60s), oil tankers were known to disappear. They'd be afloat and communicating one minute, and the next minute, they were completely gone. They disappeared from radar and had no radio traffic. Nobody knew what had happened. But we had our suspicions. There was a common thread: the tankers were usually on their return trip back to the oil fields in the Persian Gulf.

These ships were big tankers that had hundreds of thousands of barrels capacity. What would happen on a typical trip is that the ships would be filled with oil product, or crude oil, and travel to wherever they were offloaded. Once offloaded, tankers would have to partially fill their tanks with seawater to ballast the ship so that they could have stability in anticipated sea conditions on the way back to the Gulf. Once they neared their destination to pick up more oil, they would have to get rid of temporary water ballast. It would be pumped out (with some method of capturing the oil contaminants). A number of commercial units were available to perform this function. They wouldn't yet be at their destination when they started this process of cleaning up their holds to prepare for onloading oil. Of course, as they pumped out the water, air would come into the hold. There would be volatiles coming from oil clinging to walls into nearby gas space. Pressure washing walls was a common practice at this point in getting ready to load oil. This was the most critical time. A spark could ignite volatiles and cause a detonation. The detonation would totally disintegrate the boat. Typical detonation waves can be 300 PSI. Hulls are not built to withstand that level of impulse pressure. That's why these ships would suddenly disappear. It follows that everybody would be lost. A blast like that would demolish all superstructure that housed the crew and the helm as well.

We talked with the insurance people, saying, "We have a way of ensuring that this doesn't happen." It was based on purposefully using up the oxygen in the air with which you were flooding the hold. Gases entering the hold would have only nitrogen, a little carbon monoxide, a good amount of carbon dioxide, water vapor, and little else. Volatiles coming off the walls would have no oxygen to react with. No detonation could occur.

The insurance companies weren't interested. They said, "It's interesting that you came up with this, but the situation is this: our fees for transporting oil on these tankers are high enough that we're going to be making money, and if we were to have a ship fashioned with a system that could ensure it would not explode, it would make very, very little difference in our insurance situation. The value of the oil in one of these tankers far exceeds the value of the tanker. So, we're interested in the oil, and we can charge according to the value of the oil. The tanker's method of its demise is irrelevant, in a simple economic sense. There are too many other ways a tanker can be lost at sea." And that's how they looked at it.

I don't remember if tankers continued to explode or not; I think they may have developed ways to reduce that problem. Ship builders later transitioned to double-hull tankers, in which they flooded volumes between the hulls. So, hopefully, the problem no longer persists. But again, we were not able to sell our ideas to the insurance people nor to the oil transportation companies.

ROCKWELL ERA

Eventually, work became work. The last years at Rocketdyne were not happy ones for most everyone. Layoffs decimated the company. A staff of 27,000 was reduced to 2,700 as the Apollo program wound down and engine production ceased. I survived because I had an individual project that funded me full time for three years during the worst layoff period. It involved high-temperature spacecraft insulation that might have been used on course-correction rocket engines for the Mars Viking probe. NASA funded my project through its Jet Propulsion Laboratory (JPL). JPL later found a simpler and lighter-weight solution to the problem. My insulation was never used, even though I had amply demonstrated extremely low heat transfer rates in insulation operating at temperatures above 4400°F. Though I was completely funded by JPL, I also had many side projects during a time of massive layoffs. Advanced heat exchangers, water aerators, and chemical lasers were three of the technology areas in which I worked those later years.

Rockwell Corporation took over North American Aviation (NAA) in the late 1960s. As I understand the situation, it had not been intended to end that way. NAA bought Rockwell for $300 million with Apollo program profits, but within a short period of time, all NAA managers were gone and Rockwell people were in firm control of a new entity: "North American Rockwell Corporation." Even this name didn't last awfully long. Willard Rockwell (called "The Rat" by many Rockwell employees) egotistically changed it to Rockwell International shortly thereafter, with much "public" rationalization and justification given for his decision. I continued to design equipment for specific rocket testing projects.

One such program was run by Harry Arbit, an older test engineer of good repute. Harry was to test a tri-propellant rocket engine using hydrogen, fluorine, and lithium metal. I designed the heat exchangers for hydrogen and lithium. The hydrogen had to be injected at a high temperature that represented its having been used to regeneratively cool the engine. The lithium metal had to be liquefied for injection. I designed a "pebble-bed"-type heat exchanger for the hydrogen. A simple heated tank and feed line assembly fed molten lithium for testing.

Harry was an interesting soul. He had reputedly graduated from the University of Chicago at an exceptionally early age (I heard 17). He was not an "original thinker," but he was a supreme data organizer. I used to give Harry a copy of most of my work with the realization that I would lose track of some of it, while Harry would not! I could go to

Harry at any later date and ask him for a copy. He would then invariably go to his file of loose-leaf notebooks, pick out one, and let it fall open to a particular page where my report was stashed! I understand he had what is called an "eidetic" memory; he remembered everything.

CHEMICAL HIGH-POWER LASERS

Rocketdyne became one of the designer-manufacturers of chemical laser weapon systems for various armed services during the late 1960s. They were interested in this new technology. Around the same time, I was part of a group that was asked to attend a chemical laser course. I was only able to assimilate a minute portion of the book that came with the course, but, in simple terms, all I learned was that the beam spread (in microradians) of one of these devices is equal to beam light wavelength divided by the beam diameter. Basically, chemical lasers "worked" by converting combustion energy directly into laser light.

The first device Rocketdyne tested had very low efficiency. Chemical laser devices were made at first from copper, which tolerated high heat transfer rates well. However, the copper soaked up too large a portion of the combustion energy. The efficiency in terms of converting the chemical energy into beam energy was on the order of a few percent, which was not enough to allow a weapon to operate. Practical laser weapon systems would require something else. I became intrigued by how these detrimental heat losses could be minimized.

I mulled it over. We'd been told that the culprit was hydrogen fluoride (HF). Hydrogen was used in the combustion chamber to react with fluorine dimer (F_2) – it would raise the temperature to the point where excess F_2 would split into nascent fluorine (or just F). This happened around 1500°F. I decided to design the combustion system to run as close to being adiabatic (no net heat loss) as possible, planning for 1600°F to give it "cushion." I would use as little hydrogen as I could get by with in combination with helium diluent to keep combustion surfaces operating near optimum temperature as stated. I dared not use F_2 for cooling; it is too easy for fluorine to ignite most metals, especially when sharp corners are involved as in injectors. Copper could not be used at envisioned high-temperature levels. It loses all strength well below 1500°F.

Other designers had hoped to compensate for heat loss by using extra combustion energy. They ignored the fact HF acted as a poison in the cold reaction needed to get laser activity. Deuterium could not be substituted in the combustor to heat fluorine because it would act as a common heating source, thus it would not be available to participate in the cold reaction. Helium was needed as a diluent to spread out the cold reaction over a larger field of action, thereby stabilizing the effect.

Hydrogen fluoride (HF), a minor amount of unreacted hydrogen (H2), nascent fluorine (F), and helium (He) went through a supersonic nozzle bank in mixed parallel flows into the lasing region. The supersonic nozzles were about a quarter inch wide and one inch long. Each nozzle piece, rather than being a complete nozzle by itself, was actually a half nozzle facing back-to-back with a similar half nozzle. Flow occurred between opposing half nozzles in a gap (slot) only two to four mils (thousandths of an inch) wide. Expansion area ratio was enough to get Mach 10 flow speed. The high-Mach number outlet pressure was a few mmHg (millimeters of mercury). Expansion cooled the flow according to known thermodynamic laws, allowing deuterium injected into the supersonic stream to have a "cool reaction" with the nascent fluorine.

The resulting DF molecule formation in this cool reaction does not produce heat. Rather, its energy results in an electron being raised to a higher orbit. It's like a satellite in higher orbit having more potential energy were it to fall back to earth. An electron raised to a higher orbit in the DF molecule represents a higher, but metastable, energy state of existence. It can jump back down to its ground state if it is triggered by some external force, or it can jump spontaneously with no reason. When an electron jumps back to its ground state of existence, it emits a photon of energy as light.

To develop these lasers, maximizing DF molecule ions would be key. A few DF ions will spontaneously drop to their ground state, ejecting photons in the process. If mirrors were placed across the lasing region, the other DF ions would be triggered by this first photon of energy to drop to their ground state in unison with the triggering photon. The result? A coherent beam of light energy that bounces to and fro between mirrors until it is "scraped" off an edge.

To limit heat losses, I designed the combustion chamber and the nozzle bank to be adiabatic as much as possible. Walls would run at near-combustion temperature. I used the H2 and He in a counterflow heat exchange process inside the walls to cool them. In effect, I recovered the otherwise lost heat energy.

Fluorine is a difficult fluid to handle at high temperature – it will react with most anything. We needed a better candidate metal from which we could build efficient laser hardware! I spent time looking up melting temperatures of stable metal fluorides in my *Handbook of Chemistry and Physics*. Once fluorine starts burning metal, it keeps burning until the whole system is consumed! A stable fluoride layer (fluorine's equivalent of oxide) must be formed on the metal surfaces which will be exposed to hot fluorine flow to preclude fast destruction of the base metal underneath. The process to protect these metal surfaces and preclude burnout of the entire combustion system is called passivation. Passivation of a metal surface is done by subjecting it to increasing concentrations of fluorine, starting with a very dilute mixture in an inert gas carrier.

At the time I was trying to solve this problem, a friend and fellow engineer at Rocketdyne, John Wruble, was conducting a small fluorine engine study to determine some performance parameters. He was operating his combustor in the appropriate temperature range for my experiment. I talked him into letting me "piggyback" experiments wherein I inserted small samples of various metals in his combustion chamber to prove the hypothesis: "A particular metal's fluoride will or will not protect the base metal depending on its fluoride melting temperature and tenacity of the fluoride adhering to the base metal." As a result of these tests, I was able to corroborate my hypothesis that a stable fluoride was necessary and sufficient to protect base metal. However, tests of high-temperature alloys such as Incoloys and Hastelloys containing large percentages of nickel did not survive testing. Alloys of nickel would not work!

Upon further investigation, I found two materials that might work: pure nickel and pure aluminum. Both have stable high-temperature fluorides. However, aluminum melts at 1200°F, so it was unsuitable for this application. Pure nickel, on the other hand, will form a nickel fluoride that is stable, and nickel has a higher melting temperature than our expected combustor surface temperatures. It was the answer.

Passivation of the nickel was a meticulous process. You can't have any nicks or scratches in the passivation layer. You have to have perfect coverage of the final fluoride layer. It must be handled with great care! And that's what was done.

We built a small device that produced a 10-kilowatt beam. It was 10 inches long with a few dozen nozzles, each a quarter inch wide, one inch high. It cost over $50,000. It was shipped to us in a velveteen-lined walnut case like a big cigar box. I could hold it in the palm of my hand. It was like holding a Rolls Royce Silver Cloud, which was also $50,000 at that time. Lasing efficiency increased by a factor more than five by adhering to my design specifications. But I quit Rocketdyne at that point, both because of lack of recognition and a deep salary cut.

SEWAGE AERATOR

Work that Bobby Dickerson had initiated on hydrogen gas solution rates in seawater led to my work in aeration of sewage. Rockwell's Rocketdyne Division participated in a new technology agreement with a company called Envirotech which was headquartered in Salt Lake City, Utah. One of their divisions produced sewage aerators of assorted designs. It was apparent that no one in that industry understood the aeration process from basic principles. Many different aeration methods existed, and each had an arbitrary "number standard" associated with it regarding the cost of getting oxygen from air into water. Simple bubbler machines, where compressed air was injected through holes spaced along pipes laid along the bottom of a water-filled basin, were rated at a number standard of "one pound of oxygen per horsepower hour of energy input." High-speed aerators, which were essentially boat propellers attached directly to electric motors spraying water in an arc over the surface of a sewage pond, got "two pounds of oxygen dissolved per horsepower hour." Low-speed aerators, which required massive gearboxes to reduce rotation speed, got "up to four pounds of dissolved oxygen per horsepower hour." High-speed aerators cost less than low speed aerators (no gearbox). Economic amortization analysis could be done to show when total costs minimized. A municipality could decide on which device to buy based upon its own financial needs. Competition in manufacturing aerators was intense; most units of a given type mimicked competitor units.

Envirotech approached Rocketdyne asking if anything could be done to give their high-speed aerator an improved efficiency and thereby gain a decided competitive advantage, and Rocketdyne assigned the problem to me.

Over an afternoon's rumination and some basic fluid mechanics calculations, I determined that an insignificant change in a design feature would increase efficiency approximately 10%. This change was implemented, and the device was tested. It worked at the expected higher efficiency and gained Envirotech its competitive edge. By this work, I established credibility with Envirotech management, so that when a subsequent financial agreement between the two companies was signed, I received one quarter of the million dollars that was allocated by Envirotech for research work at Rocketdyne.

I was to design, build, and test a medium-speed direct drive aerator that had at least an oxygenation efficiency equal to or greater than their best low-speed aerator – ideally, four pounds of oxygen per horsepower hour. I did it on the basis of a complete analysis of the bubble trajectories and the dissolution/solution rates of the oxygen and nitrogen in the water.

I used Levich's bubble dynamics models to predict bubble histories and Henry's law constants to predict oxygen absorption rates in a finite step computer model I developed for this task. The computer did all the calculations effortlessly! I developed another computerized flow model which predicted system flows (bubble trajectories within the flow circuit), friction effects within the aeration machine, and consequent electrical power usage. All of the calculation models were verified by achieved performance of the test machine that fit these predictions to within a miniscule percentage error. A patent was obtained, assigned to Rockwell/Rocketdyne. However, what hadn't been anticipated adequately was a tendency of the machine to spontaneously go unstable.

A test series (to be described later) had been performed on a small-scale water tunnel mockup of aerator propeller blades to determine flow characteristics. These tests revealed no anomalous behavior such as blade stall with air injection. After the prototype large-scale aerator went unstable, it had to be shut down and restarted or the unstable behavior continued unabated. Above a determinable flowrate, which was within the design flowrate range, air at the inherent higher pressure caused the water flow to separate from the top surface of the propeller blade and make it stall, much as an airplane wing will stall.

My friend Bill Bissel solved the blade stall problem, suggesting use of a "splitter blade" located above the top surface of each affected aeration/pumping blade to force water flow to remain attached (acting much like the upper wing on a biplane). This "upper wing" would have been canted slightly upward with respect to a lower "aeration wing" using a higher angle of attack. However, his supervisor George Wong vetoed his idea and forced a lesser angle of attack to be used where the added blade actually caused greater flow separation. The aerator became more unstable in this configuration and testing was terminated by Rocketdyne management. Consequently, I lost project control.

Sam Iacobellis, who headed Rocketdyne's "Advanced Programs Department" had a friend, Bob Byron, who had left Rocketdyne for a marketing job with Envirotech. This friend's future with Envirotech was predicated (to some extent) on the success of the aerator that I designed. Sam was not pleased with me and this situation. I sensed that my future at Rocketdyne was tenuous, so I decided to leave the company as soon as possible. Bill Bissel took charge of the aerator project. However, he didn't know much about aerator operation, so I remained as technical advisor. The existing full-size aerator (75 horsepower) was abandoned. Nothing could be done to reverse George Wong's "wrong decision." Thus, a new design for a smaller aerator (three horsepower) was developed.

Instead of a design oxygen transfer efficiency of four pounds per horsepower hour, I elected to make the new small device with an efficiency of 12 pounds of oxygen per horsepower hour (three times as high as the initial larger test model). Actual tests of the device (which featured correct splitter blade angles) achieved *thirteen* pounds of oxygen per horsepower hour. We cheated a little bit in that we had a motor drive onboard that had variable speed. The variable speed feature had quite a bit of friction loss as compared to an ordinary motor, so we had to account for those and measure them accurately for every speed and every power load that we induced in the thing, and we did. So, we used that as a correction, and I think that we were within a few percent of real numbers. I can't guarantee it! I just believe it.

A report of these results was prepared. I left Rocketdyne, somewhat in disgrace, though I had gained vindication for my designs. I understand Rocketdyne and Envirotech never profited from the last aerator design. Bob Byron thus never made his fortune on this aerator, so that was a problem, and as he was one of Sam Iacobellis's minions, that probably gave me a black eye.

All paperwork specific to aerator design, including paper tape computer programs, was put in the round file, but I took the design principles with me – in my head. Envirotech never got the benefit of my further aerator research and development. I conceived and computer-modeled other new aerator configurations on my own time using my own computer after I had left Rocketdyne. Some of these designs promise better performance than the small three-horsepower aerator tested under Envirotech sponsorship.

A STOLEN PATENT

A postscript to the aerator story is pertinent here. As part of preliminary design work on the medium-speed direct drive aerator, I had modeled the propeller blades in a small, transparent water tunnel using a short section of congruent blading that spanned the tunnel. It was affixed to a cylindrical plug that could be rotated with respect to the incoming water flow. In this way, I changed the blade pitch and angle of attack. Air was introduced along the trailing edge as would happen in the full-size prototype. A high-speed motion picture camera recorded flow and bubble formation.

I had read a paper by David Elliot, a professor at Caltech and researcher at JPL who used the thermodynamic perfect gas law to derive sound speed in two-phase, two-component mixtures – specifically liquids and gases. He derived an expression, which indicated that sound speed in a two-phase mixture would be drastically reduced compared with sound speed in either of the separate phases. Sound speed in such mixtures can be severely reduced compared with either component's basic sound speed. For example, air has a sound speed of 1,100 feet per second at standard conditions. Snow crystals (ice) have sound speed even higher than air. When an avalanche travels down a mountain, it moves at approximately 80 feet per second. Its local speed is limited not by steepness of the slope but by the fact it travels at Mach number = one. Volcanic dust flow in air has the same limiting feature, though high air temperature allows a slightly higher velocity.

In both cases, the frontal boundary represents a shockwave that hinders the flow. The sound speed of a mixture depends primarily upon the ambient pressure and the mixture volume ratio. For example, with equal volume rates of air and water flows at ambient (sea level) pressure, the two-phase mixture sound speed might be only 75 feet per second, whereas sound speed in air is about 1,100 feet per second and sound speed in water is over 4,000 feet per second. Two cases are possible for water flow with air. In the case of a free surface of water in air, such as flow over the spillway of a dam, water velocity is limited by the analogous Froude number equaling one. When the water tries to flow faster, it shocks down in velocity and entrains air, forming a bubbly mixture. For the case of air ingested or injected within the flow stream, water velocity is the same as air velocity for initial bubbling action. If water velocity in a conduit is increased, at some point the water bubble mixture will shock, forming a milky mixture of tiny bubbles.

I ran an experiment wherein I could accurately control and measure water/air velocity and flowrates. I wanted to see what would happen to the air-water mixture when the entrant water velocity exceeded predicted mixture sound speed, thereby creating initial "supersonic flow" conditions. The motion pictures showed a "shock zone" behind the blade wherein extremely small air bubbles became dispersed widely within the water flow. This behavior led me to believe a similar effect would accrue in the large prototype aerator. A patent on this design feature alone was applied for at Rocketdyne, but the company did not pursue it. I habitually submitted patent applications to Rocketdyne's Patent Office. However, my success in having Rocketdyne's patent attorney submitting to the US Patent Office was incredibly low, although I persisted whenever I came up with something that I thought was unique. I kept a records file. I kept a log of this work, presenting much of it, including various applications deemed possible by this work to the patent officer at Rocketdyne. However, Rocketdyne did pursue and receive a patent for the overall design, which I termed "Supercavitating Supersonic Aerator Design."

After being at Argonne Labs for some time, I was summarily called into my supervisor Ken Kuczen's office where he asked me, "Larry, what have you done? There is a process server waiting for you outside the main gate." Argonne was a restricted facility; only approved personnel were admitted, so a process server could not get to anyone inside the gate. I didn't know why I would be served with a summons. Ken subtly "suggested" that I immediately find out what this process server wanted.

It turned out I was being deposed for a lawsuit brought by Baker-Hughes Corporation against a small waste oil-recovery operator who was located in Louisiana. He supposedly was "abridging one of their patents." I had to appear before two lawyers from Texas in a local Chicago area hotel room with a court recorder present to give my deposition. I had saved data from the water tunnel experiments, which showed I had done work proving small bubble formation and dispersion using supersonic shock phenomenon. Vern Lowly (I use a pseudonym to avoid harassing litigation), a former engineer at Rocketdyne who had gone to work at another Envirotech subsidiary, WEMCO, claimed to have invented the process, and for that he had received a patent at WEMCO. Baker-Hughes had acquired rights to this patent. My data proved he was not entitled and had literally stolen this patent.

I later learned the case was dismissed. I can only surmise that the "Lowly Patent" was subsequently found to be invalid by the US Patent Office. At the court hearing, which was recorded by a stenographer, Baker-Hughes was denied the patent, as I understand, from a follow-up notice. Lowly had been another friend of Bob Byron, who apparently got him the job at WEMCO. Lowly proved to me that he could live "down to his reputation" he had acquired at Rocketdyne.

A final note: I received a call from one of the patent lawyers. It seemed both had "lost" their copies of my deposition. "Could you send your copy to us?" I did, so my copy was the one used in court to present before the judge!

POWER SQUADRON

While working at Rocketdyne in the later years when college coursework declined, I took a series of night courses from the US Coast Guard Auxiliary called Power Squadron.

I was interested in sailing, having taken the basic course offered by the local YMCA. I was asked to teach basic "on the water" sailing and did that for about four years. Simultaneously, I took a series of night classes in seamanship offered by volunteer Power Squadron members.

I studied all courses up to and including celestial navigation, which was the last course offered. This was back in the days before GPS, so we learned how to take sights using a sextant. With "dead reckoning" and several stars' (sun or moon) sights and available formulas from Bowditch's principles of navigation (*American Practical Navigator*), we could determine our location in terms of latitude and longitude.

"Safety at Sea" was always stressed. In one of the courses, they had firemen come to demonstrate what would happen if safe procedures were not followed. Two example demonstrations were given. In one, they had a piece of Tygon tubing stuck on the end of an oxygen tank outlet. In the other end of the tubing, they stuck a cigarette. They blew oxygen through the cigarette for a short time, then they took this cigarette in a pair of long tongs and lit it with a long match. The cigarette did not burn – it exploded. Just the oxygen that was trapped inside the cigarette paper was enough to blow up the tobacco.

The other demonstration involved a piece of one-inch heavy wall steel pipe two feet long, capped on one end with a quarter-inch-thick steel plate. The fireman said they used to do the demonstration a different way, having the open end capped with a cork and using a spark plug to ignite a gasoline-vapor air mixture. But they ruined ceilings when the cork was blown out of the pipe. They put only 10 drops of gasoline in the pipe, tipped it back and forth a few times using a piece of Scotch tape to seal off the pipe to vaporize the gasoline. After setting the device upright, they yanked off the tape, put a lit, long match over the open end. The explosion was so loud, it felt like it shook the whole building. It sounded like it was going to rip the entire place apart! We were in a large, second-story room above a local Sears department store. All of that was just from 10 drops of gasoline in air!

All boatmen, whether sail or motor craft, are taught to always purge motor compartments with plenty of fresh air before starting an engine. I had experience. I could not understand how NASA and North American Aviation could have had such a bad design for Apollo 1. They should've had one person take Power Squadron courses! Then the Challenger and Columbia tragedies happened. Will we ever learn?

LEAVING ROCKETDYNE

There were plenty more projects that I worked on while employed by Rocketdyne, but I have not had them come back into memory. I left Rocketdyne behind in mid-October 1973. I took my remaining two weeks of vacation immediately before I quit, so I quietly "stole off into the night." Friends had wanted a big party, but I declined under the circumstances that I was leaving a less-than-glorious situation. I guess some of them were hurt by my action, but I could not stick around to be feted. During the last several months at Rocketdyne, I told some friends I was leaving. Mike Halloran, who supervised the Advanced Programs design group, hated to see me go. He had said, "When Larry came into our group, our projects started to work the first time around." The Research Department had been absorbed into Advanced Projects to form a new Advanced Programs Department. Except for specific management people, the name change meant nothing. Mike talked with Steve Domokos, who headed all of Advanced Programs, saying Rocketdyne could not afford to lose me. But Domokos said, "Let him go – we don't need him." And so, I went!

At that time, I convinced most of the senior chemical laser design staff to also leave. Several of the other laser system designers left Rocketdyne concurrently for TRW Corporation in Redondo Beach, CA, which went on to dominate in the development of lasers. (More on that later.)

Rocketdyne's laser group was decimated and never recovered its technical leadership position nor the morale we had enjoyed knowing we led the industry. I had not intended revenge – it just happened that way – but it seemed appropriate at the time that Willard's minions were disgraced in their own way. It also resulted in the company losing several (3.5) billion dollars of contract monies! Tough! They could take solace in knowing that they had "saved" maybe $100,000 a year in salaries by having junior people instead of seasoned senior engineers.

Rockwell's treatment of employees was in decided contrast with NAA philosophy. NAA wanted to treat people well and expected loyalty in return. They got loyalty while employees got a decent place to work! Rockwell seemed to have what has been termed a "dirt floor philosophy," which meant, "give the employee only what we can get by with." That might have intimidated machinists in Tennessee working in dingy machine shops having "dirt floors," but it didn't go over at all with aerospace professionals working in California's technology centers.

I sent out 150 "gold-plated" resumes when I decided to leave Rocketdyne – had them all done up really nicely and sent them all around the country – and I got two responses that were positive: one from TRW and one from Argonne

National Laboratories in Chicago. And the only reason I got them was that I knew Lydia Manson at TRW and Tom Coultas at Argonne.

Lydia Manson, a former talented office mate, had recommended me highly for TRW's chemical laser design group, but when I went down there to assess the situation, I saw a number of things wrong. The price of good or decent housing in Palos Verde Peninsula was 10 times as expensive as Canoga Park! It was well over a half a million dollars for anything you'd want to live in. Our house in Canoga Park was going to sell for $35,000 less commission, which meant $32,000 net, and we had put $45,000 into it, and there wasn't any hope of getting any better than that. TRW had a program where they would give you three years of difference in your housing costs and subsidize you (of course, it would be taxable income). I looked at that, but fortunately, when I was at TRW, a guy who had just ended his three years came down the hall screaming, "I am lost, I am lost! I do not have enough money to pay for my mortgage!" In addition, I did not know that TRW would not suffer the same cutbacks in personnel as had happened at most other aerospace companies.

At Argonne, they had been very friendly. Coultas had preceded me there by two years and had also left Rocketdyne because of Sam Iacobellis' machinations. I went to Argonne a couple times to establish the fact that I was insurable, go over my medical history, and ensure that they'd meet my conditions. They did. My wages would even go up a bit to compensate for the loss I had taken at Rocketdyne when they cut my salary. But the work was not particularly engaging.

I had a tough time choosing between them; Ellen and I spent literally hundreds of hours analyzing the prospects at both places. TRW decidedly had the most interesting work, but the cost of living and job insecurity ruled it out. Primarily because funding for personnel was assured for any foreseeable future, I chose Argonne! Yet, that was not the last I would hear from TRW.

My friend Grant Hosack took the job at TRW that I had declined, worked his way into upper management over a period of time, and TRW prospered. Unbeknownst to me, they were being funded by the CIA for covert surveillance satellite production and monitoring work. I would have been in the same building at the same time as the spy for whom the book and movie *The Falcon and the Snowman* was based... The same classified environment, working on chemical lasers! I will go into that dialogue later...

Leaving my wife Ellen behind to sell our California house, I packed the 1970 Ford LTD and headed east.

ARGONNE

COMPANY CLIMATE

Getting settled in Chicago was no easy feat. Ellen and I had listed our CA house with a firm that had hired Bob Lawhead as a realtor. Bob had been my "boss's boss" until he got fired from Rocketdyne by Sam Iacobellis. Bob Lawhead had always been a fair-minded supervisor who had the best interests of the people under him in mind at all times. He ran afoul of Sam because Sam was the opposite type of manager – a Machiavellian at heart. Unfortunately, Bob was not a good house salesman. A woman in his firm who was known as a "closer" was called in to sell our house. I flew home every few weeks to see Ellen and help as best I could on weekends. I came home to get the house packed and take Ellen and our cats to Chicago Thanksgiving week 1973. We drove in the 1973 GMC truck/camper we had bought that spring, never having gotten a chance to use it for camping in California!

The day after we arrived in Chicago, we had eight inches of heavy snow. Ellen was not happy with this weather and hated Chicago from the beginning. We stayed in a "Holiday Inn" near Argonne for several months until we bought a townhouse in Wheaton where we rented a condo from the builder until our townhouse was finished in March 1974.

Coultas had "set me up well" when he wrote a letter of recommendation to Argonne's Engineering Division's management. He stated in his letter of recommendation for me, "In an organization having the best engineers in aerospace, Larry was without peer. No one can match him." I had wondered why I was not being questioned to any degree when I interviewed there earlier. I was treated with an abundance of deference. It was hardly what I had expected after having had similar interviews at other organizations. I got to read and keep a copy of his letter the day I left Argonne some 20 years later.

My work in the Engineering Division at Argonne National Laboratory (ANL) in Chicago was decidedly different from my previous work at Rocketdyne. I thought at first that there wasn't that much to learn except my new job, which was entirely different. I had become accustomed for many years to do any required analysis, design, buildup, testing, and reporting at Rocketdyne by myself or as a Project Engineer with an assigned staff. Work at Argonne consisted almost entirely of paper studies (design analysis) and writing reports. Only a few things were ever built and tested.

Design work always went through three stages: conceptual, preliminary, and final design. Peer engineering groups approved a final design only after several cycles of independent review. I suppose this procedure was necessary because of the nuclear nature of most of the previous work. Everything had to be constantly checked and rechecked. Argonne engineers were super cautious, though I saw many of them being "next to incompetent." In fact, the old 80/20 rule seemed to apply especially well at Argonne, where 80% of the work was done by 20% of the people. Many people at Argonne seemed to be "retired" – they merely showed up at work each day, but essentially did nothing to earn their salary. There were a lot of "fitness freaks" who spent a goodly portion of each day jogging around the facility with no managers objecting! I was used to going to the lab and working with my own hands to get an experiment going, gather data, and publish a final report. I had to change my ways completely at Argonne!

The nice thing about Argonne was the fact that, even though money for building things came dearly, there was always funding aplenty for salaries. I didn't have to worry about being laid off. I learned that one can live with boredom when one's well fed and the work environment temperature's OK.

We in Engineering did have a temperature problem in our building. Our division director, Stan Davis, became "Energy Conservation Czar" for the laboratory. To set an example, we were forced to work in our offices with thermostats set at 68°F during winter months and 80° during summer months. Temperature extremes were hard to take, so, being engineers, we put a Ziploc plastic bag filled with ice cubes over the thermostat in winter to fool it and keep the heat on. Also, people brought electric heaters/fans to their offices to keep warm. Summers were more difficult to compensate for high-temperature settings… A candle burning under the thermostat would have been too obvious to Stan, who liked to wander the halls to keep track of things. We had to make do with personal fans blowing directly on us and hope our papers wouldn't be scattered in the wind.

MANAGEMENT

Over a period of time, I regained stature as a person who could get things done. I was promoted to an entry-level position in management and had a small design group working under me. In addition, there were always "side jobs" I could get involved with where and when someone needed my heat transfer and design expertise. At Rocketdyne, I had assiduously avoided management positions. I had seen too many good engineers fail at first level management, but stay in that position long enough that they lost their technical expertise. Tom Coultas had tried for years to get me to accept a management position. At Argonne, I saw no problem; an enhanced pay scale and advancement curve were a definite inducement to go for it!

I had been at Argonne for several years, and Kuczen brought me in one day and said, "It's time for your annual review." He said, "I want to show you a graph." I'd been a project engineer, you see, leading groups of people doing these jobs, but I didn't have an official management position. He elaborated, "Look at this graph – these are your projected salary increases for the coming years." And that graph showed a line that was considerably below another line that was for management. And so, I uttered, "Holy crap." He replied, "How would you like to be a group leader?" And I asked, "Does that mean that I get that kind of a raise?" And he said, "Yep." So, I said yes!

I got a new office, which was a nice little space in the engineering building, and I had half-a-dozen engineers who were working for me doing all sorts of other things. I had resisted becoming a group leader at Rocketdyne because I saw what happened there, but it didn't happen at Argonne. Group leaders at Argonne were fairly stable positions and you could count on Argonne paying your salary. You might not have made things like we did at Rocketdyne – we could do all the design work and nothing may come of it at Argonne – but at least salaries were sacred. You didn't have to worry about getting laid off and losing your job and getting to become a nothing engineer or any of that.

ENGINEERING LICENSE

During the time I was at Argonne, I decided to become a professional engineer. Now, there were colleges around that offered brush-up courses on all sorts of subjects where you could take an exam. Some people passed. Well, I decided that that wasn't good enough, so I took it upon myself to study at night after work three nights a week, three hours a night. I did this nighttime studying for three years. I studied every subject I had at college that was worthwhile and even some that I had never taken before, like engineering economics. I got a book on it, and I read up on it, and I learned how to do sinking funds and all sorts of cost amortizations and such as a result. After three years, I went downtown and stayed overnight in a hotel there, then took two days of testing. The first day was all multiple choice-type things and it was relatively simple. The second day was essay questions. I was fortunate in that I believe my boss Ken Kuczen had written the question for breeder reactors, and so I plowed into that one. I think I "ACE"ed it. So, I got my professional engineering license right away in one set of tests.

LIQUID METAL COOLED FAST BREEDER REACTORS

In my early years at Argonne, I worked almost exclusively on liquid metal fast breeder reactor design studies. Argonne had been the only instigator of nuclear reactors for the world's nuclear power/electricity production industry! It had the first water cooled reactor and the first two liquid metal cooled reactors worldwide: EBR-1 and EBR-II. The US Navy financed water cooled power reactor research for submarine propulsion under Admiral Hyman Rickover near Argonne's Idaho facilities. Rickover was absolutely against liquid metal cooled reactors in submarines, though one was built early in the program (Seawolf). Reputedly, he once said, "If the oceans were made of liquid sodium, some damn fool would build submarines powered by water cooled reactors." The American nuclear power industry almost exclusively used moderated water cooled reactors to produce electric power because of exclusive and extensive prior development "paid for" by the US Navy (and the American taxpayer). Rickover might well have saved the US Navy's bacon by promulgating nuclear power in fighting ships, but in a great ironic twist, he simultaneously screwed the American public, who wound up with low fuel utilization and large stockpiles of nuclear waste that will be around for a long, long time. If the American public ever gets smart (and that is indeed a big if) and adopts fast breeders for electric power generation, this stockpile of spent fuel rods could be reclaimed for breeder fuel. As of this writing, we would be forced to buy breeder reactors from the French.

In a rare display of intelligence, the French came to Argonne in the 1950s, studied the EBR-II design, and went home to copy it and design a larger scale breeder system called Phoenix. It generates 1,000 megawatts electric power. Later, they upgraded the design to 2,000 megawatts electric power with their Super Phoenix breeder system. France sells excess "breeder reactor electricity" throughout Europe to this day.

Argonne was a decided proponent of liquid metal cooled fast breeder reactors for one simple reason: you can "burn up" most of the uranium fuel in a breeder instead of being limited to a few percent of the less than one percent fissile material available in natural uranium. You will have, then, many times as much fuel value available from unprocessed uranium in a breeder reactor as you will from a standard water cooled neutron moderated reactor. Also, Argonne testing at EBR-II showed that the amount of fuel that could be burned before it needed reprocessing amounted to 23% rather than the few percent typical for a water cooled moderated reactor core. Further, many experimental studies showed that fuel from a fast reactor could be processed on site (within radiological containment) so fuel could be recycled locally. A fast breeder burns up the really "bad" poisons that accrue from radioactive decay, along with fuel burned. That radioactive material which is finally sent off to "storage" has been shown to decay to safe levels in 100 years, not the 100,000 years typical of water cooled reactor waste. And that's a massive advantage. The more fuel you burn up, the less you have to worry about storing, so you just add a little bit of fuel as you go along, and you're set for another cycle. In fact, much waste from water cooled reactors could be processed and burned in fast breeders.

The thing about the liquid metal reactor system is that you can ordinarily burn up something like 20% of the fuel value before you have to take the fuel out of the reactor. Then, you process it in a separate facility, reclaim the rest of the fuel value, and put it back in the reactor. You can go to more than 90% of fuel burnup with a fast reactor, see, and all you'll have is a dinky bit of wickedly hot stuff that you've got to pack away somewhere, which decays in a hundred years.

Argonne favored a "pool-type" breeder reactor system in which the liquid metal coolant (sodium) is contained in a large, unpressurized vessel. (A second containment vessel surrounding the first is used for added safety.) The sodium pool in this vessel represents a large thermal buffer that adds substantially to the inherent safety and stability of this type of system because transients are much more easily controlled than in pipe-coupled systems (such as the ill-conceived and ill-fated Clinch River Breeder Program). Argonne demonstrated that EBR-II would shut itself down in a simulated "loss of coolant flow" condition – primary pump failure. Two sodium paths are featured in Argonne "pool" designs. Primary sodium is circulated through the reactor wherein it is heated to a high temperature, thence through an intermediate heat exchanger where it is cooled before returning to the sodium pool for recirculation into the reactor for another heating cycle. Secondary sodium flows in a piping loop through the intermediate heat exchanger, in opposition to the primary sodium flow, are thusly heated with little loss in operating temperature compared to the inlet primary sodium. Secondary sodium flows next through steam superheaters and then through steam generators where sensible heat is lost. Secondary sodium is recirculated back through the intermediate heat exchanger to be reheated, repeating its cycle. Generated steam powers a turbine as in a standard electric generation cycle.

EBR-1 AND EBR-II

EBR-1 was a small test reactor that produced little power – enough to power several lightbulbs simultaneously. It was decommissioned after very little operating time.

EBR-II, however, was designed to produce 62 megawatts of thermal power and 20 megawatts of electrical power. It operated successfully, producing design electric power for nearly 40 years. It also served as a test bed for nuclear fuel evaluation. The reactor core had been designed such that fuel rods could be removed or replaced while the reactor was in full operation. Many thousands of experiments were conducted over its lifetime. EBR-II served as the model for France's extensive use of breeder reactors in their Phoenix and Super Phoenix power-production programs. EBR-II was located at Idaho's Nuclear Engineering Laboratory (INEL) site, 20 miles west of Idaho Falls. The Navy had reactors located north of EBR-II at INEL where they trained submariners. Argonne had another site at INEL called TREAT (Transient Reactor Experiment And Test). Its specialized testing was done to measure responses of various reactor components to rapid, short-term neutron bursts. ANL also had facilities near EBR-II that were used to examine used fuel assemblies.

EBR-II SUPERHEATER BYPASS

After a time, I was assigned to a project called "EBR-II Superheater Bypass." This was going to be a huge, total-facility project. I had been in research before and I had done a little bit of facility work, but nothing on this scale.

EBR-II had been built 25 years before this time. My boss, Ken Kuczen, was one of the original engineers who designed it. The design was all done with a slide rule.

NUCLEAR REGULATORY COMMISSION

The Nuclear Regulatory Commission's regulations were far less stringent when EBR-II was initially built than what they had become by 1973. Consequently, I had to learn a lot of the new nuclear regulations via a stack of binders that was a good three-feet high. When I went to Argonne, I had gotten an officemate, a fellow engineer named Ken Coover. He was a stress analyst. Ken Coover was a great help with learning this new material since he was already familiar with the rules.

The Nuclear Regulatory Commission (NRC) had a specific way of presenting material. First, they'd tell you what they were going to tell you, then they told you what they wanted you to know, and finally, they told you what they had told you. So, everything was three times larger than it needed to be, but that's the way the Nuclear Regulatory Commission did things!

The NRC promulgated RDT (Reactor Development and Test) standards from the original Atomic Energy Commission (AEC), a US government agency that had oversight and control on all things nuclear. Dixie Lee Ray was one of the first heads of the AEC. She was a "colorful character!"

SUPERHEATER COMPLICATIONS

EBR-II, no longer in commission, was a liquid metal cooled fast reactor. Fast reactor means that the neutrons are not slowed down by a moderator in the core of the reactor. Neutrons are allowed to travel at the speeds that they're emitted. With appropriate blanketing around the core of a fast reactor, sufficient new neutron emission was triggered to continue the reaction. I do not know reactor physics. I learned EBR-II's physical characteristics. The active core was on the order of a foot wide. It was hexagonal in cross section and about three feet long. The reactor was located in a large pot of liquid sodium. The tank was dual walled with an air gap between nestled tanks that had hemispherical bottoms, cylindrical top sections, and a flat deck that closed off the tank tops.

Inside the big tank of sodium was another structure called the "redan," which was basically just another thin-wall tank inside the double tank. This much smaller redan was used to separate primary sodium from secondary sodium. A pump moved liquid primary sodium through the reactor where it was heated, and then through an intermediate heat exchanger located within the redan, which transferred heat into the secondary sodium system. Primary sodium was very radioactive. Secondary sodium was not. It was a complex system designed to isolate radioactive sodium from the remainder of the power generation system. Simply put, the secondary sodium was pumped through large, insulated piping through the shell sides of two superheaters in parallel flows first, then through shell sides of eight water boilers in parallel flows. After that, it was collected and pumped back to the intermediate heat exchanger in the redan. Saturated steam from the boilers was fed into a steam drum where entrained liquid droplets were separated from saturated steam. Liquid water from the steam drum was recirculated back to the inlets of the boilers by gravity. Saturated steam went into the superheaters where it was heated to 875°F.

My first job was to handle the engineering that could result in removing both superheaters from the steam supply to the turbine. This meant that Argonne was going to take out both superheaters and run the turbine on saturated steam rather than the superheated steam the turbine had been designed to use.

Ken Kuczen and I took a trip to Lynn, Massachusetts to talk with General Electric Medium Turbine Division people. We told them of our plans, and they strongly advised against it. They said they would have to rebuild the entire turbine to use saturated steam. They'd have to use all new materials that were more expensive. They would have to redo everything. It would be a highly expensive, time-consuming job. GE basically vetoed superheater bypass.

I have to relate why ANL came up with the idea. Back when ANL built EBR-II, they had a choice of how to build the boilers and superheaters. To preclude the possibility that a flaw in a boiler or superheater single tube would permit reaction between water or steam and sodium, a decision was made to have all tubing double walled for both types of units. The probability of a flaw in one tube matching another tube flaw was considered infinitesimal. The question became: How do you get one tube inside of another and have intimate thermal contact?

ANL chose to have half of these units', four of the boilers', and one of the superheater's tubes brazed together. There was a metallurgical bond between the tubes. They still preserved the fact that a flaw in one tube would not be in the same place as on another tube. Brazing proved to be complicated, so the other half of the duplex tubes were swaged together with a mechanical interference fit. Tensile stress on the outside tube and compressive stress on the inside tube kept them intimately together. Over a period of time, operators noted that one of the superheaters that only had mechanical bonding had significantly lower temperature of superheated steam than the other unit. That meant that the thermal bonds between the two tubes were failing. It was not acting as well as the brazed metallurgical bond. As a result, you could have different temperature steam streams. Rapidly alternating temperatures on turbine blades could cause unacceptable stresses and turbine failure.

REPLACEMENT

We could not get rid of the superheaters. What we did was take one of the boilers that had the brazed bonds and put it in with the other superheater that already had brazed bonds. They were the same kind of unit, except that superheaters have a twisted tape installed inside each tube, set to help steam flow get better heat transfer. All of the units were, in essence, straight tubes inside of a jacket that contained sodium. There was a special compensation for differential expansion between tubes and shells. There was a bolt-on flange on the steam side that could be removed to add the tapes to the tubes in simple fashion.

In spite of the simplicity of the conversion, this was also a massive project. I spent several years at Argonne in Illinois and made a multitude of trips out to Idaho to talk with operating engineers. There had always been a rift between Idaho and Illinois engineering. The Idaho people thought that they should do the engineering, period. They knew the systems; they had worked on them for 25 years. Idaho guys considered Illinois people "paper pushers." I had a job at first convincing the people in Illinois that I knew how to be an engineer, and when I got out to Idaho, I had a second job convincing them that I could be an effective design engineer! Eventually, I established my reputation at both places.

A big question was: How could we get this one boiler moved over to its superheater position? I developed a comprehensive work plan. A decision had been made not to put that superheater in the boiler's place, so I had to go along with that in my work plan. It meant the sodium piping had to be drained and that an inert gas flow had to be maintained, then capped, in the area where sodium piping was cut. New welds had to be x-rayed to ensure durability. Some sodium piping had to be rerouted before being capped off to ensure sodium purity when it was reintroduced into the system. Sodium piping heaters and insulation were reinstalled. The new superheater also had its water and steam lines attached, welds inspected via x-ray.

The project was not without unforeseen problems. Ken Coover, my stress analyst, died of a heart attack in the middle of the work. It was found that EBR-II had been built over a previously unknown earthquake fault. It was now absolutely imperative that anything connected to the new system be rebuilt to new RDT standards. I was fortunate that Argonne hired another stress analyst, Habib Ahmed, who knew RDT standards as well as the new piping computer codes that could be used to diagnose what specifically needed to be done. We were given a larger office where we could easily converse about the project. Habib taught me Nuclear Regulatory Commission regulations and how to figure out what additional supports on all secondary sodium piping runs had to be added and which old ones needed to be moved to meet the new regulations. Each piping support required a large shock absorber installation to limit vibration or excessive movement during an earthquake. No significant earthquakes occurred during EBR-II's lifetime, the mid-1950s until March 1994 when EBR-II was shut down permanently.

The Superheater Replacement Project was completed successfully in several years. Downtime of the reactor was limited to two months. EBR-II continued to generate 20 megawatts of electrical power for its entire period of operation, aside from that brief two-month period. It achieved 32% thermal efficiency. In comparison, most commercial plants that burn coal or oil or gas get efficiencies in the mid-20% range. Reliability was excellent. EBR-II had regularly scheduled one-week shutdowns annually for maintenance.

SODIUM COLD TRAP DUMP SYSTEM

As a result of my promotion following EBR-II superheater and boiler system redesign work, I took on several smaller collaborative design jobs, not delegating them solely to my group. Some were related to EBR-II. One was called a liquid metal dump system. The project sought to answer a safety concern: What would happen if Argonne had to get rid of the liquid metal in the bypass system used to clean up primary sodium? Sodium attracts oxygen, so Argonne needed a system design which had the potential of trapping out all of these oxides. What would happen if something were to go wrong with that system?

With help from some of the fellows, I worked out the engineering and we redesigned the system. In this new model, we could dump the sodium into a tank automatically so that we wouldn't have to worry about the radioactivity. It would be in a room that was radiologically closed. That took a fair amount of time. The tank had to be passively cooled because it takes a while for the sodium to die down in reactivity and because, as it's doing that, it generates heat. That was accommodated. It was a smaller project, but we as a design group accomplished this task. Upon being built and installed at EBR-II, the new system worked as intended when tested.

COVER-GAS CLEANUP

My next assignment was design work on a cover-gas cleanup system. EBR-II had a lid on top of the dual sodium tanks. It was basically composed of one-inch-thick steel plates which added up to be a couple feet thick supported on the rim of the tanks. It was a monstrously heavy object. Argon gas occupied spaces between these plates and the space between the lid and liquid sodium. To a large degree, isolation from the pool of sodium, which was several feet below the lid, kept the argon uncontaminated.

As part of the safety program, Argonne decided to test the design by running the reactor with fuel tubes of radioactive material that were at the point of bursting. They wanted to find out what would happen if they purposely let one of these fuel bundles rupture. New elements, some of them gaseous, are formed by the reactivity and decaying of nuclear fuel, so the tubes had gas buffer spaces in them.

Upon testing, the radioactive gas of course escaped and bubbled up through the sodium, contaminating the argon. So, they had to make allowances for that. They reached out to a contractor and got a design for a cover-gas cleanup system. The outfit bidding on this system said they wanted $250,000. Argonne had me look at it. The proposed design would occupy a "box" at least 10 foot cubed. There was insufficient space for a system of this size to sit on top of the reactor lid as there were pumps and all kinds of other equipment already sitting on the deck (lid). I don't know where they could've put a large box. However, there were access ports *through* the deck that were big enough to place an object 10-12 inches in diameter, a foot or so long into the cover gas space.

After careful heat and mass transfer analysis, I determined that I could design a small, cylindrical, encased device approximately 10 inches diameter, one-and-a-half feet long that would fit nicely in an access port. It would serve as a cold trap for contaminant gases. My design incorporated appropriate isolated cooling and argon circulation features. It did the job, working perfectly. Again, I fall back on Coultas: find out what the problem is, figure out a way to solve it, do it, test it, and verify that it works. This cover-gas cleanup system cost about $25,000 to build and install.

BILL CANN

I was nominally a manager, but I found out that managing a group of guys who were basically independent didn't involve much management. They often worked under other project engineers. Argonne operated with line management and project management. Project management would borrow people from the line managers as they needed them and then give them back when they didn't. And so, most of my guys were busy most of the time and I didn't have a hell of a lot to do with them, except maybe once a year to do their evaluations.

I remember one guy in particular – he was kind of a lackadaisical fellow, but he was brilliant. His name was Bill Cann. He came up with a scheme of holding the redan and the nuclear breeder reactor assembly (as ANL had at EBR-II) inside of the pot of sodium without having any kind of support except from the lid. And the way he did it was ingenious.

In nuclear breeder reactors, the object is to have control rods at the same vertical position regardless of temps in the system. They have to be kept within a few millimeters of a position to be in the right place, accurately, precisely set up and down. You do not want temperature changes to affect reactivity level.

Cann's idea was to keep support lengths constant regardless of ambient temperature as happens in Grandfather clock pendulums. (Pendulum length affects the timing of a swing.) By using two different metals with different coefficients of expansion, adjusting lengths accordingly, and connecting them at opposite ends, the pendulum support arm is kept at a constant length over a wide range of ambient temperatures. "Grandfather" then keeps good time, regardless of the position of the set of weights that operate the clock.

In effect, Cann came up with a whole new concept of supporting the core using the clock pendulum concept. I got him a high mark and a better raise for that year.

EBR-II EFFICACY

As previously discussed, I was involved in the design of the cover gas clean-up system that removed contaminants from primary sodium and the argon cover gas. Tests of various kinds proved that the system was reliable and safe. That always was the rationale behind everything done at EBR-II – safety and reliability were the reigning catchwords.

Argonne had been alone in favoring a pot type of containment for secondary sodium, with its double-walled tank having the provision for sensing leaks in the primary tank. But a leak never happened. All the control rods and other devices went in from the top. No penetrations were permitted in the two tanks. Both tanks were supported on the rim of the top lid that sealed the vessels. This was a very stout, stiff structure that transferred all loads to external concrete walls. Over a period of more than 40 years, they never had a problem that I know of. There were no leaks; there were no operating problems at all. In fact, the operators set up the system to purposely operate at a higher energy-release rate. Operators watched as the reactor shut itself down after a period of time had elapsed and sodium temperature within the tank had risen a predetermined amount. The system responded slowly so operators had plenty of time to react to a potential problem. None ever happened.

In the later 1950s, French engineers came to Argonne to study EBR-II specifications. They returned home and designed France's Phoenix and Super Phoenix reactors of 1,000- and 2,000-megawatt electric power generation capacity. The design engineers behind EBR-II did an impeccable job. When I redid the secondary sodium system design calculations on a computer for pipe stress, heat transfer, thermodynamic analysis, etc., all I found was that I corroborated what they had done with slide rules. That amazes me. They were top-tier engineers.

Interestingly enough, EBR-II was also being used as a test reactor. The team at EBR-II was constantly changing out test items that they would put inside the reactor. They could change out fuel bundles "on the fly," meaning the reactor was not shut down. Fuel burnup of 25% was regularly achieved. One test achieved fuel burnup exceeding 28%. (That was the test that allowed a fuel bundle to burst.)

I was done with the original work order: replacing a superheater with a boiler. It worked out very well.

EBR-II: A NEW LARGE FACILITY UPGRADE

There were plans to build other fast-reactor systems in the United States. One of them was going to be a fast-reactor test facility located at Clinch River, which is near Oak Ridge, TN. It was going to be a big piping system. They weren't going to have a large pot of sodium; they were just going to have piping with a small pot to accommodate sodium expansion. When you have a "piping-only" system, you have fast transients to control. Things happen quickly. And the control response that you need is much faster than it is in the pot system.

The US Department of Energy decided to test the large boilers that would be installed at Clinch River. EBR-II was selected as a possible site to do this testing. The Clinch River boilers were much larger in energy capacity than anything at the time that was immediately available at EBR-II. If we were to do these tests, we'd have to build a completely new facility, including a brand-new building. It would have to be over 100 feet tall and look like the Fermi office building at Fermilab, which was a tapered arch, flying-buttress-type of architecture. The new building would have to be flexible in its ability to accommodate different boilers. It would have to be very strong, since all boilers would be very heavy. Access to interior space would be required for large equipment.

Floors, walkways, and boiler support points would have to be easily shifted to accommodate different boiler configurations. The project was immense and complex.

Argonne went through a quite serious design-analysis period. A group of half a dozen other consulting engineers and specialists from the industry were brought in for this project. I was heading all of it, managing all technical design work. In short, I planned to take 62 thermal megawatts out of the EBR-II reactor and add another hundred megawatts from Idaho's electricity grid. I would have the project syphon off as much electric power as could be obtained from the EBR-II generator (20 megawatts). The facility would need all the extra energy to heat a new secondary sodium stream that would supply thermal energy to a test boiler. We were going to have new sodium lines, new steam lines, and big air-dump heat exchangers necessary to dispel the extra heat into air because there was no cooling water at EBR-II to use as a heat sink.

All of the preliminary design work was finished in record time. The complete system looked great. There were no "dealbreakers" that anyone could see. Yet, the project came to naught. And the reason was that, once again, politics got involved.

A Senator from California purportedly told DOE that they needed to have work at the Liquid Metal Engineering Center (LMEC) test facility at Santa Susana. I had worked near there. Apparently, they had built up another facility on the mountain. Atomics International (a subsidiary of Rockwell Corporation) wanted the job, so they got it. They had nothing to start with, so they had to build a completely new facility. I heard they used gas burners to get their multi-megawatts of thermal energy to heat sodium and test these boilers.

I don't know if they ever did any testing or not, because all of this equipment, billions of dollars' worth of acquired hardware, wound up sitting on the ground in Oakridge, TN. So once more, it was a lot of work over a long period of time that resulted in nothing. I was glad, in a way, to be rid of it though, because the project would've been a real headache producer.

BIOLOGY DIVISION: MOUSEWITZ

My next major project was designing a facility for Argonne's Biology Division to test air pollution effects from coal-burning power plants on animals. The facility would use mice as subjects and coal from several different sources. Thousands of mice would be subjected simultaneously to various levels of pollution obtained by using differing dilutions of a strong, standard pollution source. The condition and probable eventual death of the mice would be studied to correlate pollution effects expected by humans at various places throughout the USA. We dubbed this facility "Mousewitz," tongue in cheek intended.

The project had progressed through two design stages (conceptual and preliminary) and we had gutted a large wing of the existing biology building (some 70-feet wide, 150-feet long, three stories) in anticipation of building the facility when the project was summarily canceled. Senator Mike Mansfield from Montana had gotten wind of the program and strenuously objected to its existence. He did not want to jeopardize selling his state's coal! DOE was threatened with funding cuts, so they acceded to his wishes and stopped the project.

I was temporarily "out of a job," but only in the sense that there was nothing for me to do. Argonne was still flush with money to fund salaries, so I would not be fired or laid off. However, I had to find meaningful work that needed to be done.

MHD FACILITIES

Argonne had been tasked with investigating gas cleanup in terms of ash removal and seed recovery in a program in cooperation with Russian work in "magnetohydrodynamics" (MHD). Argonne's focus was on finding methods of seed recovery. I wasn't responsible for conducting those studies. However, I was responsible for designing and building two new facilities for research on downstream gas-cleanup systems for MHD.

In an MHD system using extremely hot gases, you must provide some material that stimulates electrical conductivity in the gas. We used potassium salts. In a real MHD channel, the hot gases go through a channel at 5500°F. We were only able to achieve 4400°F with a 1500°F air preheat and good combustion. Our test conditions were equivalent to what would exit a regular MHD channel. Since we would look at only seed recovery, these test conditions were entirely adequate to duplicate a realistic environment downstream of the channel. Potassium cost represented a significant part of total operating cost, so it was imperative to reclaim as much potassium as possible.

The first facility was a simulated coal burner, meaning it did not burn actual coal. It was decided that we would burn a dense, "toothpaste-like" slurry of fuel oil with fly ash and potassium salt mixed in. This looked like coal when it was burned and allowed us to mimic burning various types of coal. I had to design the tankage for mixing the slurry, the stirrers that kept the slurry from settling out in tanks, and the pumps that force-fed the slurry into a combustor. I also designed other components. After designing some of the system components, I assigned another engineer to manage facility construction.

The second facility Argonne built burned actual coal, specifically Rosebud powdered, low-sulfur coal from Montana. That was a real challenge for me to design. It had never been done successfully before I tried. But I managed to do the job and get it to work right.

MHD 1

Mike Petrick, a program manager at Argonne, had brought MHD money from the Washington, DC Department of Energy (DOE) into the Engineering Division in several simultaneous areas. Magnetohydrodynamics is an electricity generation process where a high-speed, electrically conductive fluid flows through a very strong, linear magnetic field. This flow develops DC (direct current) electric potential/power that can be converted to AC (alternating current) electric power. Initially, I was involved as a program monitor for three combustor designs for which Argonne had cognizance of for DOE. I traveled extensively to the East and West coasts to monitor design progress at AVCO (Lynn, MA), TRW (Redondo Beach, CA), and Rocketdyne (Canoga Park, CA). TRW eventually won the competition and built a combustor based on its design and extensive testing at their Capistrano, CA facility.

I had been given control of a small design group with about 10 degreed engineers under me. As a line manager, I assigned one of my engineers, Tom Fornek, as project engineer to manage construction of a detailed design I made out for a new MHD test facility. Mike Petrick wanted to study the gas-cleanup process in downstream MHD flows (electrically conductive flow which had gone through a magnetic channel). This downstream gas flow contains alkali metal "seed" (i.e., cesium or potassium salts) that are used to establish high electrical conductance in the gas at typical high temperature. For MHD to be economic, alkali seed has to be recovered and reused repeatedly. I stepped in to "help" Fornek and rapidly took over the design part of the project, leaving Tom to do all project "construction overview and accompanying paperwork." First, I established design criteria to guide the actual design process. Then, the real games began.

I wouldn't call Terry Johnson an adversary; he was more of a technical equivalent in chemical engineering, but he and I never agreed on any kind of a technical solution. He had his background; I had mine. When the two of us were asked to comment on something, we always had different answers. And so, when Mike Petrick got the two of us together and said, "Design me an MHD facility," I thought for sure there would be trouble. But Terry and I sat down together, and miracle of miracles, we agreed. We said, "Let's plan on about a two-megawatt combustor, and we'll have this kind of an air supply, and we'll have to have tanks that can mix up the slurry, and run one tank until it is empty." The other tank would be filled at that time. Both tanks would have to be stirred constantly to keep slurries mixed. So, it was decided.

No combustor was available, so I designed it. Hot gas coming from our combustor had to approximate temperature coming from an MHD channel (4400°F). Thus, we needed an air pre-heater to boost the energy level of combustion gases to achieve this temperature level, since normal coal/air combustion results in a much lower temperature than 4400°F. We would also add potassium chloride salt to the slurried fuel, simulating electrically conductive seed in the actual system.

Terry Johnson and I had a general idea of what we were going to do, so we pitched it to Petrick. He said, "Okay, we've got the funding; go ahead."

MILK CAN COMBUSTOR

The combustor I designed for our MHD facility was fairly unique. It had seven burner elements. Basically, the slurry would go in a centered tube and high-velocity hot air would go around it, breaking up the slurry into fine particles. Each element had an energy output of 1/7 of two megawatts. Considering that two megawatts is approximately 2,000 BTUs per second, it was no small burner. But I didn't know if it would work!

So, in the middle of winter, we set up a little test stand outdoors with a single burner element and a two-gallon tin can full of slurry. We'd sit there with a long spoon, continually stirring it up from behind a blast shield. We fashioned an air pre-heater by running a bunch of bottled air through the system and storage heater. All I used to ignite it was an acetylene torch in front. We stood back, turned it on, and got the most beautiful blue flame that you could imagine. A blue flame indicates that you achieved great combustion. You could feel the heat coming off of it about 50 feet downstream from it – and this was in the middle of winter! I swear to God, it was probably 10 or 20 below zero that day. It was cold out there!

So anyhow, now that we knew we had a combustor, I designed what I called a "milk can combustor:" an old-style combustor that mimicked the old red stone which mimicked the V-II. The Germans had come up with a double-walled combustor which had an inside wall and an outside wall. Pins, rivets, or something of the sort welded between the two walls kept them separated because the space between them provided cooling channels.

My milk can combustor was designed and built. We'd put in a set of "Roots" blowers. We had a pair of compressors which could put out about 15 PSI. Both had a 15-horsepower motor. Each compressor had two squirrely arm configurations on the inside that mated when rotated and pressed up against each other and the outside walls. This action caused pockets of air to be squirted out continually. The two together had a fairly constant pressure output with little pulsation when discharging into outlet pipe volume.

ONE CONCESSION

Our air supply was fairly simple, but first, it had to go through a heater. Now, that was the one concession I made to Fornek. I did the whole design for the whole facility except for the air heater. Fornek found a place that would build a 600-kilowatt air heater which would take a couple pounds per second of air from ambient temperature up to 1500°F. It was basically the world's biggest hair dryer, the same design as what women use to dry their hair, except that it was huge. To fit all of the heating elements and coils of heating wire, it was probably a foot-and-a-half in diameter and 20-some feet long. When we built the facility, we would put it up on what was called the "mezzanine," which was an elevated walkway above everything else. That position kept it out of the way of working areas.

The air heater barely made it through the door. I think we had about a half-inch clearance for the thing to fit through the damned door we had built into the side of the building. We had to bring it in at a sort of canted angle going diagonally to give us the most room, then we had a travelling bridge crane pick it up, put it into place, and put the connected piping in.

TIGHT DEADLINES

The MHD project was hampered by a lack of construction funding and a tight schedule. Petrick had committed Argonne to building a facility from the ground up and testing it within a period of nine months. Apparently, DOE wanted to impress the Russian MHD people with whom we had a technology agreement. The Russians were years ahead of the US in developing actual MHD systems, already having produced electric power at megawatt levels at their Institute for High Temperature Physics in Moscow. Channel downstream cleanup was an area that had not yet been explored by anyone. The US would have something original to contribute!

There was no possibility of meeting our objectives if we were to use the usual Argonne design approach (three steps with peer review at each step). We had no time! I argued there were no other experienced combustion engineers at Argonne and we were not building a nuclear system. So, I got to design the "old Rocketdyne way:" have an independent design check, build your hardware, and test it! Fast and furious, but effective. Review came where it was needed – design calculations and installation checkouts.

I had a girl working for me, Barbara Schlenger. Barbara was a very bright girl and a hard worker. She checked every one of my calculations. I could be assured that what she OKed was okay. Everything was designed on the basis of analysis as well as my experience.

CONSTRUCTION IN WINTER OVERVIEW

Analysis and design started immediately after Christmas break, early in January 1978. It was the middle of winter, and nobody knew what constructing this thing was going to look like except that it would be built at Argonne, down by the coal plant. We broke ground in March for the footings and concrete floor of the commercial metal building. Literally, we broke ground – it was frozen solid from the previous winter cold. Preliminary testing of a combustor injector element indicated we would obtain very efficient combustion of the hot air/oil slurry (which had the same consistency as runny toothpaste). Component design preceded builds and installation by two weeks. An electric air preheater was procured from a commercial vendor. This 600-KW heater was essentially a huge "hair dryer" – heating two pounds per second air flow from ambient to 1500°F. Air, pressurized to 15 PSIG, was supplied by two Roots-type blowers acting in parallel. A control/recording trailer was located away from the test area for safety. Hundreds of control and instrument leads were routed to this trailer. Many system interlocks were designed to provide sequenced operational safety. The first successful test was run on September 28, 1978 – two days ahead of the scheduled "drop-dead date." Following initial testing and final facility installations, the facility was turned over to a permanent operating crew who installed the refined test hardware. Many tests were run in this facility.

Actual construction of this facility was not easy nor simple. Trenches for foundations were dug from frozen ground. It had to be protected from freezing. We used straw to cover it. Once concrete had cured enough, we put up a corrugated metal building that was tall, but narrow and long. It was designed so that we could have the combustor firing either vertically down or horizontally. We started with the combustor firing horizontally directly into test sections. Initial test sections were "dummies" built from thick-walled pipe. Formal test sections dedicated to gathering data were designed and installed after the initial period of testing to satisfy facility readiness and cost strictures.

We worked night and day building this facility. My designs led builds and construction by only two weeks. As I mentioned, we had a deadline because funding ended September 30. We had built many safety features into the system, consisting of interlocks that had to be satisfied in order for the system to start. Near September's end, we realized that we had so many interlocks that were interfering with things that hadn't been done yet, we had to bypass them to get the facility operational before the thirtieth. That involved mostly instrumentation, little niceties that we absolutely didn't need if we kept people out of there when we turned it on. We had to put in several hundred coax lines going from sensors for instrumentation that did not yet exist.

We also had to have a heat sink for water cooling the dummy test sections. No money was available for real test sections that would be installed to run real tests. We bought cheap, heavyweight, two-foot-diameter iron pipes, cut them into 6-foot lengths. We had welders mount huge flanges on them, bolted all of them together, put them on stands that would line up on the floor, and squirted water-jet sprays from bottom to top to cool these things. We bought an above-ground swimming pool that could hold several thousand gallons from Kmart. That was our heat sink. Water heated in the test sections would flow into the swimming pool. Evaporation would cool it. Water "makeup" came from an automatic water-supply faucet that turned on when the water level dropped a bit. Plastic lining could take elevated steaming temps. It was not elegant, but it worked.

The first successful facility operation on September 28 went flawlessly in every way except one. We noticed when we let it run for a long time, the massive pipe test sections did not heat uniformly. Apparently, cooling water was ineffective on top surfaces. Water drained down the bottom because the system was sloped toward the outlet end where it was pumped into the swimming pool. We soon had a banana-shaped set of test sections. When the midpoint of the test section assembly raised itself off the floor a certain height, we had to shut the combustor down and let dummy test sections cool. That was the one faux pas that happened during the whole check-out phase.

In mid-winter, when the pool froze over, we had to have an electric heater warm the pool area near the water inlet. Combustor energy soon melted all the ice, water steamed, and the pool operated normally even in the coldest weather.

All temporary equipment was removed. The new test sections all had individual cooling systems that ensured uniform cooling. And they all had connections to a set of heat exchangers that we had installed above the mezzanine on the side of the building opposite the active area side where all doors were located. We used a water-glycol mixture good to -20°F as coolant liquid in all of the lines going to permanent "heat dump" heat exchangers.

The following winter, Chicago had it out for us. One night, the wind blew like crazy, and the city got down to -30°F. We had some cracked fittings on those exposed heat exchangers that had to be repaired. So, we put more glycol in to go to -35°F. We never had the problem again.

The facility went on to operate for years. It had a half-a-dozen different names. I can't remember them all. It started out as "Ample" and I think it wound up as "FEUL" (instead of FUEL). And I don't know what that stands for. But it was a big success. And then we had bigger aspirations, but that's another story.

MEMENTOS FOR SUCCESS

By the time the Russians returned to Argonne the following September for technical meetings, Argonne had accrued a large amount of process data which showed feasibility of the separation processes we had already investigated. They were astounded at Argonne's buildup speed and the amount of experimental progress. People who performed all of the work in building this facility were given a formal dinner of filet mignon, etc. We sat at the end of the table, far away from the "dignitaries." Each of us was given a gift as a memento of our extreme effort, which often exceeded eighteen-hour days: a liquid crystal thermometer that might have been worth two dollars.

MHD IN MOSCOW

A number of Argonne people took a trip to Moscow, Russia in late October 1979. We visited the Institute for High Temperature Physics headed by Professor Sheindlin, a member of the Presidium, the technical support group for the Premiere of Russia. The man under him was a gentleman named Shumyatski. He came to the United States a year later, heading their delegation of half-a-dozen people. They were astounded when they saw what we had done in that short time of a year, because they had been there the year before and there was nothing at Argonne to be seen. A year later, we had a working facility.

Shumyatski and Mike Petrick (Argonne's MHD project manager) worked on a book together on MHD, a combined work of what the Russians and the United States had done up to that point in time. I've got authorship recognition of a chapter that was mostly written by the Russian engineer author. The Russians left for home in early October 1979, with suitcases full of blue jeans and other clothes they could sell for great profit.

Our American group left for Moscow again over Thanksgiving of 1979. We stayed at the Cosmos Hotel, which was brand new – so new, they still had the shrink wrap on the chrome fixtures in the bathroom. It appeared that we were the very first people who stayed there! It had been built for the 1980 Olympic Games. And I have a claim to fame that I probably had the transatlantic speed record for getting a phone call through from Russia to the United States. It only took three hours to set up the call! Where others failed, I used my sign language skills to convince a young girl, who was our "floor mother," to assist me. All to talk with my wife for three minutes. And it cost 10 rubles, which back then was $1.80 a Ruble. (Now, as I understand, the Ruble has fallen to maybe 1.8 cents and the Russians are having problems with their economy, save for the oil and gas they can sell to the west.) I stayed in Moscow only from Monday evening until Wednesday noon that trip. The other USA delegates spent all week in Moscow.

Another Argonne engineer and I were in Russia ostensibly to find out what they were doing on a secondary MHD loop. A dozen Russians and we two Americans had a series of technical meetings. In these meetings, we found out they had a secondary loop: burned methane with hot air to test some particular aspect of seed and fly-ash injection. We were looking to do the same: seed and fly-ash injections to test their system at Argonne. All of Tuesday was spent with a group of Russian engineers working out the flow-path system we would give the Russians to pneumatically transport fly ash from a supply tank to the MHD loop.

Everybody was "Doctor" in these meetings, whether they had a PHD or not (save for "Misha," our 19-year-old translator). And I imagine that most of the Russian engineers were PHDs or better because they had to be the "cream of the cream of the crop" to get this kind of job in Russia. One man in particular was a sharp dresser; he wore Savile Row suits from England, whereas all the rest of them wore baggy wool suits. The sharp dresser generally served as spokesman for the Russians. When I told the spokesman, "You can mix solid particulates into the hot-gas stream using this kind of device," he said, "No you can't." I replied, "Oh, you've already tried it and your injection flange warped?" He got beet red in the face, showing I had been correct, and I knew I had made a mistake. You did not shame these people. Because they could not afford to make a mistake. I think I might've said that if you make a mistake in Russia, you get shipped off to Siberia.

As a result of that policy, nobody did any significant new work, because if you showed up for work and put in some time during the day, that was all it took to survive. You didn't have to do anything! You'd go home and you got the same raises every year and the same better apartment every year (or whatever cycle it was). It didn't pay to work and possibly make mistakes because you weren't going to benefit; you were only going to lose. So, most Russian engineers simply never did any new work. I immediately saw that the US had no reason to fear the prowess of the "Mighty Russian Bear" in any future technology race. (Their spying was another matter.)

Anyhow, I recovered somewhat. I told him, "Well, I've made the same mistake," and I continued, "The solution is..." and I told him how to do it. How to put a flange that would heat up, expand, and warp in a hot-flow stream and keep it from warping because of its interaction with another unheated flange that's holding it there? A short cylindrical section inserted between the flanges. Our mixed group worked out a scheme for making a flow system to supply seed and fly-ash solids to their existing hot gas channel. All agreed with the proposed plan.

On Tuesday evening, our group toured downtown Moscow. I was looking for a mink hat for Ellen. Every one of the seven barioshkas (dollar stores) we tried in Moscow had only size "56" hats. There were no other sizes. Ellen required a 59! Apparently, that month the "mink hat factory" made size 56. It was a good example of Russian bureaucracy!

On Wednesday morning, we met again to conclude our talks. Wednesday afternoon, I was leaving to go back to the United States. Since we had agreed to a plan on Tuesday, I expected no problem. However, a new face showed up, a "Doctor" Sokolov. He was the Russians' boss. When we outlined the plan, he objected, saying, "NYET" – "no" in Russian. And why? "We want a general system that we can put anywhere, not just where you said you were going to put it. We might want to put it somewhere else." He then demanded that the US (Harold and I) provide a fly-ash delivery system that could place the supply tank anywhere. Harold and I did not know how to do that! But we could not admit to that fact. Our strategy was based upon the fact we thought we could exactly mock-up the Russian path of supply piping from tank-to-injector, get it to work well at Argonne, take it apart, label it all for reassembly, and ship it off to Russia! We could be pretty sure that it was going to work. But by changing line sizes, line positions, and lengths, we no longer assured success. We had no universal solution to the problem.

So, I said, "Misha, tell "Mr." Sokolov that if we don't have an agreement before I leave at noon today, tough shit, you won't have a system delivered to Russia." And that got jaws to drop. Everyone was stunned. (Most of the Russians understood English well, though they would not admit it.) Harold, who was Jewish, slid from his seat and almost went under the table because he thought we were headed for the Lubyanka prison.

RUSSIAN AIRPORT

I left for the airport and found Ellen a size 59 silver fox hat at their dollar store. I fidgeted while waiting for my plane and paced around the waiting area. There were more people in uniforms with Kalashnikovs than passengers. No gate labels were written in English. I was intimidated by a short, stocky Russian woman in full military gear carrying an AK-47 rifle, who bellowed at me to "SHUT UP AND SIT DOWN" until my plane was called. I did so, never feeling as relieved in my life as when the Japan Airlines plane lifted from the Sheremetyevo runway heading non-stop for London. It was the feeling of freedom, leaving behind a place that reeked of repression.

I got home several days later, having stayed overnight in England. The remainder of the Argonne bunch got home by the following midweek. When Mike Petrick returned, he called me to his office. He told me that Shelkov, the deputy to the head of the Russian MHD program, had asked him,

"Who was that mean son of a bitch you brought with you this time?" I felt good hearing this about my "show of force." Mike also said, "Larry, you are worth 10 of their engineers." I had to agree (without any feeling of hubris) – since I had seen for myself how they carefully avoided taking any responsibility. And these people were Russia's finest engineers.

That said, at that time, I hadn't thought about the theory of how to analyze dense-phase, two-component flow and get an arbitrary design system to work. My long, successful tutelage under Tom Coultas was not yet showing!

TWO-PHASE FLOW SYSTEM

A universally applicable method for two-phase flow system design, such as a fly-ash system for Russia, bothered me. There were no general design principles on which one could rely. I went to San Francisco to attend an ASME Heat Transfer Conference a short time later. During this technical conference, an expert in two-phase flow gave a course on the subject. I arranged to attend. There, I received a book on fluidized beds and two-phase flow in addition to extensive class notes. To me, the whole subject seemed to be in shambles. It seemed no one understood anything about two-phase bulk material transport (such as small, solid particles in air). All sorts of "correlations" existed to predict regimes of flow. However, each of these correlations was markedly limited in scope. To use one, you had to limit yourself to exactly the same set of conditions that already had been "studied and correlated." This situation was hardly conducive to "new design." How does one transport a granular solid in a gas (air) stream without experiencing plug flow, where phases separate and slugs of solid alternate with puffs of gas? This type of flow is highly erratic and does not lend itself to steady combustion or any other steady process.

I pondered the problem for some time. Finally, I had the inspiration which solved the problem. I remembered that two-phase flow of mixtures relates to Mach number – i.e.: sound speed in a mixture of solid and gas phases is much lower than sound speed of either of the separate phases. This is the problem that David Elliot from JPL had described analytically. Thus, the whole "trick" in designing a two-phase flow system is to avoid a possible approach to "mixture sound speed." If the mixture flow does approach sound speed, it will tend to segregate the phases wherein solid plugs form in pockets of gas so each flows subsonically!

I wanted to be a bastard and go back to Moscow where I could personally "thank" "Mr." Sokolov for his inspiration in helping me solve this problem. I figured he would get his free one-way ride to a gulag from such an endorsement. Unfortunately, Russia invaded Afghanistan in early 1980. Our mutual "cooperative" MHD technology program was terminated by the US State Department. I ended up using this new understanding to develop MHD II.

MHD II COAL FACILITY: GENERAL DISCUSSION

Mike Petrick got DOE to fund another Argonne program where actual powdered coal would be burned in an MHD combustor for testing candidate coals from different parts of the US. We needed a new facility!

This new facility was constructed next to the original MHD lab at a somewhat less hectic pace. TRW loaned Argonne their old 10-megawatt coal combustor. A new metal building was procured and erected on site. All we needed was a powdered-coal delivery system! Instrumentation and controls were very much like those used in the first facility. Having now already studied fluidization phenomena, I could design a flow system to deliver dense two-phase mixtures in a pipe, pneumatically supplying coal to the combustor. The biggest problem facing us was measuring instantaneous values of coal flowrate "dynamically" throughout many-hours-long testing at multi-megawatt combustion rate. Some manufacturers claimed to have these dynamic, dense-phase transport flowmeters, but some researchers did not think well of them. I assembled a team of engineers to help design the new facility.

One bright (but lazy) electrical engineer found a manufacturer of "load cells" that were 10 times more accurate than those previously available. They were just what we needed! TRW's combustor ran well at thermal power ratings of several megawatts (two to ten). Combined with the fact we wanted test runs to last for hours meant we needed a remarkably large coal tank. But a large coal tank would defeat our need for accurate coal flow measurement since those load cells had to support the coal and tank. The tank literally "hung" on the load cells! Accuracy was a fixed percent of total load capacity. All this meant we needed a small run tank.

The answer was to reload coal into the coal supply tank "on the fly" while it was pressurized. In other words, we had to have a coal supply that would permit us to refill the main coal run tank as we ran a test. But refilling could be done in batches.

I developed a coal feed system that had a pump to supply powdered coal to a fill line under what is termed "dense-phase" conditions. This means the coal has some gas entrained in it, but not very much! The diaphragm pump we used had been developed for pumping concrete, but it could also handle dense-phase coal powder with a nominal pressure rise that permitted transport to an elevation of 20 feet. This coal stream flowed into a small feed tank that was mounted on top of the main coal tank. A valve separated the two tanks. Another valve on top of the feed tank could be closed to isolate it from the coal supply line. By pressurizing the feed tank to equal the run tank pressure, one could open the valve between the tanks to dump coal into the run tank with minimum disturbance to the load cells. A gas filter system in the coal feed supply permitted discharging excess gas used to pressurize the feed tank so another load could be pumped up to it.

The coal feed system worked flawlessly from the beginning of operations. Load cells registered each refill as a short, steep upturn in overall system weight. As coal was fed from the main tank into the combustor, overall weight decreased gradually. The slope of weight versus time yielded coal mass flowrate. Electronics incorporated in the system allowed the facility operator to get short-term and long-term average coal flowrates. With my understanding of sonic flow limitation conditions in two-phase mixtures, the coal feed system between the main run tank and combustor could be designed. When tested, it worked impeccably from the outset.

To my knowledge, this was the first pneumatic, dense-phase feed system ever built which worked well the first time it was operated.

Argonne had been approached by a vendor from Park Avenue, New York City (Petrocarb Corp.) who wanted a million dollars for a coal feed system. Our design had cost the program $250,000. He had provided the University of Tennessee Space Institute (UTSI) with a powdered-coal feed system. They never got it to work properly. After the Argonne coal combustion facility was dedicated, it was turned over to an operations group who performed experiments for several years.

MHD II COAL FACILITY: DETAILS

We built a second combustion facility, this one coal-fired, and put it in another building about the same size right next door, 30 feet apart from the first MHD facility. It was my job to come up with and design a coal feed system, though I had some help along the way.

Mike Petrick had talked TRW into loaning us their combustor. TRW had been running it at 10 megawatts, but there was no reason why we couldn't run it at two megawatts, the same power level as the first oil-fueled combustor. They had pretty well characterized how it worked, and we were confident that it would hold together for our testing, and it was free! We didn't have to spend money on a combustor, and it would do what we wanted it to do. It could burn powdered coal with potassium seed particles mixed in and kick out exhaust gases at representative temperatures for analysis in downstream equipment.

We needed a stable flow for the coal feed system. Upon looking up literature and designs, I determined that, essentially, it would be a tank mounted on a stand which would then be hung on devices that could measure the weights very accurately. One of our engineers found some load cells that had one part in 100,000 measurement precision. We could determine the total weight of the coal system to within less than 1/10 of a pound accuracy. That degree of accuracy was *phenomenal*! It was 10 times better than anyone had done before!

Knowing that we also wanted to load on the fly, we built another tank, located on top of the run tank. This fill tank was rigidly attached to its support structure. I uncoupled the fill tank from the run tank with a bellows that was very "springy" so it introduced a small, constant load on the run tank weight sensors. We could fill the top tank with coal without affecting the run tank flow measurements (until coal was dumped into the run tank). We filled the top tank by pumping it full with a cement pump. Cement pumps worked well with dense-phase, dry, coal-gas mixtures. Dry nitrogen gas was used to pressurize the coal supply system to prevent unwanted ignition.

We'd pump the fill tank until it was full, shut the inlet coal valve and equalizer, fill tank pressure with existing run tank pressure, then dump coal into the run tank. There'd be a few seconds time interval of unbalance in calculated coal weight, but it would quickly recover. We'd go on, keeping track of weights every few seconds to get flowrate. We used a computer to keep a running spline fit of weight data to get more accurate flowrate determinations. This part of the coal feed system worked extremely well.

The really big problem in this system design was to obtain a stable coal flowrate into the combustor. To get stable flow, a number of design features had to be implemented. Firstly, the run tank had to have a conical bottom section. It had to have a double cone structure called a "core-breaker," which was mounted base to base – one pointed up, one pointed down, near the run tank's bottom outlet. This configuration formed a tapering, annular flow area for descending coal. The device prevented coal from only descending in the middle of the run tank, which would otherwise leave coal along the sides of the run tank. Keeping an even coal surface in descending coal was important to empty the run tank fully and smoothly. It ensured all coal settled evenly. An uneven coal level acting with unstable dynamics would have a negative effect on coal flow.

We installed a feature in the annular space between the coal tank and core-breaker called a "fluffer." The fluffer was a number of small gas nozzles injecting nitrogen gas in jets so that the coal wouldn't get bound up in the decreasing flow area. We had nitrogen in this whole coal feed system to preclude ignition. Fluffer gas flow was insignificant, incapable of affecting pressure in the run tank. Run tank pressure was set by an independent pressurization valve and control system. It worked in tandem with a separate nitrogen jet that forced the dense-phase coal to enter the piping going to the combustor. This pipe went from the bottom of the run tank and fluffer system to feed dense-phase coal directly into the combustor, and that was the tricky part.

I mentioned that sound speed in two-phase, dense flow is far less than it is in either the gas or solid. This was the most critical factor we had to pay attention to in this design. I had taken a course in fluidics at the Fremont Hotel in San Francisco for a week that was fundamentally worthless. Our instructor had written a book, which he supplied to class members, that was filled with particular sets of data showing flow regimes for different test conditions. There are three major flow regimes, called "saltation," "transport," and "slug flows." This lecturer didn't have a correlation that would fit anything except exact replica conditions of what had been done. The whole book was just a bunch of different experimental results. You had to have exactly the same configuration, etc. as that particular experimentalist had tested in order to get any data that was meaningful.

Saltation regime pertained to slow gas speeds where particulates could settle out on horizontal surfaces, forming dunes that would march along at very low speed, even compared with slow gas speeds. Transport regime occurred when particulates were swept up into the gas flow and traveled at essentially the gas speed. Slug flow occurred when gases and solids separated. In a horizontal pipe, a slug of solids would plug the pipe, keeping the gas behind it trapped until the pipe ended in a larger area. Slug flow is very erratic, unstable. It could not be tolerated in our combustor supply system.

The breakthrough in understanding came when David Elliott, a professor at Caltech (who also worked at JPL) had published a monograph with his theory based on the perfect gas law of thermodynamics that said sound speed in a two-phase, dense mixture could be calculated on the basis of a perfect gas model. He had derived the equations and given a way to estimate sound speeds. In other words, dense-phase flow was governed by Mach number.

I designed the feed line from the coal tank into the combustor, making sure it ran a little bit below sonic speed – not too much below, but not so high that it would approach sound speed, either. And, as a result, that flow system worked perfectly from the very beginning of testing. The combustor was ignited, and it ran for several years without incident. Test operators could run for hours at a time using the feature of refilling the run tank on the fly. And I guess Senator Mike Mansfield was happy because we were burning his Rosebud coal.

So, the second facility went off without a hitch. Test operators used the air supply from the first MHD facility when it wasn't running. The 600 kilowatts of hot air were directed to a given facility by simply rotating a bolt-on, flanged elbow. It worked very well.

As with MHD 1, I had done all of the design work on MHD II. The new coal feed system performed flawlessly, supplying a quarter of a ton of coal per hour to the TRW combustor, giving it two thermal megawatts of energy output. The entire coal feed system constructed by TRW for Argonne, using my design, cost $250,000. A different group of Argonne people (not designers) handled all the testing. They tested for several years, and quite a few people got quite a few papers out of their work, going on to present these at various symposia.

Although both of the MHD facilities worked absolutely beautifully from the first day on until they finally shut them down, I don't know what Argonne is doing with them now. Probably bare-bone buildings, not doing anything. That's Argonne.

MHD CHANNEL TROUBLESHOOTING

MHD had much promise when it was first proposed as an efficient energy conversion process. Supposedly, an overall energy conversion efficiency of 50% (from combustion energy to electric power) could be obtained. The hot gas coming from the exhaust of the MHD channel was hotter than the usual combustion gas that is generated for a common coal-powered steam cycle. Thus, this energy source could be used again to gain an increased total conversion efficiency approaching or exceeding 75%.

Russia led the US in MHD research, reputedly because they had developed it to power an electrodynamic laser that was used to burn up an American spy satellite as it overflew Russian territory. It was reported that the Russians merely attached a solid rocket booster to an MHD channel after trucking both up to a mountain top. The operating interval was probably just a few minutes. Exhaust gas from a solid rocket motor having the proper chemical seeding would be ideal for a short electric-power run lasting a few minutes.

In reality, long duration MHD had several severe design problems that needed solutions to make it a viable commercial power source. Extremely hot gases (5000°F+) containing alkaline salts and molten slag from burning coal are extremely erosive and corrosive. Channels had not been developed that could withstand this environment for long intervals. Also, seed recovery within the downstream gas flow system was needed to reduce costs. Lastly, burning coal in ambient-temperature air does not produce adequately high combustion temperatures; oxygen-enriched preheated air is needed to attain required high temperatures.

Engineers could devise enriched hot air supplies that were economically optimized. It remained undetermined whether the best system would be "good enough." Under the best scenarios, the MHD system would only have a 20% efficiency margin from which to subtract added operating and amortized equipment costs. The most difficult problem facing designers was MHD channel erosion from molten slag and seed constituents carried in the high-velocity hot gas stream.

In the 1980s, MHD channels were being constructed using a stack of copper plates bolted together, each separated from its neighbor plates by an electrical insulation layer. Most of the copper plates (those in the center section) were of constant thickness. Those plates at either end were tapered in one cross-channel direction. Tapering the end plates allowed the middle plates to be aligned with constant voltage potential planes that were developed at those axial locations. These middle plates were thus canted at an angle with respect to the hot gas flow. This sounds complicated, but isn't. MHD channels typically develop thousands of volts and tens of thousands of amps of direct current.

The high power MHD channel that the Russians had built and tested in their Institute for High Temperature Physics in Moscow developed 25 megawatts in a flow channel that had interior dimensions one meter across by 10 meters long! It developed thousands of volts and many thousands of amperes of direct current.

MY MHD CHANNEL DESIGN

Argonne was funded by DOE to design and build a longer-lasting "better channel" to be tested in the Russian facility in Moscow. My boss Ken Kuczen was the project engineer for this high-visibility endeavor. He had roughly $10 million to spend! Harold Herman was his deputy designer. I was not involved during the time it was being designed and built, but I saw some of the design work. I disagreed with the approach Ken and Harold took, and told them so. I was told bluntly to mind my own business. And so, I did, but on the side, I designed my own version of the channel.

Ken had Harold make the copper plate channel with "gun-drilled" cooling passages that were aligned along each interior surface and that would be exposed to a hot gas environment. Gun drilling is the only way to produce straight long holes. However, copper is known to be a "gummy" metal and is especially difficult to drill. The vendor who drilled these channel-cooling passages made a lot of money, both from rejected and accepted channel plates. It was determined that bare-cooled copper would not be able to stand up to hot gas erosion, so Ken bought a million dollars' worth of platinum bars and had them rolled into sheet stock. This stock was cut and bent to fit the channel plates and then brazed over exposed copper surfaces.

The Argonne channel was assembled and fitted with hundreds of exterior coolant hoses, valves, flow meters, pressure gauges, and controls. It was going to be shipped to Russia in a C5-A aircraft. Arrangements with the US Air Force already had been made for shipment of the completed channel when the Russians invaded Afghanistan. All technical programs with Russia were canceled by our State Department officials in early 1980. The completed Argonne channel sat on the floor in a warehouse, only subject to personnel removing components they needed for their projects – cannibalizing a very expensive relic.

I know the subject is moot now, but I will describe "my MHD channel design," which I believe would have been superior to Ken and Harold's, and which would have cost a tenth as much! I figured that thick copper plates were not needed to conduct the DC current. Water-cooled, thin-wall copper tubing had been used in experiments that had 20,000-amp currents in heat transfer experiments at Rocketdyne. So, instead of expensive gun drilling, I would have substituted commercially available copper tubing bent into "L" shapes, with ends also bent parallel to the diagonal that is formed when two “Ls” are placed together to make a rectangle. Thin copper plates (perhaps 1/16 inch thick) could be brazed onto the back sides of these tubes to maintain structural shape and add electrical cross-conductance paths. The inlet and outlet tubing pairs could be brazed together to seal and make the structure rigid. Rigid electrical insulation plates would separate each of the electrical plate-tube assemblies from its neighbors.

I had read a translated Russian paper which described their observation of the existence of electric arcs within operating channels. It appeared that current was not equally distributed crosswise along a channel plate but formed arc points which were distributed somewhat uniformly around the channel’s periphery. These arcs either emitted or collected electrical current for a given equal voltage potential “plate” from opposing sides of the channel. It seemed to me that small-diameter platinum “pins” brazed to the copper tubing at appropriate intervals (every few inches) would stabilize these arcs and be a lot cheaper than platinum plates. Platinum pins, anchored to the copper tubing, cooled directly by water flow, could be designed to tolerate any anticipated heat load. After assembly, the spaces left between tubes and around the platinum pins would be filled with high-temperature ceramic cement that would set up to a solid, leaving only the heads of the platinum pins exposed to the hot gas and corrosive seed and coal slag flows. Some ceramics were shown in both Russian and American studies to resist erosion far better than typical rigid plate insulations.

Once everything was installed, the entire assembly could be potted inside a non-conductive pressure cylinder using a low-density foam insulation encasing the whole device. Construction of my design was deemed far cheaper than Argonne's channel (which sat in storage for years). This expensive channel lost some components and reputedly some platinum as people pirated hardware.

In retrospect, I remembered another far cheaper scheme to construct the channel plates. Some cheaply made heat exchangers were constructed using two sheets of metal that are explosively welded together in patterns that allow for channels between them to be formed hydrostatically. This process works especially well for multiple identical shapes in copper!

DOE continued its MHD program for several years after their partnership with the Russians ended. They built a test facility in Butte, Montana to use their Rosebud coal and cater to Mike Mansfield, the senior senator from Montana. I did some early conceptual designs for this facility, laying out what I found as required components. My guidelines were followed in constructing CDIF.

HUNT FOR RED OCTOBER

Tom Clancy wrote and published a book in 1982 called *Hunt for Red October*. In the novel, the Soviet Red October submarine featured a caterpillar drive, or a magnetohydrodynamic pump that functioned as its propulsion system. Argonne actually built one.

The Soviets and the United States had a technology agreement in MHD going back into the '70s, which led to a technology agreement between the Soviets and Argonne. Argonne would build an immensely powerful superconducting magnet for one of the Soviets' MHD loops and it would be carted over to the USSR in a C5A. It would then be installed in Moscow in their high-temperature physics MHD facility. Argonne had built the magnet, but before it made its way to Moscow, Russia started their war in Afghanistan. The US shut down all US/USSR technology agreements. The state department decided that they didn't want us to have anything to do with Russia.

The device boasted six tesla, or *60,000* gauss, strength, the magnet had a bore of about a meter, and I recall it was about 10 meters long, so it was an impressive unit. I'd wager that it was probably the biggest superconducting magnet ever built, but now it had nothing to do. It was sitting on the floor at some physics facility at Argonne. Somehow, the Navy found out about it. They decided they wanted to see whether or not the caterpillar drive actually worked. I think Argonne was given a few hundred thousand dollars to set up a flow loop using seawater. The piping was several feet in diameter. Claud Reed was the cognizant engineer on the project.

Claud determined that this high-magnetic-field magnet, probably the best you could get, didn't yield anything worthwhile in respect to propulsion. It got a few PSI pressure, developed along the magnet, to get the seawater to flow around the circuit. This amount of developed pressure certainly was nothing in terms of producing propulsion capability like that assumed in *Red October*.

I had nothing to do with the project, but Howard Geyer, a gentleman who worked in my group, took it on himself to analyze the system with his systems analysis program. He confirmed what he had suspected: it would not work. So, the Navy threw away a few hundred thousand dollars. That was the United States' variant of the *Hunt for Red October*.

LIQUID METAL MHD NINCOMPOOPS

Mike Petrick was the project manager for MHD at Argonne; he had sway over everybody who worked in that field of study. Another little project was called "Liquid Metal MHD." He had a couple of guys on the assignment who were both PHDs and were supposed to be ever so smart. I considered them idiots. The reason for my negative assessment was that they'd worked on this system for a couple years and they were still fiddling with nothing to show for their effort.

The idea was that you started out with some liquid tin at a fairly high temperature and added water to it, thus, of course, boiling the water to become steam. This would propel the liquid tin through a magnet. You'd generate electric power from *voltage = velocity cross B* (the magnetic field). It's the right-hand rule of electric power generation.

What they hadn't seen was that, while you can put in one bit of water and speed the tin up by steam increasing the volume rate of flow (therefore velocity), you can only extract a little bit of energy from the flowing tin. So, it works a little bit, but what good is it if you'll only get a couple percent of the energy out as useful? And you have to stage tin and steam flows, which means that you need to recirculate the tin. It turns out that in order to recirculate the tin, you've got to add more water and you've got to keep enough tin to have continuous passages for electrical conductivity through the magnetic field. That means that you wind up having to circulate increasing amounts of tin. The situation keeps getting worse as you stage expansions, trying to use more of the thermal energy.

After spending an afternoon looking at the problem, I went to Kuczen and said, "this is worthless, and this is why." I showed him the thermodynamics and the hydrodynamics, and Kuczen agreed, so he went to Davis (our division director) and said, "Larry just proved that these two guys who are working for Petrick have wasted two years doing nothing."

After Davis told him, Petrick came storming over and bellowed, "Fire that son of a bitch Carlson; I don't want him around!" In the aftermath, Davis didn't fire me and Petrick finally calmed down, coming to the conclusion that I had been right. That was that.

One fellow was actually a professor at Cal-State Northridge, a full professor at that time! So, they should've known better. It just goes to show you how people "use the system" when not adequately supervised.

ION BEAM WEAPON SYSTEM

Argonne obtained a contract to house and test a US Army neutralized ion beam weapon system. This beam, formed by staged cryogenically cooled accelerators, was going to be the size of a pencil lead. Supposedly, it would be able to go through 50 feet of steel per second. Before the beam was neutralized, it could be "rasterized" by applied magnetic fields to sweep an area. Backscatter radiation could be detected so the beam could then be pointed at a specific target. It would be an awesome weapon! Of course, the Argonne test target would become radioactive in the process.

Argonne had responsibility for the cryogenic cooling system, beam, and radiation containment. I was tasked with determining how large a heat load would occur at what temperature level and what cooling system would be needed to dissipate component heat loads. Other engineers had to design and build the massive containment structure necessary to limit radiation exposure to operating personnel. They also had the job of designing and constructing electrical power supplies, controls, and instrumentation for the system.

ANL had built huge physics buildings. One was standing empty. It had three- to four-foot-thick concrete floors. It was ideal. Harold Herman and I, at this time working as friends, found a cement contractor close by, just South of Naperville, who would build the vault. He had a rather clever way of doing it. He could build it on his site, then move big chunks that weighed 20-30 tons apiece to Argonne, set them in place, and match them up perfectly. The vault he built was made of five-foot-thick borated concrete. (We had to have boron in it to absorb neutrons.) It had offsets in it to prevent any direct rays from going through. And it was all snugly put together, fit perfectly. It was probably about 15 feet wide inside, 15 feet up-and-down, and 70-80 feet long, and I think he got a couple million bucks for it. He had poured a couple-foot-thick slabs of borated concrete, much like the beams that are used in highway construction, which were laid on top to serve as the ceiling. Since everything fit together well, the generated radiation could be captured without escaping.

I worked on designing a complete cryogenic cooldown system and operating system for well over a year, designing new computer programs and integrating computer programs I already had along the way. Overall power input was several megawatts more than anticipated beam power (two megawatts). So, megawatts (exact number was classified) had to be extracted from the system at low temperatures. We had to get the copper way down in temperature. We weren't going to go superconductive on the elements that were a part of the injector and the secondary and tertiary accelerators. The beam would operate for only a few seconds duration, then I would have several hours to re-cool the system for another test. Equipment would operate at a few degrees Kelvin. I developed a computer program, specific in design to this system, that featured many elements to simulate the transient thermal characteristics of each component and their thermal interactions. I determined we would need a system with 10-kilowatts cooling capacity below 4K.

The coolant for the system would be liquid neon, which condenses at a very low temperature. We would need a lot of neon! If we had bought all of the required neon, we would have taken the total US output for approximately *a year*. However, we were able to "requisition" neon from Fermilab, which had enough for us stored as gas in railroad tank cars at their site in Batavia, IL. Fermi had somehow accumulated the world's supply of neon for a whole year before the atom bomb testing era, so this stuff didn't have any spurious nuclear radiation in it, no contaminants. Because they weren't using it and they weren't going to use it, and as Argonne was a sister lab, we could have it for nothing. All we had to do was bring the tank cars over. Thus, new neon gas storage tanks were procured for the beam site, which were about 10 feet in diameter and 40-50 feet long with a working pressure of 300-400 PSI. They traveled from some tank builder down in Louisiana, were barged up the Mississippi, went over the Illinois River, and were planted out on the Argonne grounds. One can still look on "Google Earth" today and see these huge, sausage tanks sitting on the Argonne property next to the old High-Energy Physics building, which was to be the site for the program.

Anyhow, I designed pumping systems and all the heat exchangers for both pre-cooling the neon and condensing the neon as well as getting it all ready in storage, etc. I also came up with the requirement for the helium refrigerator (10 kilowatts at 4K). It was probably one of the biggest, if not the biggest, helium refrigerator(s) built. 10 kW doesn't sound like much, but down at that level of temperatures and energies, it is incredible.

I helped write a proposal request and Argonne Procurement went out for cryogenic system bids. A design/build contract was awarded to Cryogenic Engineering Systems of Bethlehem, PA. Under the leadership of their chief engineer, an older engineer named Snow, they designed a very sophisticated, helium-based refrigeration cycle and shipped the components to Argonne on schedule and within budget. However, we were not ready to install this equipment because other contractors were behind schedule. Culham Laboratory of Cambridge, England was responsible for first-stage deuterium ion formation and acceleration, but they could not get equipment to perform correctly. Grumman Aerospace of Bethpage, Long Island, NY was responsible for second and third stage accelerators, but they had severe design problems. Though Argonne had its systems in readiness, the program foundered. Cognizant Army personnel killed the program.

Argonne had hired a former Army major named Bart Clare (who I called "Barf" behind closed doors) to oversee this ion beam weapon program. He ran it with strict, tight control. He was slated to be on a fast track to upper Argonne management. One of his decisions was to "fire" an extremely brilliant electrical engineer, Mike Rosing, who had a relevant background in ion particle acceleration. Mike made no excuse for smoking "pot." He favored its legalization. Argonne policy regarding participation in sensitive classified programs was: "You cannot be in any classified program and do any kind of drugs." So, Mike moved to a non-classified program in high-energy physics. He made important extensive contributions to a new type of particle accelerator. The irony of this story is that Clare's young daughter was taught D.A.R.E. in school – "Just say no" to drug use. She "ratted out" her parents at school one day. Police raided their house and found marijuana plants growing hydroponically in their basement! Bart was terminated and escorted immediately off the Argonne property. I had to "chuckle" over this incident. Bart Clare was no friend of mine. He was one of those managers who demanded full-time, exclusive participation on his program, knowing I had other prior responsibilities. In one incident, he demanded a six-week program be done in a month while providing quarter-level funding. I told him clearly, "I can't do it!" He did not want to hear this and caused further trouble with my division director Richard Lewis, according to friends who listened to the Clare/Lewis conversation. It was just another example of the "gingerbread man" problem I had!

In regard to the weapon system, you also had to neutralize the deuterium beam after you got it accelerated. I came up with a gas neutralizer that would have worked, but it was tremendously complicated. Basically, it had a chunk of the beam line that was at a higher pressure than the other part of the beam line, which was down to 10^{-6} Torr. I had an ingenious way of doing that, but it all became moot when some guy came up with a thin carbon film neutralizer that would do the same thing and would only take up a little dinky space, say a few atoms thick, in the beam line, and he didn't have to worry about gas loads. So, my gas neutralizer was dumped and the other one was adopted, but neither one of them ended up neutralizing the beam, because the US Army cancelled the program.

I don't know why the project got canceled, other than the fact that the three major parts of the accelerator were not being completed successfully. Whether or why that was the reason is unclear. Sometimes, DOD people would just feed companies extra money to get them to where they got things to work, but in this case, it didn't happen. As I've said before, Reagan went to Reykjavik with nuclear disarmament on his mind and met Gorbachev, who had anti-Star Wars on his mind. I have no idea whether a deuterium beam weapon was part of Gorbachev's Star Wars hysteria or not, nor how the timing of the project cancellation played into it, but it would've been one hell of a weapon if it ever got made.

THERMINOL

I was a gingerbread man at Rocketdyne, and I soon became another gingerbread man at Argonne! On one occasion, an engineer in a different building had gotten everything together and built a system for an experiment, and then found that he couldn't start it up. There was some restriction in the build that inhibited steam generation because it was not capable of going from, say, room temperature to the target temperature necessary to get the equipment to function as needed to satisfy the experiment. He was stumped, so they came to me.

I saw immediately that his problem was in using a constant heat rate from electric heaters. He had no temperature control throughout his system. He needed a heating system that functioned with intrinsic temperature control. To resolve this, I used something called "Therminol," which was a high-temperature oil, as the heat source. You could heat it from room temperature to high temperature. It fit in with his test requirements. He was able to start his experiment and run it to a satisfactory conclusion; his problem was solved.

COPPER COOLING

Kuczen came to me one day and said, "We've been trying to run a test over at 310." 310 was a building where engineering staff did unusual experiments. We had a kind of cowboy-character client who had been toying with the idea that an acetylene oxygen burner with multiple impinging jets coming out of, and devilishly close to, a chunk of copper, would serve as an *intense* heat source for an experiment his team was going to run.

Well, they turned it on, and found that the problem was that they were melting this chunk of copper that all these deaths were coming out of. They hadn't figured on that. But, because they had bought this thing as a commercial unit, they were running it overrated by maybe a factor of five or 10 more than it was supposed to. And, of course, when the manufacturer learned of their experience, he explained why they were limited to the lower range of heat input. So, the question was: What do you do when you need to run it at a higher rate? I went over to 310 and looked at it.

There was a groove in between the rows of impinging jets of acetylene and oxygen. I suggested that they could lay a small, thin copper tube in the groove, braze it in place, and run water in the tube at a fast velocity. I had done extremely high flux heat transfer at Rocketdyne using this method of cooling, so I knew what something like this could do in this instance. My guess was it would work OK.

They put this cooling system together and got a source of water that was at a high enough pressure to really zip water through the tube at a couple hundred feet per second. The copper mass behind the cooling tube didn't melt. I got some accolades on that one. It was faint comfort, knowing Stan Tykarski had died in that previous similar failed experiment.

STEAM PLANT EFFICIENCY

Another job came along that was a real stickler politically. We had a laboratory director; he was a black guy, a very nice guy, by the name of Walter Massey. He had been approached by a couple black engineers from a community in the north part of Chicago who had been working on a steam plant there and claimed they could increase the efficiency to generate more electric power. Unfortunately, neither of them was a thermodynamicist, so they didn't know a damn thing about how to do this.

I cannot remember the specific way they planned to do it, but it took me a whole afternoon to show them that it wasn't going to work. I had to write a letter to Massey and say, "Your scheme isn't going to work; it's no good." And thankfully, I didn't have to interface with them anymore. I guess an assistant division director under Massey told them, "We found out that it's not feasible, goodbye."

CARTER'S DOE DEBACLE (AND FIASCOS)

Jimmy Carter added greatly to the fiasco that had developed within DOE with regard to finding "alternate fuels." It was purportedly a three-and-a-half-billion-dollar "giveaway." I call it "Carter's Throwaway." This was back in the Carter era, I recall; it was not in the Obama era when trillions were thrown away regularly. (Joe boy is on his way to outdoing both of them combined. This has started in less than the standard 100-day honeymoon period.)

I was forced to go to DC by Carter for a month to evaluate proposals for DOE. Approximately 500 people from the various national labs were called to participate in this effort. We were each given a proposal stack a foot or more high each day and asked to "read/evaluate them." Then we had to fill out standard forms for each proposal and rank them according to established criteria! It is impossible for anyone to read that much material daily and understand it. So, we scanned all pages looking for relevant wording that would tell us a gist of the proposed program. Three evaluators looked at each program. We had to all agree on a consensus evaluation before it was submitted to senior DOE staff. After a month, we went home (we were allowed to go home intervening weekends). I found out later that "senior evaluators" had gone "upstairs" and instead awarded contractors according to a pre-established ZIP CODE distribution. I had absolutely no regard for President Carter after this experience.

THE ROAD TO CAGUAS

One of the programs Carter had funded was to do research, preliminary design, and write a proposal request for a "garbage-to-steam" facility to be built in Caguas, Puerto Rico. The facility would be able to handle 400 tons per day of garbage amassed from the surrounding area. Steam generated would be sold to Searle Pharmaceutical in Caguas. Caguas had been "granted" $750,000 in the aforementioned "Carter Giveaway" for this request – not proposal, proposal *request*.

The Department of Energy had (and has) a satellite facility located on the Argonne Labs grounds in Chicago. The people who work there are mostly program managers; they do not do any technical work themselves. As a result, when someone was nominated from DOE at Argonne to monitor the Caguas Program, not having much technical savvy, he called on Argonne for support. I turned out to be the Argonne support person. A local DOE officer asked me to accompany his representative, Jorge, to Boston to evaluate a company who had gotten the nod from Caguas to do its research, preliminary design, and prepare a formal proposal request for their facility.

I remember several aspects of the Boston meeting. 1) Their MIT-graduate engineers were incompetent. 2) The cost structure was obscene (their costs were thrice the national average). And 3) the steak dinner given at Faneuil Hall was an incredible, overt bribe. Steaks must have been at least 24 ounces. They overlapped large plates on all sides and were an inch-and-a-half thick! I kicked myself for being on a diet at the time – I ate a simple salad instead of a feast. This company was one of the highly technical, exuberantly expensive organizations of the Boston Beltway. Over a period of a few months, they had spent almost half of the $750,000 grant and had produced nothing. So, when I listened to their presentations, I had to keep from shaking my head in disgust. I waited until Jorge and I left, then I told him, "Get rid of those people. They're no good. They're absolutely worthless." So, he did! My report to DOE torpedoed this boondoggle.

As a consequence, DOE didn't have anyone to do the work. Caguas still wanted a proposal request formulated and all plant specifications filled out in detail, so the contractor in charge of the plant build would have to follow the Caguas plans exactly. Jorge came to me and asked, "Would you do this job?" I had time available, but I didn't particularly like the work; it's what's called being a Catalog Engineer. I said, "Okay," and accepted the job.

It was "obviously necessary" for the DOE rep and me to go to Caguas for a week to study their site and get a "flavor" of the proposed project. Jorge and I were wined/dined for the week, sometimes meeting the mayor himself or one of his top minions for an extended luncheon. I thoroughly enjoyed this vacation experience. The next few months were not as enjoyable. I had to become an "instant expert" in garbage handling and disposal. I scoured the Thomas Register to find the different components in a garbage treatment plant and called the companies who had advertised in it to obtain their brochures. I read these to get a "garbage" education. Eventually, I came up with a plan. I amassed all the data, put it together, and sent my report to Jorge. Jorge reviewed my report, okayed it, and sent it along to Caguas.

The plan had to be blessed by the Caguas people, so I was asked to go to Puerto Rico again for another week of consultations. This time, my wife Ellen accompanied me. (We paid her way as I anticipated another vacation.) She and I stayed at the Caribe Hilton next to Fort Geronimo at the mouth of Condado Bay. We had a small balcony overlooking the fort. I would be picked up each morning for the trip to Caguas, which is located mid-island, directly south of San Juan. My "driver" was Hiram Puig, a former comptroller/chancellor of the University of Puerto Rico, Mayagüez. He was on the mayor's staff and acting as Caguas' Chief Engineer for the proposed project. His wife would come later each day to take Ellen shopping in downtown San Juan. After work, we were taken to their best restaurants for dinner (at project expense).

Sometimes, during off days, we would be shown the sights of San Juan. We were taken where ordinary tourists never go: the bowels of Morro Castle, the basement of the church where Ponce De Leon is buried, and the dungeon of the first Spanish prisoner who wrote the first new-world graffiti! It was preserved under Plexiglas. Ellen saw a midnight festivity winding down at Fort Geronimo and wanted to go there. We waltzed on into the enclosure at midnight and saw guns that had been used to thwart Sir Francis Drake and his Golden Hind from entering Condado Bay where he was to land and then attack Morro Castle from behind its defenses. I felt old ghosts and spirits that still roamed in this place. It was an experience I will never forget.

I wrote the formal proposal request for Caguas as we had agreed and waited for follow-up work. It never materialized. The kicker is why.

Caguas sent out proposal requests to secure a contractor to build the 400-ton-per-day garbage treatment plant. During this search period, Jorge and I went down to Caguas to interview the mayor and his staff who were working on this project. Jorge was from Argentina, spoke fluent Spanish and English, and could hold precise conversations with anyone in Caguas. We toured the site selected for the plant and ate in more wonderful restaurants, escorted by Hiram. Jorge knew his Argentine beef! In our jaunts around the city, we found something interesting.

The steam part of this plant was supposed to be supplied to Searle, who had a pharmaceutical manufacturing plant in Caguas. The US government had made a big effort over the years to give incentives to various industries to come to Puerto Rico because of their extremely high unemployment. Searle had taken advantage of that inducement and had put in a large plant not only for manufacturing, but also to box product. When Jorge and I talked to Searle, we found out that Searle had never been contacted by anyone from Caguas in any government position about anything! *They didn't need steam!* So that aspect of the project was worthless!

The garbage plant project would've been in some kind of governmental miasma, but that was quickly resolved when a new mayor came into power at Caguas. He said, "I'm not interested in this project," and cancelled everything. I guess the rest of the money went back to the US Treasury. So, it became another spending fiasco. Carter was dethroned, as was the Caguas mayor who instituted the project. Well, this is the government. It's typical. Wasted man-months, wasted effort everywhere! Jimmy Carter remains my favorite living ex-president. (Trump has conceded as this story is being written.) But I'd like to emphasize a different aspect of this story. Remember, I tend to speak in irony!

Argonne, at that time, was charging $30,000 for a man-year effort. So, whereas the firm in Boston had charged $120,000 per man-year, the amount that Argonne charged DOE for my work was trivial. The Boston company had really padded their expenses. They'd had a "team of MIT engineers on the job at once" for the few months during which they had an active project. Most of the grant money was gone, but Caguas still had plenty of money left after I finished my job.

IRANIAN HOSTAGE CRISIS

I have some further comments about Jimmy's administration. He had two more aspects that I consider fiascos. One was his attempt to recover the hostages held in Iran during the Iranian Hostage Crisis. The Iranians overran the US embassy in Tehran in 1979 and held American personnel hostage for well over a year (444 days). Carter was well known as a "micro-manager." I do not know for sure how much influence he had over military personnel who ran the operation to retrieve the hostages. I only suspect he did. The distance from the starting base of operations to Tehran was too far to permit a round trip by helicopter, so an intermediate refueling station had to be set up. Other helicopters dropped fuel bladders for the remaining trip to Tehran and returning helicopters came back to the home base with hostages. But whoever selected the remote refueling area did not consider desert sand. Desert sand is much finer than beach sand: it is constantly blown about by wind, which causes granules to rub against each other and get worn down by a process called "elutriation." Turbojet engines powering these rescue helicopters ingested sand particles on the way to Tehran, ruining the engines. They could not continue their trip to the city.

Somehow, their pilots were picked up by other helicopters that did not land so they could get back to home base. The grounded helicopters were blown up with explosives to prevent Iran from using them. The hostages remained in prison until President Reagan got them released. Iran had a field day telling the world about American imperialism, using helicopter parts as proof of American transgression into Iranian sovereign territory.

INFLATION

The second "fiasco" of Jimmy's tenure as president was high inflation: mid-teens. People on fixed incomes were suffering terribly. I was fortunate personally at that time, having accepted a management position with Argonne that gave me a significant salary increase. I also worked three jobs: Argonne, consulting for the National Bureau of Standards evaluating Energy-Related Inventions, and other consulting work. Sadly, Jimmy has to accept the bronze medal for his "achievements," though, reputedly, he had the highest IQ of any president in US history. I now reserve the silver for Obama, and the gold for Joe Boy. Too bad, Jimmy. There is always the possibility that later contestants will outdo you in any chosen "sporting game!"

SUNDSTRAND'S SPACE STATION SOLAR COLLECTOR

Sundstrand Corporation, a company in Rockford, Illinois, came to Argonne to have us analyze a system that they were proposing as a power supply for the space station. It would make use of a "Rankine cycle," meaning that it would generate a vapor and run said vapor through a turbine to turn an electric generator. Vapor would be condensed and sent back through a pump to begin the cycle again in the boiler. Toluene was to be the working fluid. A large parabolic mirror focused sunlight into an aperture in a collector cavity that held heat storage material and toluene flow circuits. The collector cavity was the boiler. Heat storage material within the collector cavity was a lithium salt that had a very high heat of fusion and melted at 1200°F.

My job was to determine energy distribution within the collector cavity from incident sun radiation, knowing this distribution was necessary to engineer appropriate energy absorption material allocations within cavity walls and toluene flow circuit positions. It would be a monumental task! Even by separating the internal surface into finite zones, the resulting nonlinear integral equations could easily number in the hundreds. One also had to consider that any given sunlight "ray" would bounce around several times within the cavity with some of its energy being absorbed in each bounce and the remainder reflected back to some other position until finally, the energy would be totally absorbed! A further complication in evaluating energy distributions was the question: Is energy reflected diffusely or spectrally (i.e.: Do surfaces act as a matte or a mirror)? A further complication still was the fact that you had to follow the system while it was obtaining energy from the sun and also while it was in earth's shadow, when no energy was coming in – yet the system still had to supply sufficient energy to keep boiling off toluene.

Sundstrand engineers were not able to resolve these issues. I did not feel qualified to solve such a complex problem either! I needed help! One of my fellow engineers suggested using the "drunken walk" statistical method to solve these systems' problems. I had never heard of a drunken walk before. I learned there is a peculiarity in some equation sets as found in some called "potential equations." An example in electrical work is the equation: *V=IR (volts = current x resistance*, as determined by Ohm's law). There are many areas in physics that have the same characteristic form; all are called potential equations. They can be handled using a statistical method that says: You have a guy who is drunk. As he staggers along, he will either fall forward, backward, or on either side. Now, if you want to have him be a sophisticated drunk, you might be able to do his falling in eighths of a circle. But if you do this calculation a million times over, that drunk will go primarily in the correct direction. That's the simple fact. I can't tell you why, but it's true.

So, I set this whole system up as a drunken walk. I started with a ray of sunlight being reflected spectrally from a ring at a particular radius on the parabolic mirror – it was pointed at a particular ring segment on the collector. Ray intensity at the receiving surface was a function of its view factor. At this point, my drunk took over, calculating what happened thereafter. My computer at that time was a 486, which was not anywhere near as fast as today's machines. It was running at a few megahertz. I could have it do a million of these calculations per ring segment – it took a day or so to do them.

At one point, Steve Grammel came in and asked, "What are you working on?" I told him. I had written a section of code that was a full page long and it wasn't working. Steve wrote three or four lines of code, saying, "Try this." It worked. So, I made a deal with Steve that if I got any money out of this work, he'd get half.

My drunk got back to drinking and falling and gave me a distribution of what heat fluxes were inside this cavity. I did multiple computer runs, some with the parabolic mirror slightly off-angle, some with spectral instead of diffuse reflections, to see how large these effects might be. All cases were accommodated in the design. So, I wrote a report, handed it in for review. It was approved and shipped off to Sundstrand.

A few weeks later, a couple guys from Sundstrand showed up, demanding all of my original and supplemental calculations and all of my programming, both source and machine language material. In effect, they demanded everything I'd done for Sundstrand. "I won't do that," I said, "I have no way of knowing that you won't take my original calculations, change some material, and then say you did it. I'm not going to allow you to do that." I had even worked on the computer programming on my own time over Christmas vacation; I felt justified in not giving Sundstrand any program material on that basis alone. The Sundstrand people were livid.

I told them, "I'll give you a compiled program that you can use to calculate whatever you want. But it's going to cost you $10,000." Now, a compiled program is written in machine language from source code by the computer. There are people who can read compiled machine language, but I sure can't. And I'd say 99% of engineers couldn't either, and

I wouldn't have expected anybody at Sundstrand to be able to do it. I thought this would be a decent deal for both me and for Steve. Sundstrand totally rejected my offer.

I called in Ken Kuczen, my boss at Argonne, and told him about the situation. He agreed I had the right to withhold original material. Ken told the Sundstrand people, "I'll make sure Larry gives me everything. I'll personally destroy it all. I give you my word that I'll do that, so you don't have to worry."

Here's an after story. Sundstrand had no means to calculate anything more than I had given them in my report. So, they found some place in England that charged them a $10,000 fee upfront to provide a computer program equivalent to the one I had written that was now destroyed. Sundstrand paid the money, but they never got anything for it from England.

THE ROAD TO BEULAH

Beulah is a little town in North Dakota; it's located on a little road about 57 miles northwest of Bismarck as a crow flies. It's 200 miles west of the Minnesota border, 100 miles east of the Montana border, 10 miles north of Highway 94 (the main east/west interstate in the northern part of North Dakota).

There is some history that I was involved with in Beulah being the site for a synthetic fuels (synfuel) plant. This is where you turn coal or some coal-type material into natural gas. This story starts with the Department of Energy getting a handwritten analysis by someone who said, at that time, it appeared that synthetic natural gas could be made from coal and be competitive in the market. And considering natural gas was in short supply in Wisconsin, Illinois, and Michigan, there would be a good market.

DOE people decided to expand on this handwritten analysis and came to Argonne for support, where the job of doing further analysis came to me. I was to find out more details on the process, optimize the system, and get a better idea of economic feasibility. I was to develop a cost/benefit analysis, make a comparison with natural gas production costs. I had a Televideo 8-bit, 64-kilobyte computer at that time. I wrote a program for it that was limited in scope. However, using a recursion technique, I ran a number of cases with this program, and it showed that the process looked to be cost effective and could substantially benefit those states I mentioned. I reported these conclusions in a report to DOE, who took my analysis and gave it to another group at Argonne with a larger computer, a Unix machine. This other Argonne group could do a more extensive analysis. Their work came to the same conclusion: it looked like the synfuels project was going to be cost effective.

DOE took this information and worked with a consortium of oil-pipeline companies, deciding on Beulah as a location for the synfuel plant. I think DOE probably provided some money and help securing permitting to get the project moving. My involvement had ended.

As a result of researching for this book, I looked up the Great Plains Coal Gasification Project (GPCGP). Wikipedia has quite a large section on it, which is very intriguing. The first consortium of pipeline companies had started construction, but, at some point, they pulled out of the deal; the reason being natural gas prices had declined. They didn't think that the plant was economically worthwhile anymore. DOE bought out their interest and, after a couple years, got together with a different consortium of pipeline companies and reinstituted the project. Interestingly enough, for 25 years, the Great Plains Coal Gasification Project has been running very successfully. It processes 16,000 tons of lignite per day, which amounts to almost six million tons per year! Lignite is not the best of coals, but there is an abundance of lignite near Beulah. There's also an abundant amount of water from Lake Sacagawea about 10 miles north of Beulah.

The plant uses the German Lurgi process that was developed during World War II. 14 Lurgi units, Mark-4 models, are arranged in two banks of seven units. If any problem occurs, at least half of the production rate can be maintained. Technology has been upgraded over the years, and now, GPCGP produces not only synthetic natural gas that has 975 BTUs per cubic foot, which is just about what natural gas has, but it is dried, compressed, and routed North, where it enters the main gas line coming from Canada that supplies the northern midwestern states. GPCGP also produces ammonia, ammonium sulfate, hydrogen gas, and carbon dioxide, alongside recovering krypton and xenon, which are rare gases! They've managed to incorporate all kinds of profitable product streams into the facility. For example, they sell the carbon dioxide to Canadians who inject carbon dioxide into their oil deposits to enhance production.

The Great Plains Coal Gasification Project has been a very viable endeavor for a goodly length of time, and it has provided several hundred high-paying technical jobs in a remote section of North Dakota. As I said, I had only a small part in getting it started. I think DOE hit a home run with this project. Though the price of natural gas has fallen with the advent of fracking, still GPCGP manages to keep going strong!

SOLID OXIDE FUEL CELL

Darrel Fee was a group leader at Argonne Labs Material Science Division back in the '80s. His group developed an incredibly unique fuel cell that used hydrogen and air to generate electric power. The amazing thing about it was an efficiency of 72% conversion from the hydrogen equivalent combustion energy into electrical power! Most fuel cells did not have that efficiency. The design was also unique in that they had arranged the configuration so the current flowed across the channel instead along the channel length. Many other fuel cells had been developed in which current went from one cell to another. The current would accumulate along the length of a particular cell, then travel along that length of the cell to the end where it would be conducted to the next cell. However, the diminishing current had to flow along the length of this next cell to participate in its power generation. By such means, where cells were stacked in series arrangement, the voltage developed by the system was increased.

Now, the problem with this design is significant internal electrical resistance losses. Darrel's group had devised a configuration that used alumina – that's aluminum oxide – in thin sheets, arranged in equilateral triangle fashion that stack sideways for a cell. One cell passage would be upside down compared to its two neighbors. There were special coatings on the inside walls of these channels so that they would act as anodes and cathodes. Hydrogen passed through one channel and air passed through adjacent channels. Voltage potential developed across the alumina, which acted as an electrolyte (much as in a battery) transverse to the flow direction. The design was amazing in its efficient space utilization. They had only built one cell, a little over an inch square and an eighth-of-an-inch thick. It generated about one watt of power. On that basis, they calculated that, if scaled to larger sizes with multiple cells, you could generate five megawatts per cubic meter (5 kilowatts per liter). They never built more cells, but they also tested this cell in regeneration mode where power supplied to the cell generated hydrogen and oxygen from water vapor. Cell efficiency was also 72% in this mode of operation.

I was asked to do the electrochemical thermal, fluid-dynamic modeling of a single cell and a stack of cells, both in steady state and transient modes of operation. It was a large, complex job. I had to get all thermal and electrical properties from the material science people for these rare earths. I studied the material extensively, looked at the configuration in terms of physical attributes. I managed to create a computer program that could predict what a cell or stack of cells was doing including voltage, chemical reactants, and products, distributions within the system. With multiple computer data sets, I was able to "home in on" required air preheat level and excess flowrate required to carry away excess thermal energy.

I wrote a report and sent it to Darrel and his group with a caution that a stress analysis should be done to determine viability. Now, this fuel cell had a severe operating restriction. It operated at 1800°F. So, the cell had to be heated gingerly from ambient to 1800°F to limit thermal stresses. Excessive thermal stress could cause cracks in the alumina electrolyte. And when the alumina cracked, hydrogen could migrate through the crack instead of going as ions in the normal fashion.

I was later asked to look at a space power supply, 500-megawatt capacity, for short durations using this Argonne Solid Oxide Fuel Cell System. An assumption was made that the stress problem would have been solved and could supply 500 megawatts.

I did the preliminary design of a space system where you had four tanks for hydrogen and air, though separated. Bladders in these tanks separated reactants from products. As you depleted reactants, products replaced the volume lost. The total power system required five shuttle flights to get everything into orbit. System assembly would be done in orbit. All of the plumbing, pumping, compressing, and power supplies fit into one shuttle bay, enclosed in a separate tank.

A five-megawatt electric power supply from a nuclear reactor was envisioned to regenerate the reactants once you had depleted them. Reactor power would also keep the systems warm. On paper, this system looked feasible. Feasibility hinged on the fact that you needed to have cells that would not be destroyed by thermal stresses during transients. I saw the solution as having means to "float" individual cells so they did not interact by inducing stress with neighboring cells.

I see the Argonne solid oxide fuel cell as a boon in future hydrogen-based transportation technology. With hydrogen stored in hydride beds, cars can have ranges of hundreds of miles between "fill-ups," which can be fast yet safely done. The potential is there!

TRAILER HOUSE OFFICES

The Engineering Division was called something else after Stan Davis left. We were moved to a set of "trailer house" offices. A new manager cadre took over the division. Ken Kuczen kept his job as Associate Division Director. Don Mingesz did not. I was made group leader of a different group of techs and engineers, but my job didn't change much. My new group of engineers was assigned to a project leader who was responsible for new breeder reactor design. I had my engineering responsibility for other projects. One new manager, Sam Bhattacharrya, brought some space power design work into the division. I was tasked with coupling a large power system (500-megawatts electric) with an existing

Argonne fuel cell design that, to date, had demonstrated a few watts power output!

To expand the power range from watts to megawatts, I needed to know what design scale did to performance and its design viability. No one had done a theoretical combined fluid/thermodynamic-electrochemical analysis of the fuel cell. Hence, I developed a complex, transient computer program which took the basic Argonne-design fuel cell, expanded in size from watts to megawatts, from its initial startup conditions at elevated temperature through a steady-state set of operating conditions. The program included evaluating the changing fuel and oxidizer compositions, gas and solid material temperatures found for each position in the cell, and the corresponding Nernst electric potential. From these evaluations, voltage as developed at each layer, along with cell current (amps) were computed to obtain the entire device's power output. Internal electrical resistance values of all of the cell components were also evaluated to determine electrical losses and the feedback effect on local temperatures, as well as other coupled effects (material thermal properties).

A conceptual design of a 500-megawatt space power system was done. It featured four identical power modules, each with a fuel cell sub-module, pressurized fuel and oxygen tanks, and a water tank. Radiators were sized to condense the steam coming from the fuel cells. A hydrogen gas separator was incorporated to recover excess hydrogen that was to be used in the fuel cells for temperature control. The entire system was sized such that five shuttle flights could boost the system into orbit where it would be assembled.

This study never went beyond conceptual design. Large hardware components were never made. Argonne's Material Science Division, which had overall responsibility for all Argonne fuel cell development, used my computer program to provide input to a stress-analysis computer program for evaluation of large cell thermal stress. I was not involved with this phase of the effort and do not know specific results.

COMMERCIAL USES

If Argonne's solid oxide fuel cell were developed commercially, it would be a great advancement. Demonstrated chemical-(hydrogen)-to-electrical conversion efficiency was above 72%. Power density was five megawatts per cubic meter (five kilowatts per liter). A very small fuel cell could produce a lot of power! A small solid oxide fuel cell weighing only a few pounds could easily power an automobile! Rare earth hydride hydrogen storage is an effective and safe storage method. However, I do not see a new "hydrogen" economy developing. Hydrogen is going to be too expensive a fuel for "pedestrian" vehicles. The concept of the "average American" handling hydrogen makes me shudder. It will be impossible to make hydrogen systems sufficiently idiot proof!

NUCLEAR ROCKET DESIGN

My friend Nelson Hanan and I were given the task of redoing Argonne's nuclear rocket design that had been done 20 years earlier. We each had personal computers to do engineering calculations of heat transfer, fluid dynamics, and evaluation of hydrogen propellant properties within the reactor. Nelson was familiar with the latest core nucleonics calculation methodology using Argonne's main computer. He could accurately predict fission power distribution while accounting for neutron losses from radial and axial shielding and a rocket's throat. I did the core heat transfer and pressure drop calculations.

Though we were funded for six months, we finished validating the previous work in three months and boosted the previously determined specific impulse by 25 seconds (to 900 seconds) using old Rocketdyne technology!

This study became the basis for my work in scoping a nuclear-powered, single-stage-to-orbit shuttle that had a million-pound take-off weight and a 250,000-pound payload capability for low-Earth orbit. It featured supersonic scramjet propulsion to achieve Mach 10 at 130,000 feet altitude. Take-off was from earth, piggybacking on an aircraft like the one that then returned shuttles from California.

However practical such a system would be, no one is interested in nuclear rocket power. The public is still afraid of an incident like Chernobyl.

LISP MACROS

There was a short period of time when I was out of projects, and so Argonne put me to work making up macros in the LISP language, or as the pundits identify it, "Lost and Stupid Parenthesis" (which it has). It's a language which is used to generate such things as O-Ring Groove pieces of a drawing that you can just patch into a whole drawing and specify the numbers, etc. all automatically. I can't remember all of the uses, but the goal was basically to help the draftsmen increase their productivity on these CAD (Computer-Aided Design) machines. So, I did that for a while until some real work came along.

MPD THRUSTER FOR SPACE TRAVEL

Except for the nuclear rocket programs as previously described at ANL and GE, present chemical rocket systems are limited to relatively low specific-impulse values. Chemical rockets (solids and liquids) typically have a specific impulse of 250 seconds, meaning they can produce that many pounds of thrust per pound of propellant used per second. Hydrogen/oxygen rockets get 425 (or a bit more in space) seconds specific impulse. These rocket systems are used to place hardware and people into low-Earth orbit. Multiple staging allows going farther into space. The five-stage Saturn V went to the moon and back using lower-impulse chemical rockets.

Going to Mars, and beyond to other planets, requires a drastically different propulsion system with much higher specific impulse. A plasma engine called VASIMR (Variable Specific Impulse Magnetoplasma Rocket), invented in 1979 by astronaut Franklin Chang Díaz was described in his book, *To Mars and Beyond.* A VASIMR engine reputedly gets a specific impulse of 3,000 seconds. John Sandford mentions the VASIMR engine in his fictional thriller novel, *Saturn Run*. Another plasma rocket engine system is called "magneto-plasma-dynamics" (MPD).

MPD thrusters supposedly can achieve a specific impulse of 30,000 seconds. However, they are limited to low thrust levels, perhaps a few hundred pounds force or less. Though efficiency is high, it would take long times to increase vehicle velocity for long-distance missions. Mars trips could take months. Once halfway there, the spacecraft would have to be turned around and the engine used to slow the vehicle down to orbital speeds. Trajectory optimization is a large part of NASA planning. I will say no more on this and concentrate on the Argonne program that was proposed to help develop this propulsion system.

FACILITY AND CONTINUOUS CRYO-PUMP

Harold Herman was given responsibility to develop a facility plan and a design to test an MPD thruster under Claude Reed, Program Manager. A facility would have to provide a vacuum of about 10 billionths of an atmosphere (10^{-5} torr), while being "fed" an argon gas load of seven grams per second. No other facility in the world had the capability to handle such a large gas load at this vacuum level. A facility in Stuttgart, Germany could manage gas loads a hundred times smaller at higher pressure. Harold was not a "highly trained engineer." His English education was equivalent to a technician with some college math. Perhaps his background was equivalent to a DeVry or Dunwoody education. He was clearly out of his league for his part in this project.

At that time, Harold and I were still friends. Our boss, Ken Kuczen, asked me to help Harold with the vacuum and cooling system designs. Without help, Harold would have to be terminated. I had the time, since my funding was running low. (In later years at Argonne, we no longer had unlimited funding for all people.) So, I agreed to help him.

We quickly scoped out the size and construction of a vacuum tank. A one-inch-thick aluminum tank, 20 feet in diameter, 75 feet long, externally braced with rings at seven-foot intervals would suffice if parallel ribs were added between rings. However, vacuum pumping this heavy gas load at low pressure was a real problem.

I spent several months researching various available pumping systems. I also invented one of my own. In the end, I selected multiple types of pumping units with staged pumping between units in the system. It had a gas-diffusion-type first-stage pump that would operate at much higher inlet pressures than usual and be driven by some of the argon gas pumped from the chamber after it had been re-circulated and re-pressurized by a series of pumps. Such a diffusion pump was no longer being made, but the France-based manufacturer said they would be more than happy to restart production and build and sell us 10 units. Intermediate pumps were high-volume Roots-type blowers. Final pumping was to be done using smaller Roots-type blowers. Roots blowers are similar to superchargers used on racing cars to boost inlet manifold air pressure and engine power. A plasma physicist at Argonne, Ezzat Doss, suggested using a very high-speed linear magnetic field to move and compress argon plasma from the engine end of the chamber into the egg-crate latticework entrance region. This suggestion was never followed.

The MPD thruster had two megawatts power input. This amount of power had to be removed from the ionized argon gas flowing through the chamber before it was pumped from the vacuum chamber. I designed the lattice-type, egg-crate cooling system based on knowledge of heat transfer with help from some friends in aerospace. I called in a lot of my "markers" to get help in determining ion heat transfer rates from experts at TRW.

My invention, for which I received a patent, was a continuous cryo-pump. Cryogenic pumping had been used for high vacuum systems for many years, but never continuously. In previously designed systems, two cryo-pumps would be mounted in parallel, and each would be separately switched into a vacuum system by valving to accept the gas load as the other was switched out to allow regeneration. My invention featured simultaneous regeneration of the cryo-panel and continuous acceptance of a gas load to be condensed, solidified, and removed from the cryo-panel.

"HIGHLY TRAINED" ENGINEERS

Several personnel problems developed during the course of my work on this program. Claude Reed (I called him "Clod"), as the nominal program manager, took my progress reports, copied whole sections of them verbatim, and presented this material under his name alone at engineering society symposia. When he was questioned by engineers from other organizations who were at the symposia, he knew nothing of the subject, thereby making a fool of himself and Argonne.

Consequently, I and others were called to Princeton University to present our work before the Dean of Engineering, Professor Robert Jahn, who was acknowledged to be the "father of MPD" in the US. I gave the preponderance of the presentations. I convinced Dean Jahn that Argonne was amply capable of designing this system, specifically cooling gas flow under extremely high heat fluxes at the leading edges of the ionized, gas-cooling lattice and pumping high gas loadings from low system pressure. Following my presentation, we were given lunch in the Woodrow Wilson faculty dining room.

Our proposed facility was never constructed. The reason given was that no one at that time had made an MPG thruster that lasted in operation for a significant time duration. I write this now with hope that recent advances in fusion energy research in plasma containment will also pertain to solving durability of the MPD thruster engine.

FROM GOLDEN BOY TO UNMENTIONABLE CASTE

Dick Lewis, Engineering Division Director, called an impromptu design review of the MPD project for 10:00 AM one morning with no advance notice. I had planned to go home that day at 11:30 for a previously made appointment. No one else had much to say about the project since I had done almost 100% of actual design work. I did most of the talking, presenting the various design options and final choices. I was almost finished talking when Lewis told me to "Shut up." I was somewhat surprised by his outburst, but told him I only had one more thing to say, and I said it. I then excused myself, saying I had a prior appointment.

After I returned to work that afternoon, I was told by several people who had been at the meeting that "Lewis exploded after you left the meeting." He had said, "I never want to have Carlson in a meeting with me again." No explanation of his anger toward me was given at that time. I went instantly from being "the golden boy" of the division to an "unmentionable," like the lowest member of the India caste system. This event happened in 1984. I had 10 years of miserable work ahead at Argonne. I could not quit. My wife Ellen's medical bills were too high to permit that luxury. During one year in particular, our portion of medical bills was over $35,000 – Argonne's share was another quarter of a million!

Several years later, Lewis "bought the farm." He plowed his aerobatic airplane straight down into a cornfield on a farm south of Oswego following a stunt from which he could not recover. I was told he had not checked out his airplane after a particularly stressful stunt on a prior flight. Apparently, his seat came loose on the next flight, and he could not reach controls. I didn't miss him. However, my job situation did not improve. His replacement, Leo LeSage, was no better a manager. He apparently had Lewis's "little black book" that gave him background on each of his employees. I can only suspect I did not fare well in that book. The major difference in working for Leo was that he was incapable of bringing new work into the division and could be ignored for the most part. I probably did not ingratiate myself with him either. He had called me "Bill" one day as we passed in the hallway. I responded "Hi, George."

I had always had Ken Kuczen as an upper-division management buffer. But Ken developed prostate cancer which rapidly spread to his spine in spite of some special radiation treatment he received at Fermilab in Batavia. He could no longer work. I "inherited" another nemesis, Sam Bhattacharrya, as my immediate supervisor. He had been a Lewis disciple and did not like me. This feeling was mutual. He was mostly worthless as a manager, spending most of his time away from Argonne trying unsuccessfully to get program money. I figured he spent more Argonne money on travel than he got for programs. At those rare times when he was present, he arrived for work at 10:30 AM. He usually had a two-hour lunch and left (supposedly) at 6:00 PM. I was in the habit of arriving at 6:00 AM, taking lunch at 11:00 AM, and leaving at 4:00 PM. This way, I rarely had to see him. Normal hours were 8:00 AM to 5:00 PM.

Years later, when Sam laid me off, I was told Lewis had been "snowed" by my MPD presentation. Apparently, his ego was severely bruised. He had long had the reputation of being a "quick study." In any number of cases, it was said he would ask some expert about a subject of which he had no knowledge and then go to Washington and act like that expert. Lewis usually came back with a "bushel basket full of money." I suspect there was more than hurt ego involved in his attempt to get rid of me.

One discouragement was his "offer" to have me evaluated to become a "senior engineer." Actually, I now believe he "set me up" to be discouraged so I would quit. Argonne staffing was patterned after the University of Chicago. Senior engineers were equivalent in rank to full professors and salaries were "adjusted" accordingly to a higher level. I was interviewed by a retired former head of the Argonne Chemistry Division (Dick Adams), who then wrote a review of my many professional accomplishments, doing what I thought was a great job. Lewis rejected this "glowing report" of my achievements, though he accepted Harold Herman's case and promoted him to Senior Engineer. I was hurt by the comparison. But what really hurt were some friends telling me that Harold had repeatedly badmouthed me to Lewis in subsequent management meetings. I was no longer privy, since Lewis had also taken my design group away from me. Harold Herman was no longer my friend.

GOLDEN HANDSHAKE

Following Ellen's suicide on May 12, 1992, I felt considerably less constrained by my working environment. I remained at Argonne Labs for several years after my wife died, no longer performing at expected high levels. I found out while talking with Human Resources that I would be "eligible" for a "golden handshake" if I were laid off. So, I started plotting my departure from Argonne. I was now being assigned "skut jobs" of no real importance, so I was wasting time staying at Argonne. With Ellen gone, I had to determine for myself what my financial situation would be. I was astounded in a way – I had more money than I had thought possible, so sufficient retirement income was assured. I still came to work early, around 6:00 AM. However, I carried my lunch and ate at 11:00 AM, then took a half-hour nap and worked until 4:00 PM. I still worked more than my eight hours. However, I also left my door to my office open as I napped so anyone could see me. Sam apparently noticed (or heard about my behavior), but said nothing. I was prepared to object if he objected!

After one year, I took a month's vacation in March. Sam came up with something for me to do during that month, but I refused, saying my vacation had been scheduled for six months prior to his demand and I had made commitments that could not be changed. He was furious but could do nothing.

When the EBR-II reactor was formally shut down in March of 1994, Sam said, "I don't have funding for you anymore. If you wish to "bump" Tom Fornek, you can take his job." This ploy was a total fabrication, but I was not about to harm Tom. He had been my project manager on both of the MHD jobs, was a great guy, had a wife and had two daughters who were going to school, and couldn't live on anything except a full salary.

I made sure the golden handshake was still an option. Finding it open, I took it. I got a month's notice, which I used to clean out my office of materials I had collected over 20 years of service. It hurt a little bit. Not much work got done. I declined offers from friends for a formal send-off, but they took me (despite protests) to a local "greasy spoon restaurant" for lunch. I left Argonne in considerably higher esteem than I had left Rocketdyne. I was only 58 years old – the same age as my California "back-fence neighbor" when he had been laid off many years ago. I had vowed at that time it would never happen to me. I would make myself too valuable for any company to want to let me go! Yeah, sure, you betcha.

CONSULTING

TRW

When I first started working for Argonne, I kept getting insistent phone calls from John Hardgrove, the head of TRW's chemical laser group, to come back to California and work for him. TRW's laser program hadn't really gotten anywhere because they didn't know how to design a chemical laser yet! Even the people who had gone there from Rocketdyne were not designers. While they were engineers who handled "board" work, they were not the analytic design-engineer type that I was. As such, they didn't quite know what I had done, and they couldn't particularly help John much. So, he continually asked me to come work for him and I continually said no, until finally he asked, "Can you consult for us?"

I asked my boss, Stan Davis (head of engineering at ANL), and he replied, "Does Argonne have anything to do with these weapons?" I said, "No," and he said, "There's no conflict of interest – go ahead!"

Thus, I flew to Los Angeles many Friday evenings late in the fall of 1973 to work at TRW's Redondo Beach facility, designing their MIRCLE chemical weapon laser.

THE GRANDDADDY OF LASERS: MIRCLE

Using my knowledge of metal durability and laser efficiency with high-temperature operation that I had developed at Rocketdyne, I helped design TRW's MIRCLE laser (Mid-Infrared Chemical Laser Experiment) system and generally improved their chemical laser designs.

The MIRCLE laser was to be a 300-kilowatt device, three to four feet in length, five to six inches high, that would have a nozzle bank about an inch long in depth. The combustion and nozzle would be an adiabatic system that featured nickel fluoride for protection. I had to have TRW use an Incoloy base material because nickel by itself wasn't strong enough for anticipated stress loads on the blading. Incoloy had sufficient strength, but I had to use pure nickel plating on all surfaces exposed to fluorine. TRW knew how to do the required surface passification.

MIRCLE worked exactly as it was supposed to, except that beam power was 400 kilowatts. TRW tested it at its Capistrano test facility. It burned a five-inch diameter hole in a tank two miles away. That's all I was ever told.

The laser went on to be tested at other facilities. In the course of that later testing, reactants were changed. I understand that, instead of using helium as a diluent, they switched over from pure fluorine to nitrogen trifluoride so the nitrogen would act as the diluent. The fluorine part would be split up at some elevated temperature within the combustor to provide the nascent fluorine to the nozzles. Deuterium was then injected into the downstream supersonic flows from the nozzle bank, thereby getting DF ions in a cold reaction as had been done before.

Gomer, who was head of the engineering section at White Sands at that time, built the test facility where MIRCLE and other chemical lasers were tested. He told me much later (2020) that MIRCLE also burned a hole in a one-inch-thick steel plate at "some distance" from the beam source "in short order." No time was specified. I have not calculated an expected time from transient heat transfer theory.

Later on, based on the outstanding success of MIRCLE, TRW was awarded the ALPHA Chemical Laser program. Grant Hosack, a friend and former manager of mine at Rocketdyne who had taken the job at TRW that I had declined, became the ALPHA program manager.

TRW'S ALPHA LASER

The ALPHA Laser was projected to have a 25-megawatt beam. It would be a three-meter (or 10-foot) diameter beam and it would operate at a 3.4-micron DF wavelength. So, it would have a radian beam spread of about 1.15×10^{-7}. Thus, it would have a few feet beam spread in 200 miles. It doesn't make a hell of a lot of difference having 10-foot or 12-foot beam diameter, beam power intensity still exceeded 1,000 suns at 200 miles! The US would be able to poke this beam great distances into the Soviet Union and "toast the buns" off any Soviets, or cause havoc of one kind or another.

The United States wanted to mount this weapon on an aircraft platform, but didn't have a large enough airplane to hold the version TRW was developing. Component sizes were too big for the US Air Force Galaxy. Someone in the US State Department got the smart idea of asking the Soviets if we could borrow one of their Antonov heavy lifters, which were twice the size of a Galaxy C5A. This Soviet aircraft could carry the ALPHA Laser system. What does all this mean? I think that it was one of the factors that convinced the Soviets we were real.

The ALPHA Laser system had been in development for 11 years. Spread over this timeframe, it was a $3,500,000,000 program. As I mentioned, my friend Grant Hosack ran the program. He knew his aerodynamics too, but he was a great manager in terms of scheduling, cost control, and manpower loadings. I was told at one time, he had up to 600-800 people working at TRW and different contractors. The three-meter diameter beam mirror was good to within a *quarter wavelength* across the entire surface under the heat load it had. Laser mirrors are miracles in heat transfer engineering. I can't begin to tell anyone how they were made because I don't know. I remember marveling at the intricacies of a little mirror that we had at Rocketdyne for our 10-kilowatt device that would keep the beam collimated.

TRW had a bright young engineer by the name of Dale Hook who did all of the engineering for ALPHA, as far as I know. Dale was responsible for the critical breakthroughs and changed the design concept totally. Since the beam was going to be such a large diameter, TRW came up with an annular (toroidal) combustor that was wrapped around the mirror periphery. It was made from aluminum. We know aluminum melts at 1200°. But heat loss decreases in effect on lasing efficiency as size increases. Dale used aluminum and kept hardware cool enough while not increasing heat transfer losses such that it would influence efficiency.

ALPHA was ready to be assembled when Reagan met with Gorbachev in Iceland. Though other beam weapon systems were under development in the US at that time, I believe ALPHA was the predominant system.

Anyhow, TRW had its job, and I had nothing to do with ALPHA. But the contract had been a result of the success of MIRCLE.

THE FALCON AND THE SNOWMAN

One of the reasons I didn't go to TRW was that I didn't know how long the job was going to last. All other aerospace companies were going out of business. The only ones left were TRW and Hughes. But TRW had kept it secret that they were making spy satellites funded by the CIA.

All of TRW's secret material was stored in a vault. I had gone by this vault any number of times going in and out the door at TRW, but I didn't have clearance to go in there. There was a young, 19-year-old courier, Christopher Boyce, who would take material out of the vault and bring it to the people who requested it. You had to have proper clearance and sign for it, mark times in and out, then log everything. What Boyce didn't tell people was…

He had made copies.

Christopher Boyce was a falcon enthusiast. He flew falcons. His buddy was a cocaine addict. Boyce would hand off secrets to his cocaine buddy who would go to Mexico City to the Soviet embassy and sell this data to the Russians. And I don't know how much money they made, and I don't know what ever happened to the cocaine addict, but Boyce eventually got caught and was sentenced to federal prison. There's a book about them called *The Falcon and the Snowman* if you want to read all the details. It's in the open literature. I've read the book. I can attest to that which I know is true. What does this story have to do with anything?

REAGAN AT REYKJAVÍK

In 1986, President Ronald Reagan went to Iceland to meet with Mikhail Gorbachev to discuss nuclear disarmament. Reagan's hope was to achieve a gradual reduction in nuclear weapons over a period of time that would eventually result in no nuclear weapons for either side.

I listened to an audiobook written by the interpreter who was working for Reagan. Gorbachev had his own interpreter. Reagan's interpreter attended all of the otherwise closed meetings, so he knew what was said and what the ambiance was during these meetings. From what I remember, Reagan was his usual imperturbable self at the meeting, chewing on his jellybeans placidly. Gorbachev was raging mad, red-faced, screaming, as it's described – he was decidedly unhappy with Star Wars and wanted the United States to cancel it, period! In effect, Gorbachev's agreements on nuclear disarmament were contingent on the US abandoning Star Wars. Reagan tried to assure Gorbachev that the US would share the final design specifications with Russia once the system was tested and found to work. Gorbachev didn't believe Reagan. And what Reagan didn't know was that Gorbachev was probably far better informed about future US beam weapon capabilities than Reagan! He had all of the spy data to look at, or his people did. Alpha was a critical part of Star Wars equipment. ALPHA was well enough along that the Russians could see that things like the mirror were already ready to test! And then the US asking about putting it in an Antonov heavy lifter was icing on the cake. You know they knew that we were serious!

Reagan and Gorbachev went home, nuclear disarmament talks a bust. The US press considered Reagan a failure. What the American populace and Reagan did not know was that Russia was going bankrupt spending over half of its GNP on new nuclear super submarines. Russia didn't have the gas and the oil revenues that they now have. They couldn't keep up with US weapons development. And they didn't take Reagan's word when he said, "We'll develop this thing, and once it's done, we'll give you all the details – you can have your own defensive system. We'll both be protected from incoming missiles." The Soviet Union imploded. All the outlying satellite countries withdrew from "Mother Russia." Russia was alone.

There was a lot of infrastructure that the Soviet government had controlled up for the taking. It became possible for some Russians to buy whole industries for "kopeks on the Ruble" (equivalent to our "pennies on the dollar"), getting something for nothing and then turning it into billion-dollar empires. Quite a few billionaires were created literally overnight. Corruption was the norm. I had gone to Russia in 1979 as part of a MHD delegation. Russia was a pretty dour place at that time. Half the people you saw on the street wore military uniforms and had "Kalashnikov rifles" slung over their shoulders. Military presence seemed to be everywhere.

In 1996, my sister Ruth and brother-in-law Len and I went to Russia on a cruise through the Baltic and wound up in St. Petersburg for two days. We went through the Hermitage Museum and saw much of the artwork that Catherine the Great had accumulated. It was incredible. One thing you noticed was that women on the street were wearing flowered dresses. It was in early May; the weather was nice. Ordinary people had a completely different demeanor than what they had in 1979 when I visited Moscow on a technical tour.

Unfortunately, things have changed again. Putin has taken control. He's trying to reestablish the Soviet Union and, as a former KGB colonel, he knows all the ways to intimidate. It seems he has somehow gotten the minds and the spirits of the populace to back him. They elected him twice, had an interim fellow for two terms, and now, Putin is back in power. The Soviet Union is, in effect, being resurrected, at least in part. Eastern Ukraine was taken as part of an effort to recover Sebastopol, a port on the Black Sea.

International politics have once again prevailed, but my claim is that, for at least a brief time, the weaponization capability of the chemical laser system was shown because of my work. TRW built a much larger laser that cowed the Russians to some extent, maybe hastening the demise of the Soviet Union, giving the world a semblance of peace for a short time. So, I had nothing to do with Alpha, but I was kind of its great granddaddy.

ROOF BOLTING MACHINE

Beyond TRW, I also consulted for Salt-Lake-City-based Envirotech Corporation, both in their mining division and also in their process division. (The sewage aerator I developed for their process division is described elsewhere.) For their mining division, I developed a roof bolting system which could be used in low overhead mine shafts, drilling and bolting continuously. Roof bolting in mines is done to prevent roofs of wide shafts from collapsing into the workspaces. It provides a means to transfer overburden loads from the center of a shaft to its outer edges where mined material is left to support such loads. Mines that had shafts 15 feet wide might be two or three feet high. Whereas they had to extend a bolt up into the rock roof 10 feet or more. How do you do that?

The old answer was to assemble short lengths of drill rod vertically, stopping for each as you drilled upward. This was a slow and cumbersome process. When you were done drilling, you had to disassemble the drill string and retrieve the cutter assembly. It was time consuming and halted mining operations in the affected area. A twisted steel cable could be used for the bolt. A fast-setting cement was used to grout and anchor the bolt in the hole. The bolt had a plate attached at the lower end with a screwed-on nut.

The new way to drill a bolt hole straight up into the rock above the ore or coal required a machine no more than two feet high with a cutting device that had a bendable shaft supporting a cutting head at its tip. The cutting head has a rotating diamond cutter to grind and pound the rock simultaneously. You have to flush the rock dust from the hole as it is generated. The required operating functions of the drill shaft are: 1) It must have an internal, bendable air supply passageway. 2) It must have a bendable structure that will transmit shock forces. And 3) It must have a bendable means to transmit high torque loads effectively in either rotation direction. The cutter shaft must traverse a 90° bend through a guide channel with a radius of one foot from horizontal to a vertical direction.

The air passageway solution was a series of small segments of tubing as core fitted end to end with no gap between them. They extended the full length of the drill shaft. Next, around these tubing segments, seven solid rods were nestled against each other in the circular direction and against core tubing segments radially inward. Rods acted as hammers. Ken Coover (my office partner at that time) suggested having a one-full-turn twist in the hammer pack to keep a constant effective length as the rods traversed a 90° bend. Hammer rods were wrapped tightly, first in a clockwise direction, then in a counterclockwise direction for the full length of the assembly. These wire wraps provided torque transfer capability in either direction. Rotation in the clockwise direction was used for cutting. Counter-clockwise rotation was used to ease removal of the cutting assembly. The new cutter assembly could be incorporated in a standard roof bolter.

I spent most of a weekend in Salt Lake City reviewing the US Bureau of Mines proposal request and wrote the proposal for the machine I've just described. Envirotech won the proposal competition and got a contract to build a demonstration machine. It was tested successfully, and they incorporated the new design in their line of roof bolters. I worked with Lars Olavson, who was Envirotech's new product manager. I also helped him design a hydrogen fuel storage system for engines to be used in underground mines.

HYDROGEN-GAS-POWERED COMBUSTION ENGINES IN MINES

One of the largest problems in mining anything underground is getting material from where you're mining out to where you can lift it up to the surface (or wherever else you'd like to carry it). A lot of lateral transport is done with electric-battery-powered locomotives. Limited useful productive time of battery use occurs when the mining is being done far from recharging stations to switch battery packs. A lot of energy from the battery pack is wasted going back and forth. Yet electric power is preferred because of its safety.

A combustion engine has much more energy potential. You can't burn any hydrocarbon fuel because you'll make carbon monoxide. If you have a rare earth nickel metal hydride, which has notably high hydrogen storage capacity, you could couple this hydrogen source to a combustion engine to provide substantially better range capability in locomotives in underground mines. Lars Olavson successfully ran a Caterpillar supercharged diesel engine on hydrogen. His engine had three valves per cylinder, one each for air, exhaust, and fuel. This engine would exhaust only water vapor and nitrogen. He needed a hydrogen source to take into a mine with sufficient storage capacity to operate the engine for a full shift.

HYKSOS HYDROGEN STORAGE TRANSFER SYSTEM

Another project I was involved with was called "HYKSOS," named after the Egyptian god. We had a chemical division at Argonne, and there was a brilliant chemist there by the name of Dieter Gruen who came up with the scheme of configuring hydride beds (hydrogen combined with some rare earth metals) to direct hydrogen flows. By heating and cooling different hydride beds, he could get hydrogen flowing from one to the other through a turbine to produce mechanical power. But he had to prove the basic concept. That involved building tanks filled with rare earth hydrides, one of which was lanthanum nickel hydride. Hydrides have a 25% volume increase when they go from the non-hydrided state to the hydrided state. When they lose their hydrogen, they shrink back to their original higher density. Some hydrides contain more hydrogen by mass per unit volume than liquid hydrogen!

No one had ever made a tank that would withstand hydride expansion. I knew what the problems were, but how could I solve them?

I had to build tanks that had heat exchangers inside to transfer heat into or out of the hydride in a timely fashion that met other system requirements. These heat exchange elements consisted of coils of tubing flowing heat transfer fluid. Coils had to have a certain spacing as the timing of the heat transfer from one place to another would be critical in limiting system response. The system had to have a minute time response.

Additionally, I had to have a way to distribute hydride material that also distributed expansion space among the coils. I put trays inside, interspersed among the coils, to hold hydride material. Tanks were sealed and pressure tested. The HYKSOS system was tested with hydrogen circulating back and forth between tanks. It worked beautifully. It was the first time that tanks never split open. That was the major achievement.

It's important to note that these particular hydrides are safe as a hydrogen storage medium. The liquid or high-pressure gas forms can be very hazardous to handle. It only takes 10^{-8} erg energy to initiate hydrogen combustion/detonation with the correct mixture ratio in air or oxygen. With hydride beds, hydrogen is released at low pressures. Adequate ventilation prevents burning or detonation. I remembered these design principles in later consulting work. HYKSOS was considered an outstanding success.

HEAT TREATMENT FURNACE FANS

I got a phone call from a fellow who managed a high-temperature fan manufacturing company just north of Argonne in Darien, Illinois. It was just a couple miles north on Cass Avenue, the East boundary of Argonne. Chester Johansen, the manager, asked me if I'd be interested in consulting for him. I said, "sure," and went to talk with him. Chester would call me in, and he'd have a particular problem with a high-temperature fan that his staff could not figure out and solve. It usually involved heat transfer or fan blades were falling off. If so, the rest of the fan would shake apart. Sometimes, bearings would fail.

Fan materials were the best alloys you could buy: Incoloys and Hastelloys. But operating conditions were pushing these materials to their limits. I did analysis for Chester, showing him how to fix certain problems. For example, with fan blade "departures," Chester's engineers had not considered bending moments at the blade root caused by fan forces moving hot gas. They had only considered integrated centrifugal loads on blade root welds. Adding stiffener strips at the blade roots solved the problem. An overhung fan and its bearing assembly had to be located within the hot furnace. Lubricants could not tolerate the high temperature, at least 1700°F. I had Chester's staff redesign the fan shaft to be a hollow, thick-walled alloy tube. It was in intimate contact with the inner bearing race. I had them install an inner insulated stationary tube within the rotating tube shaft with outlet nozzles directed on the outer tube in contact with the inner bearing race. A small, high-speed centrifugal fan blower (such as in vacuum cleaners) fed warm air to the inner tube. Hotter air returned from the furnace end through the annulus between tubes. Though heat was transferred from the returning air to incoming air, it had little effect. The bearing worked well.

It was simple engineering, but it was fun. And I really enjoyed working for Chester. He was always gracious, and I got paid right away!

NATIONAL BUREAU OF STANDARDS

After three years at Argonne, Tom Coultas quit and went to work at the National Bureau of Standards in Gaithersburg, Maryland. The National Bureau of Standards (NBS, soon to become NIST, or National Institute of Standards and Technology) had an interdepartmental program funded by the Department of Energy, called the Energy-Related Inventions Program. NBS solicited proposals from anybody throughout the country who thought they had a new energy invention.

Most replies (90%) were perpetual motion machines, dismissed out of hand by NBS staff. However, a few proposals merited closer evaluations. A particular proposal might be sent to three outside evaluators for review and comment. A cadre of the top 400 or 500 engineering professors in the US was assembled for this job, and Coultas was the head NBS evaluator. He kept bugging me to become one too. I kept refusing until finally I asked my boss at Argonne if it would be a conflict of interest. He said, "No, go ahead and do it."

It was the interesting ones that NBS staff really had no way to handle and would send out to specialists. I was rated among the top five of the hundreds of outside consultants because I took an interest in the work and I always went the extra mile. If I could write a computer program that would allow a person to optimize a system, I'd check out the program to see that it operated correctly, then print an example, then send that along in my report with how to install the program on a PC.

I have two examples of standout proposals. The first involved a truck driver who hated to stop at night in a truck-stop parking lot because there would be hundreds of trucks with their diesel motors idling. They would have their air conditioning running so they could sleep in their cabs. Truck-stop parking lots were smelly, noisy, and possibly downright dangerous because of carbon monoxide generated.

His idea was this. As you're going down the road, your air conditioner provides abundant, even excess, cooling. Compared with engine power output, air conditioner power demand is minimal. Excess cooling could be used to cool a cold storage locker. He had the idea of using a material called a clathrate to store the cold in the locker. If you mix water and Freon, it forms a clathrate molecule. Freon clathrates have a melting temperature (or freezing temperature) that you can vary depending on the amount of Freon mixed with water. As an example, if you had a mixture that froze and melted at 45°F, cold air coming from the air conditioner at 35°F would solidify it. The rate of freezing would not be critical, because you would have all your time on the road to accomplish this process. That night, you could run a little fan with a few watts power draw from a battery and get a sixth of a ton of air conditioning for eight hours while not having to run your diesel engine. You also would save diesel fuel cost. I thought it was a great idea. I did all the heat transfer calculations, constructed a PC program to allow optimization of the design, and included this program in a report to NBS. I never heard back whether the truck driver had capitalized on his invention.

A second fellow, Julius Czaja, was a 77-year-old, retired engineer from Kodak in Rochester, NY. Julius had developed a thermodynamic analysis for predicting the effect of net isentropic (no total entropy change), two-phase, two-component expansion (i.e.: a vapor and gas). What does this mean? Well, it's what happens in a tornado; it's what happens in a hurricane. It's the driving force that develops when water vapor condenses and transfers this energy to the surrounding air. Added expansion causes buoyancy or rotational energy if the air/vapor mass has an initial angular momentum.

Julius' application of his idea was rather lame: putting a small vortex generator out in the desert to provide pumping power to draw water from subsurface storage basins. However, his thermodynamics were a phenomenal insight. I used Julius' concept to develop a computer model that could predict tornado activity knowing temperature and humidity. Tornados are possible at temperatures as low as 60°F. I've heard it happen. And you can get pressures down to two-thirds of an atmosphere at ground level. There is a lot of power in a tornado.

The question is: Can we have controlled tornadic activity in a structure built like a cooling tower such as are found at electric power generation plants? I don't know if anybody would ever risk doing it. Thermodynamics indicates it's possible to get 200 megawatts of electric power per square mile of area covered by a transparent membrane. This power system would be an interesting alternative to solar panels. A thorough design and cost analysis will show relative merits if the risk factor is acceptable for tornado power.

UNITED STATES URANIUM RECOVERY COMPANY

I got a call one day. I thought it was a telemarketer, so I hung up the phone on him. He called right back, saying, "I'm not a telemarketer. I want to hire you." He was from a place called US Uranium Separation Company in Paducah, Kentucky. He had read about a patent I got on a continuous cryogenic pump to trap argon gas at low pressure (a few millitorr). He wanted me to come to Paducah, KY to talk to them about the cryopump. I replied, “I’m not in a position to travel; if you want to come to Houston, you can avoid any travel, housing, and per diem expenses. I only charge for hours I work.” We arranged to meet a few days later at my house. The fellow came and we discussed what his company was trying to do.

It turned out they were trying to come up with a new way to separate uranium 235 from 238. Now, the interesting thing is, Dieter Gruen had come up with the same scheme, several years before. I had solved the problem for him. Thus, the problem was solved for this other guy. The problem was that they would have mixed uranium fluoride gases. It could be U-238F6, or it could be U-235F6, not very much difference in molecular weight. But they could tune a laser to a wavelength to excite one or the other type of uranium fluoride molecules, then nudge it electrostatically in a mass spectrometer. They’d have a little pile of 235 over here and a bigger pile of 238 over there. Dieter had introduced me to the concept of macromolecules. It turns out that either UF6 molecule, which are amazingly high molecular weight molecules to begin with, tends to agglomerate as it’s cooling in the expansion process. The thermodynamics of a macromolecule gas is totally different than what the UF6 started with. The macromolecule has a higher freezing point. It will deposit out on the walls and plug the nozzle. You wouldn’t get a stream of supersonic gases.

I solved the plugging problem by building an electric heater into the nozzle. A kilowatt heater was more than adequate for the task. It was powered with a variable-voltage power supply transformer. A thermocouple indicated operating temperature. The nozzle was thick copper to facilitate conduction to its end. According to Dieter, the nozzle worked well. However, the program at Argonne did not continue. I never heard why. US Uranium was interested as I discussed the Argonne experience. They had contracted with a place in Australia, South of Sydney, that was doing the experimental work. I don't know the outcome of these experiments.

SEARLE AND NUTRASWEET

Stan Davis, a former Director of Engineering at Argonne, retired after both parents died and left him a large inheritance. He got bored and started looking for work, winding up with a contract with Searle Pharmaceuticals. At the time and in a separate facility, they also made NutraSweet sugar substitute. (They later sold the rights to make NutraSweet to Monsanto Chemicals.) Stan Davis was consulting with Searle to show how they could improve production. He had come in the fall, telling me about problems Searle was having with trying to supply oxygen to the special bugs that convert sugar into aspartame – the precursor to NutraSweet. What people don't know is that aspartame is bug poop. I don't know anything beyond the point where the bugs do their duty. But Searle somehow could collect all this excrement and process it further, and then they had to dilute it by a factor of 1,000-to-one to make it into a product that you can put in your coffee.

In essence, they wanted to find out how to better provide oxygen to their bugs.

I had done a lot of aeration work in the past at Rocketdyne, so I sat down and went through Searle's whole system. I had to write a computer program with a number of floating variables because Searle was not about to tell us much. I did find out that there were about 400 kilowatts of thermal energy generated by these bugs in each of four 500,000-gallon tanks. From these numbers, I could calculate how much air was consumed. Then, knowing bubble dynamics and tank configuration, I calculated how much excess air would be required.

I decided on an oil-free compressed air system using a bubbler design I had success with at Rocketdyne and optimized the design using my computer program. I did all of this on my own time over Christmas vacation, both because it was interesting, and as I didn't have anything else to do that Christmas. Stan came by again in January saying, "I got this job if you're interested. Would you look at the aeration of this system and find out how to optimize it so that they could maybe double their production rate?" I said, "Yes, I can." He then asked, "How long would it take?" "Maybe six weeks," I replied. What I didn't tell him is I already had it done. He said, "How much do you want?" I said $10,000. He said, "Do it in that time, you got a deal and you get your money." I called him in four weeks, told him the job was done, and got my check for $10,000. I thought I was really doing well!

We had a guy working in our area who was taking flawed diamonds and putting them in a reactor. Somehow the neutrons going through these diamonds would recrystallize carbon and get rid of defects. He worked with people in Switzerland. When I told him my story of what I had earned with my NutraSweet project, he one-upped me. "I went to Switzerland last weekend, flew first-class both ways, was put up in a first-class hotel, saw some people, came home with $10,000," he reported. I said, "Get out of here." He said, "Well, come on out to my car." So, I did, doubting he had a check for $10,000 from some bank in Switzerland. It was real, dated the weekend before. So, he had done in a single, relaxed weekend what I had done in many days of work. And he had done it with a reactor that had been available – didn't cost him anything to do this "work!"

PERSONAL LIFE

MEMORABLE ADVENTURES

I have had several memorable adventures in my lifetime. They remain "frozen" in memory to an extent that I wish to share them in writing.

When I was seventeen, I spent a summer in Colorado working for my brother-in-law Len Jones in Canyon City where he had leased a Standard Oil gas station. In those days, gas was not "self-serve," so help was needed to aid customers. I was a "gas pumper," engine oil checker, and window washer! This was in an era when "full service" was the normal way of doing business – customers expected an attendant to check engine oil level, wash all windows, and check all tire pressures – at no extra cost. Gasoline cost about 30 cents a gallon! Another local fellow, Jim, worked there too. We became buddies. His uncle had an old WWII jeep with open sides and no top. We would go from the gas station on our "off time" to explore the mountains around town.

On one such occasion, we were at 14,000 feet elevation when we spotted some deer grazing near us. I decided to chase them. I got about 20 feet and collapsed. The air was too thin to breathe! The deer just scampered away, unconcerned about me. I learned about lack of conditioning the hard way.

Another time, Jim and I took the old "shelf road" that ran from Canyon City to Cripple Creek. Long ago, it had been the stagecoach road, and had not been maintained ever since. It was barely wide enough for the jeep. There were times when the passenger side tires (my side) seemed to be running half off the road's edge, and there was an 800-foot drop-off on that side – straight down. It was definitely exhilarating, but scary beyond description. I was glad when we reached Cripple Creek and took another road (Phantom Canyon) home. I learned a little exhilaration goes a long way. There is no way I would ever attempt such a passage again. Once in my life was more than enough!

DEVIL WIND

My first wife Ellen and I took a vacation in eastern Utah in late October of 1970, camping in a tent in the Manti LaSalle Mountains at 9,300 feet. I set up the tent with the usual tent pegs holding the edges and corners of the tent floor to the ground. We had cots to sleep upon. About midnight, a terrible wind arose. It was eerie to an extreme. There seemed to be a pocket of wind that swept around the rim of the bowl where we were camped. This natural bowl was formed by mountains on three sides and a drop-off to the valley 4,000 feet below on the fourth side. It took about a minute for this pocket of wind to make a circumference of a mile, so it must have been traveling 60 miles an hour! The ground shook when it passed. I was afraid it would rip the tent pegs from the ground and blow us off the mountain. We both huddled on the ground on the windward side of the tent to help the pegs hold. It must have worked because we were still there after the wind suddenly died an hour later. The next morning, I noticed that all of the trees were bent in the direction toward which we had heard the wind blowing. Obviously, this phenomenon had happened many times before. Later, I asked some locals in Moab, Utah about it. They knew of this "Devil Wind." Early Indians of the area had been afraid of it!

As we camped, we listened to news using the car radio (sparingly – since this was before transistor radios). After several days, we heard about a heavy snowstorm in Salt Lake City that was headed our way. It was time to leave. We packed the car and I attempted to start the engine. Our 1970 Ford LTD would not start – it kept flooding out. I knew enough about engines to remove the spark plugs, which were coated in soot. After cleaning thoroughly, I reinstalled them and tried again to start the car, being careful to not flood it. No luck. I pulled one plug only to find it was coated with soot again – which meant all the plugs were being shorted out and would not spark. Our car was located about 1,000 feet from the rim of the bowl. There was a very slight incline from where our car sat up to the rim. There was no way that I could push a heavy sedan by myself. I was ready to cut a sapling tree, use it as a lever, and try to "inch the car" over to the rim where we could coast downhill. Even the prospect of inching the car to the rim was not good in two respects: it would be an inordinate amount of work and take "God only knows how long." Also, if I managed this feat, we would be careening down the mountain with poor brakes as the car had power-assisted brakes that required the motor to be running. I despaired that we wouldn't get off the mountain in time to avoid the snow.

Thankfully, a little Toyota Corolla appeared. I asked them to push us. The driver hesitated, thinking it would ruin his little car. He acceded when I told him our options. He was able to get us over the rim and we started down the mountain. I had the car in the lowest gear, hoping the automatic transmission would slow us some and help me brake the car's descent. However, we were extremely fortunate in another way. It turned out the transmission rotated the motor, which some automatic transmissions won't do! So, I had some braking assistance! After a half mile, the motor caught. It ran fitfully at first, but eventually "smoothed out" as the soot was burned off the plugs. I was able to use the disc brakes for the rest of the trip down the mountain! We made it back to Moab and were very thankful we could stay in a warm motel for the night before we headed home to California.

Sometimes, one will be caught in a situation over which he has no real control. If potential help comes, one must ask for it! I believe we had help from above this time with assistance arriving in time. No telling what would otherwise have happened.

LAKE MINNETONKA DUNKING

Floyd Larsen was another grad student who worked in the heat transfer lab with me back in the day. He was a great engineer in terms of having a "hands-on" mechanical bent. In fact, he was responsible for putting in a complete high-pressure, high-flowrate air flow system throughout the mechanical engineering building *as a grad student.* It supplied and made available 250 or so PSI air through eight- or 10-inch piping all over different labs. I thought that was quite an accomplishment. It would've scared the hell out of me to have to do something like that in those days. I later built my ego up to an ability to build facilities, but I was a long way from doing that in grad school.

Well, Floyd was the son of a fellow and his wife who lived out on lakeshore property off Lake Minnetonka, one of the hoity-toity sections of Minneapolis. One day, we decided that we were going to go sailing. Floyd had set up a really big canoe – an "Indian War Canoe," he called it – for sailing. I think it was 20 foot long and really wide. Floyd had rigged the canoe with flat side lee boards in lieu of a keel. He also rigged a mast with two booms and a lateen sail. (Lateen sails have both top and bottom booms.) Floyd invited Woody Talbot, me, and Roger Schmidt to go sailing on Lake Minnetonka on a fine, spritely spring day with a crisp westerly wind of 15 knots. Most of the lake laid to the East. Floyd rigged the lateen sail after we other three settled in and we took off across the lake, heading downwind, going like a bat out of hell.

Now, Minnetonka's not a small lake. It would be several miles, easily, before we got to where we'd have to turn around. However, Floyd had made one mistake in rigging his sail. Instead of having a loop to hold the bottom boom onto the mast, he had a U-shaped oarlock, so when we came about, the bottom boom came loose, fluttered up in the wind, and tipped that canoe over. Suddenly, we were wet and topsy-turvy!

Winter ice had been gone only a few weeks, so the water was still cold. God, it was COLD! It must've been less than 40 degrees. We had maybe 150-200 feet to get to shore. But all of us stuck with the boat and tried to gather up whatever floated. We paddled with hands or oars. All of us made it to shore, thank God! After pulling it onto shore, we got the canoe upright and bailed out. Then we tried to dry off enough before we attempted to head back against the chilly wind. Fortunately, we all had left our shoes, socks, and outerwear on the dock in front of Floyd's house.

On our arduous return, some of us used salvaged paddles and the rest of us just used hands. All made it back, thoroughly worn out. "Going back against a chilly wind" was strenuous. It had been quite an experience, one to remember. Later, when I finally got to learn how to sail on the Pacific Ocean offshore from Los Angeles, I noted that it had been that initial thrilling experience (not the dunking) that got me addicted to sailing.

We all parted ways for a while. I went to California, Roger went to work for Honeywell in Minneapolis, and Floyd went to work for a place called Fluidyne in Minneapolis.

Woody went to Battelle Research Institute in Columbus, Ohio.

THE GIRL WHO BECAME DAISY DUKE

Norma Bachmann was a pert, vivacious, lively woman who was also our group secretary at Rocketdyne a few years after I joined Research. She was interested in play acting. North American Aviation had an employee's recreation center in Canoga Park near where I worked. My wife Ellen and I were "invited" to watch a play in which Norma was acting. We went one evening sitting near the back row of seats in the small theater. Norma's two kids, a girl of 12, boy of 10, were sitting in the front row, cheering wildly whenever Norma appeared on stage. I know Ellen and I got more of a kick out of watching the two kids than enjoying the play. I think the rest of the audience did too!

Five years later, I met Norma's daughter Catherine. She was a stunningly beautiful 17-year-old woman. She was meeting her mother at the guarded entrance gate to the facility at Santa Susana Field Laboratory. We only had a short conversation, but I was told that Catherine was interested in getting into the movie or television business.

A few years later, after I left Rocketdyne and moved to the Chicago area, I got a letter from Norma asking me to write a letter to CBS "praising" the *Dukes of Hazzard* TV show. Norma was concerned the show was not getting high enough reviews for CBS to keep it on the air. I wrote a glowing letter, emphasizing the cast's ability to portray their roles in a fun-loving, happy way. The Dukes show caught on and continued.

Another few years later, I got an additional letter from Norma asking me to go to the Chicago Stock Yards Auditorium where some of the cast of the "Dukes" were showcasing the car featured in the series and doing skits for the public. Norma indicated her great concern that the show's producers were "using Catherine badly." I was given permission to go "backstage." I was able to talk briefly with Catherine alone. Without makeup, she looked to have aged well beyond her years. Actually, she must have still been in her 20s. I reported back to Norma, who told me her concern was because the producers gave actors uppers regularly to get them to perform, then gave them downers to get them to be able to sleep. I don't doubt that Norma was correct in her assessment.

After a long run on TV, *The Dukes of Hazzard* went off the air. I didn't follow the life after for the young, beautiful girl who had been Daisy Duke, except the fashion she set of extreme cutoffs to allow girls to show off their legs.

MYSTICISM

As far back as I can remember, I was always somewhat of a "mystic." I got it from my mother. She had been born in that part of Sweden where the "black Swedes" lived. These people were reputed to be very superstitious – believing in omens and having a proclivity to develop defenses against "bad spirits." While I was growing up, we kids had to follow certain rules: "Never walk under a ladder," "Don't step on cracks," "Get your hair cut at the correct phase of the moon," etc. Throughout my life, I seemed to have had spiritual guidance. I can relate several personal instances and those times related to my work are too numerous to mention. I can now say that many "breakthroughs" that happened throughout my career must have had spiritual help. I cannot honestly claim authorship now, though at the time they happened, I certainly did so. My ego demanded its due! But, I must say emphatically that all of the following really happened – whatever the case, cause, or circumstance.

During my career at both Rocketdyne and Argonne, I would have "inspirations" which would allow me to solve technical problems other people could not handle. At first, it was an ego thing. After an initial phase of not having any confidence in my abilities, I became egotistical, thinking I was "just better" than anyone else. However, my attitude extracted a terrible price. I was almost constantly under extreme pressure to "perform," solving other people's problems as well as doing my own assignments. Late in my career, I finally had an epiphany of sorts. I realized that a "higher power" intervened many times to help me solve a difficult problem. This is what I mean by spiritual guidance. Once I had this realization, a large load was lifted from my shoulders. I could say, "If God wants it done, he will see to it!"

One example suffices. It involved a solution of a Green's Function representing combustion dynamics in the moon ascent engine (see Rocketdyne chapter). I had hated higher math in college. I was no good at it! When we studied Green's Functions to solve differential equations, I was stuck as usual. Fortunately, another engineer, Carl Oberg, who was a brilliant theoretician, had done the particular theoretical solution. But it didn't work! He had made an error which he could not find. Somehow, I found the error in the infinite series of terms of his solution. It had to be because of divine guidance. I certainly cannot claim any credit. This type of "help" must have been given to me thousands of times during my career. Was it a friendly angel? Well, no deceased member of my immediate family had been to college, let alone studied higher math, so ancestral spirits were probably not the source of this help!

CHRISTMAS TREE THEORY OF LIFE

When I was a kid growing up in northern Minnesota, the family ritual at Christmastime was to go out into the "woods" to find a tree. We didn't have far to go since our little town was surrounded by pine, spruce, and fir forests. No one in those days worried about someone stealing a tree from some out-of-the-way place, so "Christmas trees obtained in the woods were free!" I remember many times wading through three feet of snow back into the woods for perhaps a half mile, carrying a rope and an axe looking for that perfect tree – usually a top from a larger tree. Invariably, we would return to the side of the road to chop down and haul away that "first tree" we had seen! Over the years I developed my "First Law" or "Christmas Tree Theory of Life:" You should go after the first thing that you discover in your search for an answer to a problem. You'll eventually come back to it anyhow. With few exceptions, this principle served me well. It's still a mystical conundrum!

PART FINN, PART SWISS, AND PART IRISH

Three other examples illustrate mystical phenomena in my personal life. Two involve both women I married. While I was in my third year of college, I had a habit of coming back to the dorm after classes and taking a short nap before supper, which began at 5:00 PM. One time as I yet lay awake in bed, I started to wonder, "Who will I marry?" The answer came to me immediately: She will be from New Jersey, be part Finn, part Swiss, and part Irish.

When I met Ellen, my first wife, seven years later, I fell in love and told myself I will marry this girl – all in the space of the first 10 minutes after meeting her! And after six weeks of dating, she informed me that she was ¼ Swiss, ¼ Irish, and ½ Finn. I already knew from her accent that she was from New Jersey! We were married nine months later after a very stormy courtship. I told myself many times throughout our marriage that I should never have married her. We were almost totally incompatible. But, I had made a commitment and "no one in our family got a divorce" and I did not want to be the first!

After 30 years, she committed suicide, not willing to live in increasing pain from arachnoiditis in her spine. I had grief, relief, and a host of other emotions at that time. For all the trouble we had during our marriage, I gained a lot from her, which made me stronger, wiser, and a wealthier person. And, without Ellen, I doubt that I would have had the amount of technical success that I acquired during my long engineering career, often obtained by staying away from her to avoid personal problems. I often used this time to study or do research on a technical problem.

MAKE A CHOICE

It's quite a shock to have a near-death experience! Mine happened after Ellen and I ate seafood at a restaurant on the end of the pier in Santa Barbara, CA. I had abalone and a salad which was sprinkled with bacon bits. I don't know which food caused my poisoning, but I will not eat abalone to this day!

I had to throw up on the way home several hours after eating. I pulled off the freeway a number of times. After we got home, I had "everything" coming out both ends simultaneously. After several hours of sitting on the toilet while holding a plastic bucket in hand, I got terribly dehydrated. Ellen called neighbors to help. Their response was, "We're going out to eat now and can't help you." So, Ellen called local paramedics who came out immediately from the fire station. I had dragged myself into our kitchen and sprawled on a chair. They lugged me to a stretcher laid out beside the chair.

As the paramedics fussed over me, I could look down – seeing myself and them while they were working on me! I drifted away. I know they got me to the local hospital only because that is where I awoke. Yes, there was this diffused white light around me while I lay on the stretcher in our kitchen. I seem to remember that I had been told to make a choice at that time – to live or die! After several more hours recuperating at the hospital, the doctor allowed me to go home. A concerned neighbor had showed up to inquire about me and took us home, since Ellen had apparently accompanied me in the ambulance.

The net effect of this incident was that for several ensuing years, I was not afraid to die. That sense of serenity which I had at that time has dissipated. My old fears of death eventually returned. I had no such effect when Stan Tykarski died.

STEVE

Steve Grammel was a fine young analyst who had previously worked in my Argonne group. He had an innate ability to simplify the solution to a problem and implement it with concise programming. Once, during a Christmas vacation, I was working on a computer solution to a problem (and staying away from Ellen) when he helped me solve a vexing coding section. With only a few lines, he eliminated a page or more of code I had written (that would not work), and made the computer do the thing I wanted it to do! Steve had been assigned to another group, so I had little contact with him for several years. I heard then that he had become increasingly "odd." At Argonne, "odd" was often the "norm" and indistinguishable sometimes from "normal." One can often see distinguished people doing odd things! It was definitely an academic type of organization.

One day, one of Steve's coworkers came to see me. He told me Steve had gone blind and had something terribly wrong with his brain. He also told me Steve was seriously considering going to a local neurosurgeon for brain surgery. Something told me this was absolutely the wrong thing to do. I called Steve and told him to do nothing until I contacted him again. I dropped all of my own work for the remainder of the next two days and started to look for the "right doctor" for Steve.

Argonne is associated with the University of Chicago. So, I started with contacts in their medical service. Within a short time, one name stood out among Chicago's many neurosurgeons. He was associated with Evanston Hospital, just north of Chicago. I had Steve get an appointment with him. Howard Geyer and I took him to see this doctor, who when looking at the MRI and other test results, said to the three of us, "Sit down! Steve, you have at best a one-in-a-million survival chance. Your tumor is unprecedented in my experience. I have done over 700 operations on the human brain. This tumor extends from invading your sinuses back to include and infuse your brain stem. The tumor occupies 90% of your skull! If an operation is performed, the shock of quickly releasing pressure would snap both of your optic nerves, leaving you permanently blind. There is possibly only one surgeon in the world who would even attempt to operate. I would not. That is the best scenario I foresee!"

I was so stunned by these pronouncements that I felt nauseous. Howard looked ashen. We both started to cry. Steve's look cannot be described, but as best I remember, he looked unconcerned. His look could not fit the gravity of his situation. The doctor said he wanted Steve admitted immediately into Evanston Hospital for observation and tests. And he wanted a hormone specialist to examine Steve and test his blood. "There is an extremely small chance that your problem is caused by an excess of the human growth hormone." Within the past two years, this other doctor at Evanston Hospital had developed a chemical treatment that could reduce the level of human growth hormone (HGH) and shrink any tumor the excess HGH had caused.

It was determined that Steve's tumor was caused by an excess of HGH. He received the chemical treatment and over a period of time recovered his sight and sensibility. Miraculously, he's alive today and continues to be my friend, though I no longer live in the Chicago area. I had no part in helping him other than responding to an urgent call from some unknown source to stop his course of action and find the best medical help for him.

THE WOMAN ON THE PLANE

Have you ever been touched by history? I have. The experience was another of my mystical moments.

On one of my frequent jaunts to Los Angeles, where I was monitoring two MHD contracts, I sat next to a "little old lady." She had flown in from Israel and had changed planes in Chicago. It was my usual 6:00 PM Wednesday flight on Continental to LAX. She would catch a "puddle jumper" flight on to Santa Barbara where friends from close-by Montecito would pick her up. (This suburb is one of the most affluent in the US.) We had a nice chat on the three-hour trip. While getting to know one another, she mentioned she had been one of the original settlers of Israel and knew such people as David Ben-Gurion and Golda Meir, the first and fourth prime ministers of Israel. They had slept together in tents in the desert in the earliest days, just to survive. It was a fascinating story.

We intended to part our ways at LAX. I went to get my luggage and do the paperwork to get a rental car. At that time, rental cars were parked inside a "Loop" of Century Blvd that ringed LAX airport terminals. I came out of the building and saw her standing, forlorn, next to the taxi stand. She had found Santa Barbara's airport was closed – they were resurfacing runways. No taxi would take her that far (90 miles) and limo service was not available. She could not drive a rental car. I made a quick decision: I would take her. I told her no one would know I had put an extra few hundred miles on the rental that weekend; I would enjoy taking her to Montecito. Relieved, she accepted my offer.

We had an extended conversation on the way. I could point out landmarks since I had lived in the area while working at Rocketdyne. I had to inquire at a gas station to find the particular address, but we found it readily. As we said goodbye, she said, "If you are ever in Israel, look me up, you will have a place to stay as long as you wish." I never went to Israel; I do not remember her name. But I am certain I was meant to be on that plane to be able to help her.

ARACHNOIDITIS

My first wife, Ellen, had a weak back. She was stubborn; she could never accept responsibility to care for anything she thought "wrong" in her life. We had moved from California to Illinois and bought a townhouse in Wheaton, 30 miles west of Chicago's Loop. After moving in, she was lifting a box onto an upper shelf (not heeding my advice) and felt her back "go out." It seems now that she had ruptured two disks in her spine. The circumstances leading up to the eventual problem are vague in my memory. However, she was treated using a then-new procedure. Supposedly, this procedure had a success rate that was identical to that for spinal fusion – 80%. The advantage over fusion was a short recovery period and the possibility of later doing a fusion in case it didn't work! Patients would get up from the operating table and walk away with no pain! Two adjacent disks were found to be ruptured, so both were injected.

For six months, during which we thought all was well, her back pain was greatly alleviated. But then it started up again throughout her spine. We went to an ER for help and a doctor prescribed Benadryl shots! No help in pain relief was obtained. After another visit to the ER, he advised us to get a regular doctor to assist us. A fellow who practiced internal medicine in Illinois was nominated. We both became his patients. In the ensuing 10 or so years, we were directed by him and other doctors to various specialists to find what was wrong. Endocrinologists, neurologists, urologists (her bladder became affected due to her deteriorating spine) were consulted with no help given. A doctor at a rehabilitation center tried to convince her that the pain was all in her head. Psychiatrists did the same. One of the neurosurgeons to whom we were referred had saved the wife of a friend of mine. She had suffered brain hemorrhaging. Her doctor put her into a coma for a week. It worked – she recovered, and the couple spent many more years together. Yet even this neurosurgeon announced that Ellen had been *"FOISTED ON HIM"* and he deeply resented that fact!

Finally, a chief neurosurgeon at another hospital announced that she had "arachnoiditis" – inflammation and deterioration of the middle layer of the spinal cord cover. I researched on the topic extensively in numerous libraries, databases, and facilities. Support groups were being formed by people who had the disease back into the late 1960s. The founders of these support groups were trying to help others cope and to get whatever solace they could find for themselves.

It all became a moot issue after Ellen committed suicide in 1992 after suffering for 15 years with the disease. Perhaps it is ironic. That is also the average length of time it took for a person with arachnoiditis to die from the disease. I read that one went through increasing pain until the nerves in the spine finally atrophied and died. Then one experienced total paralysis. One finally died when internal organs, such as heart muscle, were affected.

Ellen had been on narcotics since the mid '70s, each time starting with lower doses of less powerful narcotics and gradually building up dosage and strength until her doctor decided she had to get detoxified. She would then spend a month or more in a hospital, sometimes general, sometimes psychiatric, to "get clean" and start over. She took a powerful opiate for a period of time before she killed herself. Her doctor threatened to take her off all opiates and leave her without any pain relief. That was enough to push her over the edge in May 1992.

In the 1980s, there was no internet. I recently "Googled" arachnoiditis and found many thousands of references, so many that I could not continue to pursue the topic emotionally. But, in one paper, I saw that now people have developed new, openly advertised support groups and are still battling the disease.

RETIREMENT

After Ellen died, I was alone and without purpose. My career at Argonne was stagnant at best. I asked myself (prayed),

"What are you going to do with the rest of your life?" I had no real ties to or inclination to stay in the Chicago area anymore, so I started to plot my "egress strategy" for leaving Argonne. I roamed around the US for four years in my little Ford Probe, looking for a place to roost in retirement. It took two years for Argonne to get rid of me – I left in March of 1994. So, it's been more than 27 years now that I've been retired. I rapidly grew accustomed to retired life. My story continues to be interesting and that has, as you might gather, both good and bad connotations, but I did get the "golden handshake" I had plotted for my initial retirement income. I managed to pay off my mortgage on the house and I bought myself a little Ford Ranger pickup. So, then I had a Ford Probe car and a Ford pickup to drive. I liked them both. I won't say too much more about cars.

Retirement turned out to be lonely. I took lots of trips around the country visiting people and getting rid of excess stuff I had accumulated over the years. I'd take loads of furniture up to Minnesota, down to Kentucky, or out to Colorado that I really didn't need or want in the house. My life was simple, but not very satisfying with no companionship to rely upon. I had Dish TV to watch, but after a while, Dish TV had all the same programs in reruns. I quit watching anything on Dish and started to listen to music that played on Dish. In fact, I recorded some of that music. When I went to Minnesota, I gave music tapes to my sisters-in-law, Elaine and Myrtle. They really appreciated having good ad-free music.

I had a small, but sufficient income coming in each month. It amounted to $19,000 a year. It was enough to pay for my needs, insurance, taxes, heating in winter, summer cooling, electricity, food, and incidental expenses. I wasn't hurting financially during this period of time, from age 58 until age 62, when I applied for and got Social Security. My income went up enough that I could start traveling more and enjoy eating out in good restaurants.

I went to Florida in the middle of each winter to escape winter cold and to visit with relatives in the St. Petersburg area. My sister Ruth, her husband Len, and I took a cruise through the Baltic Sea in May of 1996. We departed Dover, England, went to Amsterdam, Oslo, Copenhagen, Stockholm, Tallinn, Helsinki, and St. Petersburg, Russia. It was a mind-opening experience! Even having these trips, I still was lonely most of each year.

A NEWLY WIDOWED WOMAN IN THE SOUTH OF HOUSTON

After almost three years of retirement (December 1996), following a visit with my brother Kenny and his wife Elaine in Florida, I extended my annual winter trip in the south by heading west to visit a friend in New Mexico and relatives in Colorado. I took highway 19 up the west coast of Florida to interstate I-10, then headed further west. As I was driving through Houston, I had a "message" come into my head: "There is a widow in South Houston you should get to know." My response to myself was, "How in Hell am I going to find one woman out of millions?" I never put much credence in that experience. I continued on I-10 west to Las Cruces to see my friend. After a few days visiting, I angled northwest to pick up I-25 northbound to Pueblo Colorado where my sister Ruth and her husband Len lived. Winter weather driving this far north was "iffy." I listened to radio reports to find a "good weather window." In a few days, the weather looked OK for the next day, so I left, going north on I-25 through Colorado Springs. It started to snow. By the time I got to Denver, I was skating on ice. Radio weather reports were eight inches of heavy snow to be falling throughout Nebraska within several hours. I angled northeast going as fast as I dared on mostly dry pavement. At the state line, the road cleared. I headed east on I-80. I barely kept ahead of the snowstorm all through Nebraska, Iowa, and western Illinois. Having left Pueblo at 3:00 AM, I made it home at 10:00 PM. I traveled 1,200 miles nonstop (except for gas and PEE breaks). By the next morning, I awoke to eight inches of heavy snow to shovel. I was happy to be home safe, not having had to drive in a snowstorm.

During the Fall of 1997, Ruth, Len, and I planned another cruise. This time, we would go from San Juan, Puerto Rico to various Caribbean ports, then through the Atlantic side locks into Lake Gatun in the middle of the Panama Canal, turn around and come back out into the Atlantic Ocean, and go back to San Juan. I also had planned to go to Florida for a couple weeks in mid-December. I would be back in Illinois with plenty of time to prepare for the Panama Canal trip that started in early January. 20 minutes before I left to go to Florida, I got a phone call from my sister Ruth, saying that they were now thinking of taking a cruise through the Panama Canal from San Juan to Acapulco, Mexico. "It's a longer trip that costs less! Will you want to do it?" I said, "Sure, go ahead. Send me the details. I will be at Kenny and Elaine's for the next week starting tomorrow."

Early January 1998, Ruth, Len, and I met on board the Regal Princess in San Juan. A few days later, I met Deann.

Ruth and I had started the habit on a prior cruise of getting up early and taking a mile walk (or jog) around Promenade Deck before breakfast. However, on this trip, Ruth could not. She had found out days before the trip that she had ovarian cancer. She was feeling ill, but had the grit to go on this trip. I had no desire to walk alone, so I went up to the buffet area to have coffee early. I saw a woman sitting by herself at a table. No one else was around. In the previous two days, I had found some men to talk with while drinking my morning coffee, but none of these men were there this day. Though it is against my nature to be forward in social situations, I approached this woman and asked her if I could sit and talk. She said, "Yes." So, I sat down and introduced myself, even showed her my passport. Deann was a poised, impressive woman. I found out quickly she didn't smoke, didn't drink much besides soft drinks, didn't like sailing. (Two out of three ain't that bad.)

At lunch that day, she came to our table where Len, Ruth, and I were sitting (a fourth chair was empty), plopped herself down, and made their acquaintance. I had been trying to remember her name. Ruth nudged Len, saying, "we've got to go," leaving the two of us to talk alone. Later, Ruth told me Deann is a keeper! Deann was from Clear Lake City, TX – 20 miles south of Houston, and had been a widow two years!

In the ensuing days of our trip, we walked and talked. We had so much in common. We never got to see the Panama Canal! I cried when she left the ship in Acapulco; I was scheduled to leave the ship at a much later time.

When we got home, we talked by phone many times a day for a month. In spite of our sharing phone calls, we both had large phone bills, which were not getting any smaller! If I came to Houston, we could talk for free. I just "had to go see her" in late February. I drove the thousand miles in one day.

A NEW LIFE TOGETHER

Deann had a two-story house in Clear Lake City. Neither of us like a two-story house. She also had a swimming pool. All I can say about swimming pools is if she hadn't had one, I probably wouldn't have lasted for that first summer in Houston. I lived in her swimming pool to avoid the hot, humid, miserable weather. Soon, Deann and I developed an understanding and commitment to each other. We decided to buy our own, new single-story house. We would each sell our old one.

We took a trip back to Illinois in late March to do my income taxes. I'd been in Texas since early February to visit Deann and talk about our future. That is when I sold my house. I sold it (by myself) in 20 minutes. It was an easy sale. The neighbors next door said their daughter and son-in-law wanted my house. I took their "kids" on a tour and pointed out everything that was wrong with it. They still wanted it, so I sold it to them.

The house that Deann had took a couple months to sell, but she sold it to a single fellow from California who had sold his house there for much more money than he needed to buy Deann's house. We had enough money then to pay for our own house that was being built in League City.

The model home had three bedrooms and a den or study. We decided to convert the study into a fourth bedroom with a huge closet. Our house was to have a four-car garage, but we "only" had two cars! So, I had the architect redesign the extra space in the garage. He made the extra space into three rooms: a den, a shop area, and a storage area. Other design changes were made throughout the house. The builder was quite accommodating with what we wanted. Construction started in March 2000; we moved into our new home in August. We have been living here ever since.

MR. & MRS. CARLSON

When we had gone back to Illinois to sell my house, of course, there was a snowstorm, with six inches of heavy snow. I managed to get my snow blower to work finally and cleared off the driveway. Deann came out to help in her thin-soled shoes. I had to shoo her back into the house. Deann was reintroduced to the winter she had left, having been born and raised in Chicago. I did not want to put up with winter any longer either, so we decided to take a cruise in Hawaii! With help from the buyer and my friend Gomer, we packed a moving truck and headed for Houston.

Our preliminary plan was to cruise around the islands of Hawaii on an American ship. However, Deann found a Norwegian liner to cruise around the islands with an added cruise to Christmas Island, 1,200 miles south of Hawaii. Longer trip at less cost! We jumped at this choice. It was a small ship (20,000 tons) and they had never done that cruise before. When we got through with cruising Hawaii's Islands, we finally headed south on the open Pacific Ocean. It was not "pacific," it was rough; I got seasick on the way down and Deann was seasick on the way back.

We got to Christmas Island, and it was hot. It was probably close to 120 degrees, and nearly 100% humidity. I had already decided to propose to her on Christmas Island. It would be a memorable place. We went down to the beach. Our ship was anchored offshore a little distance. It was a beautiful backdrop. The beach sand was so hot it burned our feet through the soles of our shoes. I told her, "I'm not going to get down on my knees because the sand is so hot. But, once in a man's life, a woman like you might come along, and I don't want to lose this opportunity. Will you marry me?" And she said, "Yes."

We announced our engagement at the supper table that evening. A girl at our table was a singer who gave a performance later that night in the main theater. She related our engagement to the crowd. We were asked to stand and got a long clapping ovation.

Back in Houston, we had to wait for the church to be renovated before we could get married. We were the first couple to be married in the new church setting. Our wedding took place a year to the day after we met. Deann has since become the most important person in my life. In the very least of her being, she ended my loneliness. In the most of it, I am alive today because I met her. (See later details.)

CRUISES

Our honeymoon cruise was from Miami on Superbowl Sunday, an inconvenient coincidence we had not planned. In spite of traffic, we made it to our ship on time and thoroughly enjoyed cruising the Eastern Caribbean islands as far as Barbados. Our cruising lifestyle had begun. Over 10-12 years, I had 34 cruises and Deann had 33. We went to many different places: the Mediterranean, the Baltic, the South Seas, Hawaii, Alaska, and, of course, in the Caribbean, where we sailed the most. My favorite place was Topkapi Palace in Istanbul, Turkey.

These cruises were always learning experiences. You'd find out things that you'd read about or heard in history courses, but didn't mean anything, all of a sudden, became alive. We've been fortunate to have cruised so many times and enjoyed every bit of it.

FAMILY

As I view it now, Deann and my life with her in Houston is the reward for a previous 30-year commitment to a bad marriage. With Deann, I inherited three little grandkids: two boys and a girl. They were about two-and-a-half, three years old. I became (and stayed) their "Grampa." I also got another girl who was about eleven, and another boy about fourteen, but they never accepted me as anyone except the person who had married their grandmother. Deann had five adult offspring, two girls and three boys: George, the oldest, Mary, Michael, Elizabeth, and James (Jim). The girls and Jim live in the Houston area, George lives in North Carolina, and Michael lives in New Jersey.

Mary and Elizabeth are loving women who treat me as they would their natural father. My grandkids, Randy, Billy, and Melanie, are the joys of my life. I never expected to have such an incredible family, since Ellen and I had no children of our own. Surely there has been, once again, some "upper-level help" in achieving this state of grace.

THEY MUST BE LOCALS

Traveling with Deann was always memorable. Sometime after marrying, Deann and I took a car trip from Houston to northern Minnesota for me to attend a high school class reunion. We had gone past Iowa and stopped for food and drink at a McDonald's in Owatonna, a small Minnesota town located just north of the Iowa border. I had been teasing

Deann along the way. She had to learn "MINNESOTA TALK" if she was going to fit in and understand the people up north! I used to be able to mimic the "old timers" from the "old country" when I wished to do so. I laid it on thick. *"U've got to larn da old vay ov talkin' if'n U vant to be unnerstoot!"* Another couple was sitting next to us; I had my back to them. The lady said in a very clear voice, "They must be locals!"

A TOUCH OF ROYALTY?

A few months ago, I got an email from relatives, Eris and Bob Hyrkas, who live in my old hometown of Grand Rapids, Minnesota. Eris is deep into finding ancestry. Eris not only got her own DNA tested, but also Bob's, and one of my generation of Carlsons. According to DNA, I am 22nd generation-removed of Swede Royalty, Catherine of Bjorum, who was Queen of Sweden and Norway in the 15th century. I told my wife Deann that she would henceforth have to bow and scrape before me since I am 1/4,000,000 royalty. I got a big '*Harumph*' from her. "That's like a fart in a windstorm, you can't even raise a stink with that," she declared! Well, I did have my 20 seconds of glory, but now I sit, just being a common man.

THE ONLY DOWNSIDES OF RETIREMENT

I won't go into Deann's and my medical problems too much except to touch on each. Deann had breast cancer about 15 years ago. She was treated with a new radiation procedure called "Mammosite" and chemotherapy pills (Tamoxifen and Arimidex), and has been breast cancer-free ever since. In early 2015, Deann was diagnosed as having the worst kind of thyroid cancer one can have. It's called "anaplastic undifferentiated thyroid cancer." She was treated at M.D. Anderson Cancer Center in Houston. Dr. Gary Clayman, chief of head and neck surgery operated. She endured 35 high-intensity targeted radiation treatments to her neck. She had three platinate chemotherapy treatments at M.D. Anderson. These only seemed to mess up her blood chemistry. She was given at-home chemotherapy treatment with a drug called Lenvima. She was part of a trial to test this drug's efficacy with thyroid cancer. It had many bad side effects. But, it seems to have killed her cancer. Deann has over six years survival now. She is one of only five patients at M.D.A. who have this length of survival. Her main doctor said, "Deann is on a very short list of patients." Hers is not an easy life. She has to be fed through a PEG tube (plastic tube leading directly into her stomach).

Deann caught double pneumonia in early 2019. One was easy to treat with antibiotics. The other called "MAC" lasted over six months with intensive, specialized antibiotic treatment. She has a lingering cough. She cannot swallow anything, yet she gallantly soldiers on. I am immensely proud of her.

I had problems with my bowels for years, and I finally was convinced to have a colonoscopy, thank God. Well, actually, I thank Deann and my friend Gomer (who couldn't do it alone), as well as Deann's personal physician who became my doctor, for convincing me to get a colonoscopy. The gastroenterologist found a four-inch-long polyp that was precancerous but was going to turn cancerous any time soon. It and a third of my colon were removed in 2000 with the surgeon's promise that "I had been cured." My mother had died from colon cancer at the age of 55. I was 64! I have had no problems in that regard since then.

Sight in my remaining eye has been deteriorating since 2008. I have Fuchs' dystrophy, a cornea disease that causes blurred vision. Also, the detached retina "jiggly field" I've had since I was 17 has descended a bit, now covering my center field of vision.

In March 2019, I broke my right hip, tripping and falling from standing up! A real unexpected, freaky incident. I also had an E. coli infection that went systemic, and I've had problems from that which I'm mostly over. Most recently, following a sore throat and issues with pain, a mass, and an ulcer on my tongue, I have been diagnosed with Hodgkin's lymphoma. OLD AGE is the only downside of retirement (if we are lucky).

LIFELONG LEARNER

Learning has always been a core part of my life. Well, actually, I probably never learned during the first few years of my life by being curious, except whatever any little kid learns, but after I was three or four, I was very curious. I had a favorite question for everyone: "Why for? For why? Why for?" I'd drive people nuts asking that same thing over and over again as I was growing up. I guess I became known as the "Why For, For Why" kid. People would tease me about it, but it didn't stop me from being curious. I've been curious all the rest of my life. I'd say that's probably one of the most important things to drive you forward in terms of learning.

Over two decades of formal schooling in tandem with field work and research throughout my career, I was always learning. Particularly at Rocketdyne, the atmosphere was one of constant learning. There were courses in the company during the day. Some of the guys I worked with taught things like rocket heat transfer. One fellow went to a college nearby, took a combustion course, and then started teaching combustion. Over the years, the company sent us on junkets around the country to interview different people and find out what they knew about the rocket business. We would get proposal requests for really outlandish things that nobody had even thought of, and we had to become instant experts and submit a proposal on it! So, we'd go to the libraries around and find out what they had on the subject and read it. Then we'd write proposals. Rocketdyne Research had an outstanding record as far as getting programs from proposals. I think we had something like a 50% capture rate, which was probably the best in the industry. We always had new things to learn. In university, at Rocketdyne, at Argonne, and while consulting, it helped me immensely to be surrounded by a large group of intelligent, well-educated people I could talk with and learn from.

In later years, being stuck here in the house, especially with Covid pandemic, we don't get out much. Getting a new streaming service on my computer called CuriosityStream has been a godsend. It features all sorts of projects and documentaries in genres of science, history, technology, and nature that the BBC primarily has done. There are hundreds of them. I've gone through a good part of them! I learn an awful lot from this source. It's amazing how much that can add to one's breadth of knowledge. Continued learning has been a big part of my life that I hope to maintain.

PURPOSE AND GRATITUDE

I hope that this book will give younger people a flavor of what engineering is about – at least the kind that I practiced, which I think is the most general and the most satisfying. It's having a theoretical basis for something and then having the idea of how to solve problems that results in building hardware and testing it and finding out whether it works or not. It's a great life. I hope I've given young readers some incentive to be favorable toward learning what to do and how to do it. It takes work, but most anybody can do it. So, all I can say is: Have at it!

My story doesn't end here. I still have purpose in a life to yet live. I am indebted to many people who either started me on a certain path or helped me along the way as we went together. Most all that I accomplished and hope yet to do, I owe to someone else in no small measure. I am truly grateful to all. To those who still live, I say thank you. To those having passed, I say sleep well. God bless us all.

INVENTIONS

FOR THOSE WILLING

I'll give a general discussion on inventions. I've got seven patents, and I'm not going to bother to go through all of them. Some of them are kind of meaningless. But the supercyclone is one that has not been patented, and it's probably one of the greatest things that I came up with. It took 20 years of thinking before I got it figured out. I've never been an entrepreneur, but I have a computer program that will design any kind of supercyclone that you might want. I wrote in Turbo Pascal, a computer language that is no longer used by scientific workers. Its syntax and print options would have to be converted to a modern language. I do not intend to give away source code, but interested parties can contact me to discuss consideration.

A share in the success of the following ideas I leave open to those willing to reach out.

THE SUPERCYCLONE PARTICLE SEPARATOR

While at Rocketdyne, I read a secret paper about a nuclear rocket engine that used granular nuclear fuel swirling inside the chamber. The fuel was driven by hydrogen gas diffusing radially inward as it was injected tangentially at the periphery of the cloud of nuclear fuel. I understand one such engine was built and tested. It did not work because the fuel particles eroded by friction while bumping into each other. The smaller, "elutriated" particles being formed were blown out of the reactor – eventually causing the engine to shut down from lack of fuel. At a later time while working at Argonne, I came across an article in the *Chemical Engineers' Handbook* which showed a similar design cyclone as had been depicted in the nuclear engine paper. It had multiple rows of tangential inlets that had a constant injection angle with respect to the transverse tangential direction. Thus, I found the design was no longer secret. But I reasoned any commercial cyclone based on this design would have similar, if not identical, limitations that the rocket cyclone had: poor retention of smaller particles.

I mulled the problem in my mind for many years. Finally, an answer came to me. I developed a computer program to predict separation performance of this new device I had envisioned. The angle of each injector is determined by analysis of an integral boundary layer according to Theodore von Kármán's criteria for momentum transfer. At least two rows of inlets are needed for internal swirl flow stability. (Try to spin a top with one finger!) By varying the inlet angles, one can control the swirl flow and radial flow so all radial gas flow is outward over most of the cylindrical length. Radial inward gas flow will occur within the conical section of the cyclone that is located at the end opposite the gas outlet. This results in some particles being recycled a number of times through the cyclone before being eventually trapped, but the size of particles that escape retention is significantly reduced.

Radial outward gas flow along most of the cyclone axis is necessary because it complements the centrifugal force acting on the particle. If radial inward flow exists (as occurs in all standard cyclone designs), Stokes' drag dominates in comparison with centrifugal force as particle size diminishes. That is why there always is a "cut size" associated with each cyclone design. My "supercyclone" delivers a "cut size" at least five times smaller in diameter than an equivalent-size commercial cyclone having the same pressure loss. Since mass loss is proportional to particle diameter cubed, mass loss in a supercyclone will be about one percent that of a similar, old-style device.

The computer analysis was formulated using an integral boundary layer model that considers momentum exchange at subsequent axial positions starting at a location where the outer edge of the momentum boundary layer is attached to the wall. This attachment position is located near the gas outlet end of the cyclone. Using Stokes' Law for particle drag forces, Schlichting's formula for wall friction, and a mass balance for the segment of axial integral boundary layer that is being considered, an injection angle is calculated.

This injection angle represents the circumferential to axial velocity ratio of the boundary layer flow field at that axial position. Viewed as an initial value problem, the succeeding tangential injection angles are calculated at increments of axial position using input of flow variables known from the previous axial position. In addition, the necessary radial outward gas flow velocity that is necessary to sweep particles (by Stokes' drag in conjunction with centrifugal force) from the outer perimeter of the boundary layer to the wall is calculated. Different particle sizes can be inputted to find the particular "cut size," which is no longer separated from the outlet gas flow. Again, since particle mass depends on size (diameter) cubed, this means 30-100 times better mass separation with this new type of cyclone.

My supercyclone model was tested having a six-inch bore and 27-inch length at 20 inches of water pressure drop and at an air flowrate of 400 cfm. It achieved a 95% capture of each of several materials, including baking flour, baking soda, and baby's talcum powder. I'd like to acknowledge Dr. Paul Chung (Dean of Engineering, Univ of Illinois, Chicago Circle Campus) for making the first model I tested. He also helped me write a proposal to Army Tank Command, Warren, Michigan.

APPLICATIONS

I envision many different commercially viable applications for supercyclone devices. Cyclones that are used commercially for separating materials such as flour, pharmaceuticals, etc. often have bag-type filters to augment their "less-than-ideal" separation characteristic. This dual-separation system could be replaced with a supercyclone acting alone, not needing additional problematic hardware – filters clog.

Military applications abound. One example would be to use multiple parallel flow supercyclones in the turbine engine air supply of M1A1 battle tanks. These tanks have gas turbines for motive power instead of diesel engines. Gas turbines are susceptible to compressor blade erosion from fine sand particles. Sand particles with a size greater than five microns ingested with air will erode turbine blading. Desert warfare has proven that tactical deployment of tanks had to be changed to prevent ingestion of small sand particles swept as a cloud into the air from previous vehicles. Tanks could no longer be deployed in a line along a roadway, for example. Even with this change, dust filters are clogged at too short a time interval for effective fighting tactics to be used. I have been inside an M1A1 battle tank filter housing. It is large enough to house a set of supercyclones that would provide all airflow necessary for the turbine to operate at full-power output. There are two such filter housings in an M1A1 tank that now act in parallel to provide air flow to the turbine. When these filter sets get plugged, the tank has to cease fighting, and someone has to go outside the tank to shake the dust out of the filters – not an especially desirable duty. Though not normally needed for air cleanup, the second filter housing could either house a second set of supercyclones or be used for storage of other items.

A supercyclone can be used at high temperatures when constructed with appropriate materials. Another application might be as a "soot"-removal device in diesel engine exhaust systems. Many diesels are operated with poorly adjusted fuel injectors. One often sees clouds of black "smoke" coming from exhaust pipes of large trucks, especially as they start moving. Soot particles are typically a few microns in diameter. With the ability to separate fine particles and having a catalytic surface inside the supercyclone, long residence times of capture would allow oxidation of soot to carbon dioxide gas with air injected into the boundary layer flow. Exhaust temperatures in diesel exhaust systems are high enough to provide fast chemical reaction rates. Catalysts would be similar to those used in home ovens.

I have read that the pharmaceutical industry loses a significant portion of product (as much as five percent) during manufacturing because ingredients are often finely ground before mixing and pelletizing. However, all of the equipment used must be totally sterile. It is difficult to manufacture filter assemblies that meet stringent sterile conditions.

WASTEWATER AERATION MACHINES

While at Rocketdyne, I developed a sewage aerator I called the "**supersonic super-cavitating downdraft aerator.**" It had evolved from my study of gas bubble formation in water/air mixtures flowing under certain conditions. I had studied the seminal work of David Elliot of JPL who developed the theoretical description of supersonic flow of two-phase, two-component (e.g.: gas/liquid) mixtures. In his work, he determined that air and water flowing together at roughly equal volume rates have a sound speed of approximately 75 feet per second at atmospheric pressure. Small solid particles in air at equal volume flows also have roughly the same sound speed at standard atmospheric pressure. Avalanches of snow and air mixtures travel at roughly 60 miles an hour. These phenomena contrast with an air sound speed of 1,100 feet per second and a water sound speed of 4,400 feet per second. Solid materials have sound speeds in the range of 1,000-4,000 feet per second. When a two-phase (e.g.: gas/liquid) flow system is purposely set up for higher flow velocities than predicted sound speed, it tends to form a shock wave with a gross reduction of bubble size downstream of the shock. Mixture velocity is reduced commensurate with the pressure increase and volume reduction of the gas flow.

I set up an experiment at Rocketdyne to study shock-induced bubble breakup. I essentially repeated and confirmed some of Elliot's JPL work with a "water propeller air injector design" I envisioned for a wastewater aeration machine that was to be built for Envirotech Corporation of Salt Lake City, Utah. Once I determined that the "shock" process was effective in reducing bubble size, I proceeded to analyze required mechanical characteristics for the rest of the system.

Small bubbles are preferable in water aeration because the rate at which oxygen is transferred into water is directly proportional to the total surface area of the bubbles. For a fixed-mass flowrate of air, total bubble area increases inversely with bubble size. Thus, bubbles 10 times smaller in diameter have 10 times the area for a constant air mass flowrate (lbm/sec). This is just algebra.

I started to study wastewater aeration using “U-tube” aerators. In this setup, water/air mixtures are directed down in a flow channel to a design depth and then are directed up again back to the surface. Using mass transfer theory, one finds that mass transfer rate of a gas into liquid is proportional to a “Henry’s Law” gas constant, the surface area of the gas and the difference between gas specie concentrations in the gas bubble and gas specie concentration in the liquid at any given position in the flow field. Initial gas specie concentration in the bubble is directly proportional to total pressure, which includes pressure due to depth in the liquid added to atmospheric pressure. As a specific gas specie is absorbed from the bubble into the liquid, subsequent changes in gas concentrations in both bubble and liquid must be accounted for in the calculation sequence. Bubble size shrinks with increasing pressure. However, the net overall effect is that an increase in system pressure increases mass transfer rate in spite of the decrease in bubble size.

A computer can accurately “keep track” of all of these simultaneous effects when a sufficiently small step size in bubble position (depth in liquid) is considered in the analysis. By running the computer program with a given step size and rerunning the program again with a smaller step size, one can determine whether the analysis is providing correct answers.

In a simple U-tube device, the liquid entrained bubble flow field is down a certain distance and then goes up to the surface. The computer program keeps track of the bubble dynamics in small increments of bubble location. Analysis is by finite difference approximation, which mimics the governing differential equations to an arbitrary accuracy. Since initial conditions are known, we have what is termed an initial value problem.

The supersonic super-cavitating aerator had complicated outlet flow field dynamics. Since the actual device would be located in a large diameter tank, the average bubble trajectory in the tank had to be determined as bubbles first went down into the tank, flowed sideways, and subsequently ascended to the surface. I did this analytically, considering liquid flow spreading out radially in the tank while bubble buoyancy changed vertical positioning of gas bubbles undergoing partial absorption.

Once the fluid mechanics of the system were worked out, mechanical and electrical requirements were addressed. Pump power was determined from drag and integrated propeller surface friction using Schlichting's turbulent flow boundary layer wall friction model. Three different computer programs were developed to support the design. As stated earlier, the machine performed exactly as analyzed, with the exception of water and air flow stability problems. Low bubble depth aeration machines are limited in their effectiveness to transfer oxygen from air to wastewater. The aeration machine I designed for Envirotech transferred four pounds of oxygen into wastewater for each horsepower hour of electricity expended. It was designed to match the performance of the much more expensive Envirotech low-speed aerator design. A smaller aerator model subsequently achieved a value of 13 lb per horsepower hour. This seems to be the practical design limit for such machines. However, a design which uses extreme water pressures might have significantly higher aeration effectiveness numbers!

In studying wastewater aeration, I also invented another type of aerator which uses very high water/air mixture pressures in a part of the flow field. Some existing centrifugal pumps have double annular inlets, each one located along each of the axle shafts. Such pump designs feature a double-vaned impeller which rotates within the outer enclosure. There is only minimal clearance space between rotating impeller and a fixed enclosure to minimize leakage. Only low-pressure shaft seals are required in these devices. Discharge is from a central volute located on the stationary housing perimeter. Such a design could be modified for use with air and water flows, minimizing leakage while providing high intermediate pressures.

If one were to modify this design so the impeller and housing rotate together and flow enters only from one side and exits the other side, one could have a high-, though variable, pressure U-tube equivalent machine. A "bubbly" mixture of air and water would enter on one side at a nominal low pressure. As the mixture traversed radially outward, it would progressively experience higher pressures. Rotational speed and outer diameter determine maximum pressure obtained. As in the simple U-tube, bubble absorption is followed analytically using a finite difference stepping procedure. A set of flowrates and initial bubble size and machine operating conditions is chosen to optimize performance. Power is required to compress the bubbles isothermally (which is the most efficient method). Power would be expended to provide for bearing and flow friction losses. Preliminary calculations show effective gas absorption ranging up to hundreds of pounds of oxygen absorbed per horsepower hour.

Based on my research, I designed a specific wastewater aeration machine for Envirotech. Due to mismanagement at Rocketdyne, this design, which had progressed to a full-scale working model to be used in actual wastewater treatment plants, was abandoned. This aerator had a stability problem. It amounted to the same thing as an airplane wing stall, with consequent loss of lift. My friend Bill Bisell, a talented turbomachinery engineer, solved the stability problem using a "splitter blade" leading each aeration blade of the propeller. It would keep the aeration blade from stalling, much like a biplane's set of wings. Bill's boss insisted that the splitter blades be installed in a fashion contrary to what Bill had specified. Forever after, the aerator was totally unstable.

In tests done at Salt Lake City, conducted before the splitter blade fiasco, the aerator (while running stable) achieved an oxygenation efficiency equal to the best machines on the market at that time. It had a 75-horsepower, 900-RPM electric motor that turned a specially designed propeller. This propeller induced air flow that was broken into very fine bubbles in the downflow wastewater field. It obtained four pounds of oxygen transfer per horsepower hour and would have run continuously for years without maintenance. It would have replaced existing slow-speed aerators as made by Envirotech that had periodic gearbox failures that were a constant headache and replacement expense to sewage treatment plant operators.

This new design aeration machine was only a small step forward in treating sewage. There are other devices based on theoretical models I developed that are a lot better. These models suggest machines that could obtain 50 or more pounds of oxygen transfer per horsepower hour with throughputs of millions of gallons of wastewater per day. But, for want of a nail, a kingdom was lost! Envirotech is no longer in business.

A COMPACT STEAM BOILER/TURBINE CAR ENGINE

I remember going to an ASME meeting in downtown Los Angeles many years ago where Bill Lear (of 8-track tape and Lear Jet fame) gave a lecture on steam cars. He had set up another corporation in Reno, NV to engineer such a vehicle. And he "reinvented" water. Supposedly a different water molecule had more favorable steam properties. I doubted that part of his lecture presentation totally. And I also looked at his steam boiler with disdain. He wanted to sell a steam car for a small increment over gasoline-powered cars of that time. (Cadillacs were selling for $6,000.) The stainless steel tubing in his boiler alone would have cost him $6,000! I knew stainless steel tubing pricing from my work at Rocketdyne, where we got the lowest possible price in industry. His design made no sense. So, I started to think of an alternative steam boiler design.

My college major was in heat transfer. One of the dominant factors in convective heat transfer is the effect of passage size on convective heat transfer coefficients. Smaller passages have larger heat transfer coefficients! In convective heat transfer limited situations (boiling is such a very much better transfer agent that it can be ignored for the moment as it relates to restricting heat transfer), heat transfer rate depends directly on a heat transfer coefficient times an area times the difference in temperatures between the gas and the surface. And then I remembered the double-sided inlet, centrifugal pump configuration!

The overall boiler design would feature a high rotational speed disk assembly consisting of alternate layers of gas and steam/water passages. Feed water for boiling would be fed radially in a separate flow-isolated and thermally insulated passage wherein pressure would increase to a high value. High-pressure water would be distributed to each of the steam generation passages at the outer periphery of the device. Each steam generation passage would consist of two thin sheets (disks) of metal, separated and welded together using a lattice of expanded metal. Not only would this expanded metal lattice hold the two disks together, but it would also serve as a very effective conductive fin structure, supplying heat to the steam by increasing the surface area while also decreasing temperature losses. This type of structure was built at Rocketdyne using inexpensive diffusion welding techniques. For example, merely putting a stainless steel structure in a good vacuum and heating it to moderate temperatures while applying moderate clamping pressure results in diffusion weld bonds that are equal in strength to parent metal.

Water and then steam would flow radially inward. The interleaved hot gas passages would be tied together with coarse metal mesh of expanded metal acting to weld the structure together. The expanded metal would work as fins to accept heat from the hot gases with high film coefficients and transfer this heat to intervening disk surfaces and thence to the steam generator part of the system. Combustion gases would be generated axially on one side of the steam generator. Only a low-pressure, low-temperature gas seal would be required to prevent hot combustion gas losses. A large diameter bearing/seal would be fitted to this end. A steam turbine would be fitted coaxially to the other end of the device. An electric motor/generator attached to the turbine would be used to spin the unit up to a preliminary rotational speed so that it could then bootstrap to operating speed by the steam turbine.

Preliminary hand calculations of a combustor and steam turbine system having a two foot outside diameter with a total disk thickness less than six inches, spinning at 6,000-9,000 RPM, could produce 200 horsepower with an overall thermal conversion efficiency of 25%. Electrical power could power individual wheel-mounted motors and/or charge a battery system for hybrid operation.

A COMPACT STEAM GENERATOR

During the early 1970s, several of us Rocketdyne engineers were considering leaving the company to go into business for ourselves. Grant Hosack, Bob Schnerstein, and I considered making a number of products, going so far as attending a USC marketing course, ultimately settling on a steam cleaner I had designed. It was a small, handheld unit that had an instant on/instant off control feature. At that time, all other steam cleaner units used in such places as gasoline service stations required five minutes to start and five minutes to stop and cool down for safety reasons. A lone mechanic working the service part of the gasoline station could not stop and serve customers needing gas. Our unit would solve that problem.

We made a complete portable unit, brought it to a downtown service station, and demonstrated it by cleaning our marketing professor's car engine. He was impressed. He was a member of the Los Angeles Millionaires Club that invested in start-up ventures. They were, indeed, Venture Capitalists! We gave a presentation to them and received an offer of $100,000 if we agreed to two provisions: 1) We had to put half of our salaries into the business for five years and 2) We had to sell the business after five years, turning over half a million dollars to them. It took only a short minute to see we would be putting $100,000 into the business ourselves, so we said no. The steamer project was abandoned. We all left Rocketdyne to work for other companies. But our steamer worked well! However, gasoline service stations went out of vogue with self-service being the new norm. Service people went to other establishments for employment.

Now, the question is: Can an instant on/instant off steamer be used for other purposes? Well, I think maybe it could! We use pressure washers for cleaning many things now. Steam with entrained water droplets is gentler on some surfaces such as car paint. It is easy to strip car paint with a high-pressure water jet. There might be plenty of cleaning jobs for steamers. I realized recently that it could also be used in other applications to heat things more efficiently. Two examples: residential swimming pools and houses.

POOL HEATING

Presently, for swimming pools, you might have a heating system in those areas that get cold enough that people do not want to swim without the water being heated to a comfortable temperature level. But the heaters now available barely generate enough heat to keep the pool warm. The current practice is to run pool heaters 24 hours a day, even if the pool is used only a few hours each day. A lot of natural gas is wasted. An alternative is to have a pool heater with a much larger heat generation rate, one that could reheat cold water to a comfortable temperature within an hour. Plan ahead, turn on the pool heater an hour before an intended swim! After your swim, turn the pool heater off and let the pool cool until your next intended swim.

Current pool heaters have a heat generation rate of 300,000 BTUs per hour. Much of that heat goes up the flue stack. Also, pools lose heat by radiation and evaporation. You might have half of the heat generated left to heat water. With a 25,000-gallon capacity pool needing to be reheated from 50° to 80°F, it would take a half day to reheat. A pool heater putting out a million and a half BTUs per hour would take less than an hour to reheat the pool. A design having no flue losses and the short duration of heating would show radiation and evaporation losses to be trivial.

HOUSE HEATING

Regarding the aforementioned heating unit, there's another application that comes to my mind, and that is home heating. It has the same advantages, same limitations. If you had a heater that would be big enough for most houses, it would probably be the size of a large coffee can at most. Hot water and steam would circulate through piping in a tank and keep that tank hot while clean water or glycol (whatever would be necessary for your particular climate) continuously circulated through tubes, and when the tank temperature got down, the heater would come on. And so, you would have heat available all the time, anywhere you wanted it.

Using this system, you would have the possibility of individual-room thermostats, which would click on or off. A fan would extract heat from the circulating fluid flow, and you'd be able to have a much easier and more controlled zonal heating system. Thermostats aren't particularly costly, so it would be doable.

This piping would be small; it wouldn't be the large ducting that you use now for air systems. I think there's a significant advantage in my system. In addition, it would probably be much cheaper than what a standard furnace and duct system costs now. However, it has the same possible disadvantage as the pool heating system: you'd be dumping carbonated water into the sewer. So, someone would have to evaluate whether that's a showstopper or not.

Carbon dioxide, in the past, combined with calcium in nature, formed our coral reefs, so it might be possible to use some sewage plant add-on that would take care of this acidic carbonic acid. Again, it's something that could be evaluated, and if it turns out that it's either no problem or that the problem can be alleviated or minimized or eliminated, it will open up a new means of home heating. Another advantage, from an environmental perspective, would be that if this method of trapping carbon dioxide is effective and you just formed solids, it would eliminate at least home heating as a source of carbon dioxide in the atmosphere regarding the global warming situation that we think we're going through.

As I see it, both applications of this heating system are worthy of consideration and would serve as valuable business opportunities for someone so inclined.

HOUSE COOLING

Thinking in terms of the cooling needed in a house or commercial establishment, you could use this new water or glycol fluid system that I've described for heating instead for your cooling cycle. Instead of being a hot tank, it could also be a cold tank, depending on the season. For total flexibility, one could have two tanks: one hot, one cold.

A standard freon system could be used to chill the water or water glycol fluid in the device. And once the fluid temperature got down sufficiently, the cooling system would turn off. If the fluid temperature rose, the cooling system would turn on. You could have the same zonal cooling controlled by multiple thermostats as you would for the heating system. The difference, of course, is that you wouldn't have any carbon dioxide consideration. But you would have some possibility of having drip lines in the individual cooling units that would be in each of your rooms, and that would have to be considered.

Now, the big advantage that I see? In the South, we have large ducts in the attic, and the attic is either warm or hot in the summertime – and I mean, it could be 150°F. There's a lot of heat transfer from the attic into the cooling ducts just because of all this surface area. Whereas with a small amount of surface area from small ducting and adequate insulation, that's much less heat loss or gain than what you have now. Unwanted heat transfer would pretty much be eliminated. The efficiency of this liquid-transfer system would be far better than the air systems that we have now. That fact should be considered. Somebody could do cost amortization economics, of course, but it looks to me like it's a no-brainer.

PLASTIC/KRAFT PAPER "UNDER-THE-RAFTERS" INSULATION

As I've mentioned, here in the Southland, it can get devilishly hot in the summer. The sun beats down on your house's roof with a heat flux of 400 BTU per square foot per hour (for surfaces normal to the sunlight). It is rough on roofs. Roofing material is quickly heated and inadvertently re-radiates energy to the ceiling joist and insulation over your living spaces. Over half of air conditioning cost is associated with this unwanted heating. Several manufacturers have recognized this fact and now supply "under-the-rafters" insulation kits to block this unwanted heating to some degree.

For houses with soffit vents and ridge venting, this under-the-rafters system can be most effective in keeping attics cooler in summer. Heated air trapped between the roof and the new under-rafter insulation can flow by natural convection from soffits to ridge vents, reducing temperatures seen by the new insulation and thus reducing heat seeping into your living space.

Another company (we no longer hear about) had a different approach to supposedly solve the attic heating problem. It advertised a "Radiant Barrier" paint for under-roof application that would mitigate the problem with "low emissivity paint." In other words, this paint was supposed to radiate less heat at any given temperature. Such claims are patently false. Any paint of any color (including white) in sunlight has nearly the same color (dark grey to black) in the infrared spectrum of low temperatures (less than 150°F).

Metal-foil coverings tarnish with age and also collect dust that radiates like most other materials. Thus, metal foils can also be dismissed as effective radiant barriers.

The only problem I have with under-rafter insulation kits is **cost**. Home improvement stores are charging from 40 cents to $1.30 per square foot. With several thousand square feet of roof in a typical house, material costs can't be ignored. And the cost of installation by anyone except the homeowner is to be added to get a total cost. Purchased labor can easily double the total cost.

My suggestion to reduce material costs of under-rafter insulation is to use plastic sheeting (several mils thick) and/or kraft paper doubled over with a little air space between layers. Either of these materials will serve as a barrier to radiation from undersides of the roof. They will also act to establish free convection air flow between soffits and ridge vents. The cost is pennies per square foot. A handy homeowner could prepare rolled up, double-layer insulation packets and install them over a winter to save costs. An electric staple gun would make installation fast. You might have to provide backing patches at intervals along the insulation roll to prevent staples going completely through the insulation.

Attics that are not ventilated can easily reach 140-150°F in the summer. When we built our house in 2000, I had the builder put in a special opening under a portion of the patio roof so I could install a 36-inch fan. It's belt driven, made by Master Flow Fan Company. It has a quarter-horsepower two-speed motor. This fan moves 7,000 cubic feet of air per minute, discharging it through both soffits and ridge vents. It keeps the attic within 12°-15°F of ambient outside air temperature. We run the attic fan perhaps six hours per day in the summer. A remote temperature sensor in the attic alerts us when the attic temperature exceeds 100°F. I have estimated that our attic fan costs 30 cents per day to operate, yet it saves us 10 times that much in not having eight tons of refrigeration operating a few extra hours per day. I wish I had thought of under-rafter coverings when we built the house. It would have enhanced the effectiveness of attic fan ventilation. Maybe it will still be done some winter, but not by me.

STEAM BALLOONS

I'll touch on another subject that I thought would be interesting to the Navy. Never went anywhere, but this is it: steam balloons. We probably all know about hot air balloons, or recreational ballooning. It's an exuberant, colorful sport in which participants take to the skies in wicker baskets suspended from enormous balloons that float about, sometimes vying with others, trying to beat each other to desired destinations by predicting wind speeds and directions at various altitudes. I suppose it's a lot of fun, but hot air balloons don't amount to much value beyond sport.

A hundred years ago in the 1920s, Germany developed their dirigibles and the United States came up with blimps, difference being: dirigibles have an internal metal structure that supports everything, including multiple gas bags inside the outer skin. A blimp can have multiple gas bags, all enclosed within an outer balloon skin. A blimp has no internal structure except the supports for a passenger cabin that hangs below the balloon.

Ordinarily, the United States used helium as the lifting gas, so our blimps could cruise around with relative safety. Germany had no source for helium and the US would not sell them any. Germany was thus forced to use hydrogen gas as a lifting medium, accepting the hydrogen flammability. For years, Zeppelins roamed the skies around the world without incident. We all know about the Hindenburg and its tragic burning in Lakehurst, New Jersey in 1937. That tragedy ended dirigible flights.

The US continued using blimps in WWII for spotting German submarines along the East coast and Japanese subs along the West coast. According to a naval officer I spoke with years ago, the US Navy considered using steam as a lifting medium. While human skin is extremely vulnerable to steam burns, steam itself will not burn nor explode. However, the US Navy dismissed it as a useful lifting agent because there was too much heat loss from the balloon surface. No one could design a structure that would minimize heat loss, thereby permitting long-duration flights using only engine exhaust heat to regenerate steam.

I've analyzed the situation extensively. The heat loss from a balloon surface is mostly radiation. That's the problem you have to solve.

You would have to have multiple layers of very thin, reflective materials that could readily tolerate steam temperature. Mylar with a metallic film would be a good candidate. Keep the mylar films separated with "dimples" and a dry air space so the inner surface can keep this insulation package free of steam. One could also intentionally introduce a small percentage of air into the steam supply to the balloon envelope. The effect of air intrusion in steam condensers is well documented. Air has a decidedly suppressive effect on steam condensation rate. A simple test rig could be constructed to test this combination of insulation features to determine whether a steam balloon would be feasible where you could get by with only engine exhaust heat. With that fact established, all other details could be worked out.

Steam balloons could be used for many purposes besides sport. Heavy remote lifting, transportation (both commercial and personal), advertising at sporting events like the Goodyear blimp, etc. It would be a fairly expensive way to travel. However, people are drawn to that these days. Somebody might be interested!

SAUDI RAIN

After thinking a little bit about my somewhat unctuous remark to Jack Silverman on "Let's have rain and no smog on Tuesdays" (see Rocketdyne chapter), an idea struck me. It came about because a nuclear salesman visited Argonne.

We were going to buy a huge amount of equipment from his company, so he made a special trip to come out and introduce himself. As we got to talking, he told us about his family. They lived in Palatine, one of the ritzy sections of the suburbs northwest of Chicago, and he was doing well financially for his family. His daughter had gone to college and met a Saudi Arabian boy, fallen in love, and the two of them were going to get married. Sometime after the marriage decision was announced to their families, the Saudi family came to visit the Palatine family. The remark of the Saudi father was, "We can't afford to have our relatives live in such squalor." Thus, this salesman was going to quit his job and move to Saudi Arabia, where he would be given a job supervising construction of hospitals, schools, and other large public works. Apparently, the groom's family was involved in large construction projects. And the salesman was high as a kite about getting this opportunity of a lifetime because of his daughter.

In the course of our informal conversation, I started talking to him about my ideas of recovering the desert. Of course, Saudi has a little bit of desert land! This conversational exchange took place back in the early 80s. The Saudis had huge quantities of natural gas that were simply flared. At that point in time, liquified natural gas and tanker ships had not come into vogue. There was a lot of natural gas being flared that could be used to fuel gas turbines to power large pumps. Rocketdyne had a detailed design for a high-pressure, high-volume flowrate axial pump. It would couple directly to a large gas turbine such as those provided by GE for use in electric utilities supplying peak power. These GE turbines matched the Rocketdyne pump needs exactly. Expected pump pressure was 1,000 PSI with a flowrate of 60,000 gallons of water per minute.

Putting one of these turbine/pump units every half a mile along the coast would provide vast quantities of water (yes, saltwater) to inland areas. The saltwater could be sprayed on the downslope side of coastal hills. You'd have to accept losing a certain amount of land to salt deposits, but as prevailing coastal winds carried the moisture-laden clouds inland, super-saturated air would gain altitude and cool, whence rain would fall. Large tracts of land would be watered, possibly every day, or on a schedule.

I spoke previously with meteorologists about this proposal and was given encouragement to proceed. So, when this nuclear equipment salesman showed up at Argonne, he got the speech! He promised to speak to his new relatives in Saudi Arabia. I never heard from him again.

PING PONG BALL THEORY OF LEVITATION

Bob Dickerson had a passion for "antigravity" – though here on earth, antigravity is more properly termed "levitation." When I was still quite young, I fancied that I would like to work in three major areas during my life: space travel, unlimited energy production, and "antigravity." I was able to get a good bit done in the first and second areas during my tenure at Rocketdyne and later at Argonne Labs in Chicago. The third area is still a mystery, but Bobby D. gave me a clue as to a possible solution to levitation of physical objects above the earth's surface. He termed it his "ping pong ball theory of antigravity."

Consider a ping pong ball bouncing between a table and a paddle that is held parallel to the table at some fixed distance above it. If the paddle is slowly lowered toward the table with the ball bouncing between, the ball will bounce at a faster cycling rate and exert a larger force on the paddle as it lowers! Lowering the paddle makes up for system losses, which accrue because of air friction and the less-than-perfect coefficient of restitution of the ping pong ball. Bobby worked out the governing dynamic differential equations to show this was indeed the case. His answer to the inevitable losses in a real system was to install a battery aboard the paddle and have it drive an oscillating surface on the bottom of the paddle, adding just enough energy to balance the bouncing ball's losses. This theory and analysis sounded good to me. But I could see no practical application with such a "loss-prone" system.

Much later, it occurred to me we have lossless particles surrounding us already: air molecules. How could one make use of this fact of nature to invent a levitation machine?

With air mean free path lengths of 10^{-5} centimeters at standard temperature and pressure, and sound speeds of 35,000 cm/sec, the frequency required for a vibrating surface to displace air molecules is in the range of 300-500 megahertz. Controlling a levitation process (mimicking a ping pong ball system) at this frequency might become possible sometime in the future. Computer frequencies are now in the range of 2.4 gigahertz, so controlling a process with a fraction of that speed should be possible. How the surface of a levitated vessel might be made to vibrate at these frequencies, but at very small amplitudes, is a problem for future engineers to solve!

My research so far indicates quartz or calcite crystals (which have para and diamagnetic properties with thickness of a millimeter) might be the answer. Thermodynamic calculations of perfect gases suggest one watt of power provided per square inch of levitation surface might produce one pound of lifting force, if good coupling is achieved. Of course, power requirements will dictate whether an economic system design will be feasible.

TIDBITS/MISCELLANEOUS

OMELETS AND SUPERFLUIDITY

I once worked with a fellow whose last name was Fisher at Rocketdyne in the early years. Fisher had received a PHD from MIT using a Lagrangian approach for analysis of superfluidity of super cold helium liquid. I never understood his explanations of the effect, why helium would ostensibly climb the inside wall of a dewar to flow down the outside surface and dissipate into the air. It seemed almost magical.

A few years ago, I started making omelets for breakfast. I bought a cheap ($3), thin-wall aluminum fry pan from Walmart. It had a rudimentary Teflon surface coating to prevent sticking. I use a dollop of water to thin the batter, making the omelet fluffy. I spread extra virgin olive oil over the bottom to help keep the omelet from sticking. At some point in time, I noticed a ring of oil had formed around the edge of the pan on the stovetop, a glasslike, smooth ceramic, after everything had cooled. I thought, at first, that the pan had cracked along the outer edge. Yet, I could see no crack.

Eventually, the Teflon wore out, so I tossed the pan into recycle. I bought a much better pan with hard Teflon and a thick aluminum wall. I noticed the same phenomenon with the new pan: a ring of oil around the base at the outer edge. What was happening?

I have concluded this phenomenon is due to binary (two) fluid (vapors) thermophoresis. Water vapor transports oil vapor by temperature gradient. In single phase, water vapor is known to migrate through air along a temperature gradient, especially in closed boundary systems where liquid water can collect on the surface when the dew point is exceeded. Liquid helium is known to have two isotopes, He3 and He4. I suspect that He3 is transporting He4 over the edge of the dewar. I have heard that the process eventually stops with some liquid He left in the dewar. Am I wrong?

MAGIC GOUT CURE BY BOB DICKERSON

1. Procure a plastic tub – two-gallon capacity (as given by most hospitals for morning washes).
2. Obtain a digital thermometer (approximately $17-20) from Bed Bath & Beyond that has a six-inch-long, eight-of-an-inch-diameter steel probe, good to within a fraction of a degree over a range from 40°F to several hundred degrees Fahrenheit.
3. Warm a gallon of tap water to 105°F. Warm the second three-quarters-of-a-gallon water to at least 125°F or 135°F from tap or microwave. Put bare foot in warm water. Slowly pour hot water into the tub. Mix, avoiding direct contact on foot. Raise combined water temp to 115°F (if you can stand that heat). Leave the foot in heated water for 15 minutes while it slowly cools.
4. Repeat twice more the first day.
5. Do procedure for several more days. You can expect the gout to go away. If it returns, do the entire procedure again. Eventually, the gout will not come back.

The procedure is based on the fact that the crystals which cause gout (by blocking capillaries in feet) dissolve at higher temperatures.

ACKNOWLEDGEMENTS

WITH GREAT APPRECIATION

I believe none of us walk through life alone; we have help along the way in many different forms. So, I'd like to acknowledge with great appreciation a number of people in my life, some who not only helped me along the way, but also started me along a certain path to an accomplishment I would never otherwise have.

Mom is the first. She had me as a 22nd pregnancy, so I came along late, of course. I'm sure glad I did, but it was hard on Mom to have that many pregnancies. Only eight survived into adulthood. It was telling on Mom – the Great Depression, and then World War II. Both of my brothers went off to war: Vincent as an airman in Europe, Kenneth a sailor in the South Pacific.

I also appreciate my Dad, who was a very strong man. He could handle most any situation and come through for the family. He taught me three things that I used throughout my career to excel and survive. The first one is a little flippant, but it has meaning. He taught me how to wipe my butt! That meant using a certain amount of toilet paper and no more. It taught me conservation: don't waste anything that you're going to just throw away. I believe that my conservativeness stems from that teaching. The other two things were even more important throughout my life. He told me many times, "Always be honest with yourself, and you can be honest with others, and you will lead an easier life." Dad and Mother never went beyond eighth grade school, so they never read Shakespeare. Shakespeare said the same thing: "To thine own self, be true, And it must follow, as the night the day, Thou canst not then be false to any man." The last thing was most important! He said, "Never be afraid of hard work." Dad was undoubtedly the hardest working man I've ever known. He preached and lived these precepts. I tried to live by them, too. They held me in great stead in my career because, by hard work, I could sometimes surpass other people who were far brighter than me.

The third person I'd like to acknowledge is Mr. Michelson. He was the principal of my high school in Grand Rapids, Minnesota. I can't prove it, but I believe that he was the person who had the State of Minnesota Department of Public Service come see me. When I finished high school, I was legally blind. The State of Minnesota paid for my first three years of college.

In my fourth year of college, I had an undergraduate advisor, Roger Eichhorn, who I believe was more of a humanitarian than anything else. He was a brilliant engineer, but he loved helping people. He certainly helped me. I was extremely fortunate to have him as an advisor because I had run into trouble financially. I lost my funding from the state when my sight returned somewhat. He got me a $500 grant from the William Morris Foundation that paid half of the cost of my fourth year. Then, he also got me a job in the Heat Transfer Laboratory doing experimental work. That paid for the rest of my fourth-year expenses. I continued working in the heat transfer lab and was able to pay for my grad school education. My getting through college was possible all because of Roger Eichhorn. He started me on my heat transfer career.

In grad school, my major professor was Dr. Ernst R. G. Eckert, who was probably the most respected heat transfer expert in the United States, if not the world. I was very fortunate to study with him.

When I got my first job at Rocketdyne, my boss was Tom Coultas. For some unknown reason, he took me under his wing and mentored me. (And sent me back to school for 10 years!) As a result, I went from being one of the least talented engineers to one of the best engineers in the company.

Tom's boss was Bob Lawhead, who was another true humanitarian. Bob loved everybody who worked under him. He cared for his people and undoubtedly cared for me. Bob helped me immeasurably at times.

When it comes to fellow workers at Rocketdyne, the first is Bob Dickerson. Bob was truly brilliant; he could analyze anything. I used some of his models in my own work, extending them to fit my needs. He was one of my path finders.

Another great Rocketdyne engineer was Harland Burge. He provided me with a book called *Heat Transfer Solutions by Finite Differences* by George Dusinberre. As a result of that gift, I was able to solve problems that had been *impossible* when I had to do them by using calculus. It was a real boon to my existence.

I left Rocketdyne after 14 years and went to Argonne Labs in Chicago. My first supervisor was Ken Kuczen. He was yet another humanitarian and he was surely instrumental in helping me find my way in working there. He was an honest, bright engineer, but he always took care of his people first. One of the notable impacts he made was convincing me to go into management. Thus, I was given a group of seasoned engineers.

One seasoned engineer was Howard Geyer. Howard had an incredible, brilliant mind that was very agile in mathematics. He developed a means to solve multiple nonlinear algebraic or differential equations simultaneously using a computer. I used Howard's computer program extensively in many work endeavors.

I had another fellow in my group, Steve Grammel, who was a PHD engineer in nuclear physics (originally a farm boy from Michigan). I did a lot of programming. Sometimes, I'd get in a bind and could not find a solution. Steve would drop by, look at where I was stuck, write three or four lines of code that would be the solution. I'd use it and it worked.

We had another fellow at Argonne, Mike Rosing. Mike was a PHD electrical engineer out of Madison, Wisconsin. He helped me with one particularly difficult problem that was almost impossible. It was a method of characteristic solution with boundary layer friction effects for supersonic flows. I was given the problem of providing a region of higher pressure in a high-vacuum beam line, isolating this section from high vacuum with only fluid dynamics methods. Mike's help in analysis helped me design a workable system.

There are people you work with who are a pleasure to be around. One was Nelson Hanan. Nelson was from Brazil. He loved strong, black coffee! I had a four-cup coffeemaker in my office. We would sit down with our coffees, talking about various projects. We both got to work two hours early. I looked forward to going to work each day knowing coffee time was coming. Nelson had a PHD in nuclear engineering from Madison, Wisconsin. He did everything with a passion. We were given a six-month job together to corroborate designs of two nuclear rocket engines Argonne and General Electric had done some 20 years previously using slide rules. We had personal computers. Nelson did the nucleonics, I did the thermal hydraulics. We got the job done in two months, upping specific impulse by 25 seconds to 900, using hydrogen as the propulsion fluid.

I had a good friend at Argonne, Jim Bailey. Jim was a quiet person, a hard worker who told me about a "binary chop" method to solve transcendental equations. Those are equations where you need to know the answer to get the answer. (Yes, these exist. You get them once in a while!) I used this method many times in computer programming to get around a difficulty in analysis. An example is: $X = sin(X)$. What is X? Use the binary chop to solve it! Further, if the US government ever gets around to having nuclear plants reprocess their spent fuel, a process Jim developed is available to do this work which eliminates the need to store radioactive waste for 100,000 years. 5,000 generations of the world's humanity might pay homage to Jim Bailey, a truly great man.

Ron Merkle was another giant among men. Though he stood at 5'10", he towered among all others beside him. He was a humble giant who could solve any electrical problem, whether it be power or electronic (TV, computer). His accomplishments for NASA were legendary. Several Shuttle flights were successfully launched only after he flew to the cape to fix an electrical problem. His life was replete with success wherever he chose to participate. He's sorely missed, having died of kidney cancer several years ago. Ron was a dear friend.

I'll end this section with sincere thanks to my wife Deann. She not only has been a steadfast companion for 23 years, but she also saved my life three times (so far!). It is difficult to adequately describe such a good person. I can only say she is beautiful in every important way a person can possibly be. Thank you, my love.

GALLERY

Childhood home in Grand Rapids, MN.

Jack and Larry, ages 24,
Van Nuys, CA apartment.

Sniggle, Larry's favorite cat.

Larry and Ruth.

House in Oswego II.

Hippy the cat.

Larry, 1970.

Kenny, Bing, and Larry with Beech King Air plane.

Department of Registration and Education

State of Illinois

CERTIFICATE NO.

This is to certify that LARRY WILLIAM CARLSON [illegible]

IS AUTHORIZED TO PRACTICE AS A

REGISTERED PROFESSIONAL ENGINEER

REGISTERED UNDER THE PROVISIONS OF THE LAWS OF THE STATE OF ILLINOIS

In Witness Whereof, The Director of the Department of Registration and Education has hereby affixed his hand and the seal of the said Department this [illegible] day of [illegible] A.D. [illegible]

Attest

No 1597

Engineering license.

Recognition for invention contributions.

UNITED STATES
DEPARTMENT OF COMMERCE

CERTIFICATE
OF APPRECIATION

Presented to

Larry Wm. Carlson

for outstanding contributions to the scientific and engineering evaluation of inventions.

Director, National Bureau of Standards

Chief, Office of Energy-Related Inventions

November 1985

US Department of Commerce Award, 1985.

Extended family at the Carlson wedding.

Larry and Deann's bridal party.

The Carlsons, wed early 1999.

Cutting the wedding cake.

Exploring Seattle, WA with the grandkids (2008).

Writing Moiety of a Gingerbread Man.

Larry Carlson, 2021.

Personal library.

GLOSSARY

ACOUSTIC DRIVER	The part of an acoustic speaker used to emit soundwaves.
APERTURE	The measurement of the diameter of the part of a camera that lets light past the lens towards the film or sensor.
APOGEE	The highest point of a rocket's ascent; the vertex of the parabola of its travel route.
AUXILIARY BOOSTERS	Either the first stage of a multistage launch vehicle, or else a shorter-burning rocket used in parallel with longer-burning sustainer rockets to augment the space vehicle's takeoff thrust and payload capability.
BINARY CHOP METHOD	A search algorithm that finds the position of a target value within a sorted array. Binary Chop compares the target value to the middle element of the array. If they are not equal, the half in which the target cannot lie is eliminated and the

search continues on the remaining half, again taking the middle element to compare to the target value, and repeating this until the target value is found. If the search ends with the remaining half being empty, the target is not in the array.

BIPLANE — A fixed-wing aircraft with two main wings stacked one above the other. Advantages over monoplanes being more stiffness and a better stall resistance, disadvantages being more drag and diminishing returns on lift increase.

BOOMS — In sailing, a boom is a spar (pole), along the foot of a fore and aft rigged sail, that greatly improves control of the angle and shape of the sail. The primary action of the boom is to keep the foot flatter when the sail angle is away from the centerline of the boat.

BORE — The measurement of the diameter of a hole.

BOUNDARY LAYER — The Boundary Layer is the layer of fluid in the immediate vicinity of a bounding surface where the effects of viscosity are significant. The liquid or gas in the boundary layer tends to cling to the surface. The friction is the measurement of effect the surface has on the layer.

BTU — The British Thermal Unit is a unit of heat; it is defined as the amount of heat required to raise the temperature of one pound of water by one degree Fahrenheit.

CENTRIFUGAL FORCE	An apparent force that acts outward on a body moving around a center, arising from the body's inertia.
CFM	Cubic feet per minute is used to measure the amount of air that is being delivered, and is a common metric used for carburetors, pneumatic tools, and air-compressor systems.
CHERNOBYL DISASTER	The Chernobyl disaster was a nuclear incident that occurred on Saturday April 26, 1986, at the No. 4 reactor in the Chernobyl Nuclear Power Plant, near the city of Pripyat in the north of the Ukrainian SSR in the Soviet Union. It is considered the worst nuclear disaster in history both in terms of cost and casualties and is one of only two nuclear energy accidents rated at seven – the maximum severity – on the International Nuclear Event Scale. The initial emergency response, together with later decontamination of the environment, ultimately involved more than 500,000 personnel and cost an estimated 18 billion Soviet rubles – roughly US $68 billion in 2019, adjusted for inflation. Caused unknown numbers of deaths directly attributed to the accident. Varying estimates of increased mortality over subsequent decades.
CHICAGO PILE	The world's first artificial nuclear reactor. On December 2, 1942, the first human-made self-sustaining nuclear chain reaction was initiated in CP-1.

COMPUTER TOMOGRAPHY	A CT scan or computed tomography scan (formerly known as computed axial tomography or CAT scan) is a medical imaging technique used in radiology to get detailed images of the body noninvasively for diagnostic purposes.
CONDUIT	An electrical conduit is a tube used to protect and route electrical wiring in a building or structure. Electrical conduit may be made of metal, plastic, fiber, or fired clay. Most conduit is rigid, but flexible conduit is used for some purposes.
CPM	CP/M, originally standing for Control Program/Monitor and later Control Program for Microcomputers, is a mass-market operating system created in 1974 for Intel 8080/85-based microcomputers by Gary Kildall of Digital Research, Inc.
CRYOGENIC STORAGE TANKS	Cryogenic tanks are used for the storage of cryogenic liquids. Cryogenic liquids are typically liquefied gases at -150 °C or lower.
DAISY WHEEL PRINTER	Daisy wheel printing is an impact printing technology invented in 1970 by Dr. Andrew Gabor at Diablo Data Systems. It uses interchangeable pre-formed type elements, each with typically 96 glyphs, to generate high-quality output comparable to premium typewriters such as the IBM Selectric, but two to three times faster.
DERIVATION	A sequence of steps, logical or computational, from one result to another.

DEWAR	A double-walled flask of metal or silvered glass with a vacuum between the walls, used to hold liquids at well below ambient temperature.
DIFFERENTIAL EQUATIONS	In mathematics, a differential equation is an equation that relates one or more functions and their derivatives. In applications, the functions generally represent physical quantities, the derivatives represent their rates of change, and the differential equation defines a relationship between the two.
DOT MATRIX PRINTER	Dot matrix printing, sometimes called impact matrix printing, is a computer printing process in which ink is applied to a surface using a relatively low-resolution dot matrix for layout.
DSL	Digital subscriber line is a family of technologies that are used to transmit digital data over telephone lines. In telecommunications marketing, the term DSL is widely understood to mean asymmetric digital subscriber line, the most commonly installed DSL technology, for Internet access.
ELUTRIATED	The process of separation (lighter and heavier particles in a mixture) by suspension in an upward flow of liquid or gas.
EPOXY	Epoxy is the family of basic components or cured end products of epoxy resins. Epoxy resins, also known as polyepoxides, are a class of reactive prepolymers and polymers which contain epoxide

groups. The epoxide functional group is also collectively called epoxy. The IUPAC name for an epoxide group is an oxirane.

EXISTENCE THEOREM — In mathematics, an existence theorem is a theorem which asserts the existence of a certain object. It might be a statement which begins with the phrase "there exist," or it might be a universal statement whose last quantifier is existential.

F-1 ENGINE — The F-1, commonly known as Rocketdyne F1, is a rocket engine developed by Rocketdyne. This engine uses a gas-generator cycle developed in the United States in the late 1950s and was used in the first stage of the Saturn V rocket. Each F-1 developed 1.5 million pounds of thrust.

FAT CITY — A very comfortable condition or situation in life. (Slang)

FERMILAB — Fermi National Accelerator Laboratory, located just outside Batavia, Illinois, near Chicago, is a United States Department of Energy national laboratory specializing in high-energy particle physics.

FINITE DIFFERENCE EQUATIONS — A finite difference is a mathematical expression of the form $f(x + b) - f(x + a)$. If a finite difference is divided by $b - a$, one gets a difference quotient.

FLOWMETER — A flow meter is a device used to measure the volume or mass rate of flow of a gas or liquid.

	Flow meters are referred to by many names, such as flow gauge, flow indicator, liquid meter, flowrate sensor, etc.
FORTRAN	FORTRAN is a general-purpose, compiled imperative programming language that is especially suited to numeric computation and scientific computing. Originally developed by IBM in the 1950s for scientific and engineering applications, FORTRAN came to subsequently dominate scientific computing.
FREON SYSTEM	A cooling system using a patented blend of halocarbon products made by Dow Chemical.
FUKUSHIMA DAIICHI NUCLEAR DISASTER	The Fukushima Daiichi nuclear disaster was a 2011 nuclear accident at the Fukushima Daiichi Nuclear Power Plant in Ōkuma, Fukushima Prefecture, Japan. The event was primarily caused by the 2011 Tōhoku earthquake and tsunami. It was the most severe nuclear accident since the Chernobyl disaster in 1986.
GATLING GUN	The Gatling gun is a rapid-firing multiple-barrel firearm invented in 1861 by Richard Jordan Gatling. It is an early machine gun and a forerunner of the modern electric motor-driven rotary cannon.
GREEN'S FUNCTION	In mathematics, a Green's function is the impulse response of an inhomogeneous linear differential operator defined on a domain with specified initial conditions or boundary conditions.

HELMHOLTZ RESONATOR	A Helmholtz resonator or Helmholtz oscillator is a container of gas (usually air) with an open hole (or neck or port). At the Helmholtz resonance, a volume of air in and near the open hole vibrates because of the ‘springiness’ of the air inside.
HENRY’S LAW CONSTANT	In physical chemistry, Henry’s law is a gas law that states that the amount of dissolved gas in a liquid is proportional to its partial pressure above the liquid. The proportionality factor is called Henry’s law constant.
HYDROPHONE SYSTEM	A hydrophone is an underwater device that detects and records ocean sounds from all directions.
HYPERGOLIC PROPELLANTS	A hypergolic propellant combination used in a rocket engine is one whose components spontaneously ignite when they come into contact with each other.
IMPEDANCE FUNCTION	Acoustic impedance has the symbol *Z* and is defined as the ratio of acoustic pressure to acoustic volume flow.
JPL (JET PROPULSION LABORATORY)	The Jet Propulsion Laboratory is a federally funded research and development center and NASA field center in the city of Pasadena in California, United States. Founded in the 1930s, JPL is owned by NASA and managed by the nearby California Institute of Technology.

KEEL — The longitudinal structure along the centerline at the bottom of a vessel's hull, on which the rest of the hull is built, in some vessels extended downward as a blade or ridge to increase stability.

LAPLACE TRANSFORMS — In mathematics, the Laplace transform, named after its inventor Pierre-Simon Laplace, is an integral transform that converts a function of a real variable (t) to a function of a complex variable (s). The transform has many applications in science and engineering because it is a tool for solving differential equations.

LATEEN SAIL — A lateen or latin-rig is a triangular sail set on a long yard mounted at an angle on the mast and running in a fore-and-aft direction. Dating back to Roman navigation, the lateen became the favorite sail of the Age of Discovery, mainly because it allows a boat to tack "against the wind."

LEEBOARD — A leeboard is a form of pivoting keel used by a sailboat in lieu of a fixed keel. Typically mounted in pairs on each side of a hull, leeboards function much like a centerboard, allowing shallow draft craft to ply waters fixed keel boats cannot. Only one, however, leeward is used at a time, as it does not get lifted from the water when the boat heels under the force of the wind.

LENS EFFECT — Refraction of force or light to increase the size of the beam or force.

LEVITCH'S BUBBLE DYNAMICS — Bubble dynamics in a microchannel refers to the nucleation of a bubble on heated flow channel walls and its subsequent interaction with the single-phase or two-phase flow field.

LOCAL MASS BALANCE EQUATIONS — The mass balance equation forms basis to a number of process engineering calculations and states that total mass in any system is always conserved: *Total mass in = Total mass out + Total mass accumulated in the system.*

LUNAR ASCENT ENGINE — The ascent propulsion system or lunar module ascent engine is a fixed-thrust hypergolic rocket engine developed by Bell Aerosystems for use in the Apollo Lunar Module ascent stage. It used Aerozine 50 fuel, and N_2O_4 oxidizer.

M1A1 BATTLE TANK — The M1 Abrams entered service in 1980 and currently serves as the main battle tank of the United States Army and Marine Corps.

MARS VIKING — The Viking program consisted of a pair of identical American space probes, Viking 1 and Viking 2, which landed on Mars in 1976. Each spacecraft was composed of two main parts: an orbiter designed to photograph the surface of Mars from orbit, and a lander designed to study the planet from the surface.

MAST — The mast of a sailing vessel is a tall spar, or arrangement of spars, erected more or less vertically on the centerline of a ship or boat. Its purposes include carrying sails, spars, and

	derricks, and giving necessary height to a navigation light, look-out position, signal yard, control position, radio aerial or signal lamp.
METASTABLE	In physics, metastability is a stable state of a dynamical system other than the system's state of least energy. A ball resting in a hollow on a slope is a simple example of metastability.
METHOD OF CHARACTERISTIC SOLUTION	In mathematics, the method of characteristics is a technique for solving partial differential equations. Typically, it applies to first-order equations, although more generally the method of characteristics is valid for any hyperbolic partial differential equation.
METHOD OF ISOCLINES	Isoclines are often used as a graphical method of solving ordinary differential equations. In an equation of the form $y' = f(x, y)$, the isoclines are lines in the (x, y) plane obtained by setting $f(x, y)$ equal to a constant.
MICROCOMPUTERS	A microcomputer is a small, relatively inexpensive computer with a microprocessor as its central processing unit. It includes a microprocessor, memory, and minimal input/output circuitry mounted on a single printed circuit board.
MIE SCATTERING THEORY	Mie scattering theory is the generalized solution that describes the scattering of an electromagnetic wave by a homogeneous spherical medium having RI different from that of the medium through which the wave is traversing.

MS-DOS	MS-DOS is an operating system for x86-based personal computers mostly developed by Microsoft. Collectively, MS-DOS, its rebranding as IBM PC DOS, and some operating systems attempting to be compatible with MS-DOS, are sometimes referred to as "DOS."
MYLAR	Mylar, also known as BoPET (Biaxially oriented polyethylene terephthalate) is a polyester film made from stretched polyethylene terephthalate (PET) and is used for its high tensile strength, chemical and dimensional stability, transparency, reflectivity, gas and aroma barrier properties, and electrical insulation.
NAVIER-STOKES EQUATION	In physics, the Navier-Stokes equations are a set of partial differential equations which describe the motion of viscous fluid substances, named after French engineer and physicist Claude-Louis Navier and Anglo-Irish physicist and mathematician George Gabriel Stokes.
NEC	NEC Corporation is a Japanese multinational information technology and electronics corporation, headquartered in Minato, Tokyo. The company was known as the Nippon Electric Company, Limited, before rebranding in 1983 as NEC.
NUCLEONICS	The branch of science and technology concerned with atomic nuclei and nucleons, especially the exploitation of nuclear power.

OARLOCK	A brace that attaches an oar to a boat. When a boat is rowed, the rowlock acts as a fulcrum, and, in doing so, the propulsive force that the rower exerts on the water with the oar is transferred to the boat by the thrust force exerted on the rowlock.
P-3 ORION AIRPLANES	The Lockheed P-3 Orion is a four-engine turboprop anti-submarine and maritime surveillance aircraft developed for the United States Navy and introduced in the 1960s.
P-51 FIGHTER	The North American Aviation P-51 Mustang is an American long-range, single-seat fighter and fighter-bomber used during World War II and the Korean War, among other conflicts.
PETROCARB CORP	Now defunct engineering corporation with numerous patents.
PRESSURE TRANSDUCER	A pressure sensor is a device for pressure measurement of gases or liquids. Pressure is an expression of the force required to stop a fluid from expanding, and is usually stated in terms of force per unit area. A pressure sensor usually acts as a transducer; it generates a signal as a function of the pressure imposed.
PT BOAT	A PT boat (short for patrol torpedo boat) was a motor torpedo boat used by the United States Navy in World War II. It was small, fast, and inexpensive to build, valued for its maneuverability and speed but hampered at the

	beginning of the war by ineffective torpedoes, limited armament, and comparatively fragile construction that limited some of the variants to coastal waters.
RANKINE CYCLE	The Rankine cycle is an idealized thermodynamic cycle describing the process by which certain heat engines, such as steam turbines or reciprocating steam engines, allow mechanical work to be extracted from a fluid as it moves between a heat source and heat sink. The Rankine cycle is named after William John Macquorn Rankine.
REYNOLDS NUMBER	The Reynolds number (**Re**) helps predict flow patterns in different fluid flow situations. At low Reynolds numbers, flows tend to be dominated by laminar (sheet-like) flow, while at high Reynolds numbers, flows tend to be turbulent. Reynolds numbers are an important dimensionless quantity in fluid mechanics.
ROLLS ROYCE SILVER CLOUD	The Rolls-Royce Silver Cloud was a luxury automobile produced by Rolls-Royce Limited from April 1955-March 1966. The J. P. Blatchley design was a major change from the pre-war models and the highly derivative Silver Dawn it replaced.
SATURN V	Saturn V was an American human-rated super heavy-lift launch vehicle used by NASA between 1967 and 1973. It consisted of three stages, each fueled by liquid propellants.

SEAWOLF	The Seawolf class is a class of nuclear-powered fast attack submarines (SSN) in service with the United States Navy. The most expensive SSN submarines ever at $3.5 billion each, only three were made.
SHOCK TUBE	The shock tube is an instrument used to replicate and direct blast waves at a sensor or a model in order to simulate actual explosions and their effects, usually on a smaller scale. Shock tubes are also used to investigate compressible flow phenomena and gas phase combustion reactions.
SLIDE RULE	The slide rule, also known colloquially in the United States as a slipstick, is a mechanical analog computer. As graphical analog calculators, slide rules are closely related to nomograms, but the former are used for general calculations, whereas the latter are used for application-specific computations.
SODIUM-COOLED FAST REACTORS	A sodium-cooled fast reactor is a fast neutron reactor cooled by liquid sodium. A fast-neutron reactor is a category of nuclear reactor in which the fission chain reaction is sustained by fast neutrons, as opposed to thermal neutrons used in thermal-neutron reactors. It needs no neutron moderator, but requires fuel that is relatively rich in fissile material.
SONOBUOY	A sonobuoy is a relatively small buoy – typically 13 cm diameter and 91 cm long – expendable sonar system that is dropped/ejected from aircraft

or ships conducting anti-submarine warfare or underwater acoustic research.

SPECIFIC IMPULSE — Specific impulse is a measure of how efficiently a reaction mass engine creates thrust. For engines whose reaction mass is only the fuel they carry, specific impulse is exactly proportional to exhaust gas velocity. A propulsion system with a higher specific impulse uses the mass of the propellant more efficiently. Specific impulse relates how many pounds of force are produced by expelling so many pounds per second of reaction mass. It has units of seconds.

SPECTROMETER — A spectrometer is a scientific instrument used to separate and measure spectral components of a physical phenomenon. Spectrometer is a broad term often used to describe instruments that measure a continuous variable of a phenomenon where the spectral components are somehow mixed.

STOKE'S DRAG — An expression, now known as Stokes' law, for the frictional force – also called drag force – exerted on spherical objects with very small Reynolds numbers in a viscous fluid. Stokes' law is derived by solving the Stokes flow limit for small Reynolds numbers of the Navier-Stokes equations.

SUPERFLUIDITY — Superfluidity is the characteristic property of a fluid with zero viscosity which therefore flows without any loss of kinetic energy. When stirred, a superfluid forms vortices that continue to rotate indefinitely. Superfluidity occurs in two isotopes of helium (helium-3 and helium-4) when they are liquefied by cooling to cryogenic temperatures. The theory of superfluidity was developed by Soviet theoretical physicists Lev Landau and Isaak Khalatnikov.

TEFLON	Teflon is a brand name for a synthetic chemical called polytetrafluoroethylene (PTFE). Teflon is used to coat a variety of products because it's waterproof, cuts down on friction, and creates a nonstick surface. Teflon has been used since the 1940s and it's found in everything from heat lamp bulbs to catheters.
TELETYPEWRITER	A teleprinter is an electromechanical device that can be used to send and receive typed messages through various communications channels, in both point-to-point and point-to-multipoint configurations.
THERMAL ANALYSIS PROGRAM (TAP)	Thermal analysis software analyzes heat transfer processes and aids in their design. The software provides solutions to methods, including conduction, convection, radiation, and changes of phase. Thermal analysis programs offer functionalities such as modeling, editing, analyzing, and post-processing.
THERMAL HYDRAULICS	Thermal hydraulics (also called thermohydraulics) is the study of hydraulic flow in thermal fluids. The area can be mainly divided into three parts: thermodynamics, fluid mechanics, and heat

transfer, but they are often closely linked to each other.

THERMOCOUPLE JUNCTIONS — An electrical device consisting of two dissimilar electrical conductors forming an electrical junction. A thermocouple produces a temperature-dependent voltage as a result of Seebeck effect, and this voltage can be interpreted to measure temperature.

THERMODYNAMICS — The branch of physical science that deals with the relations between heat and other forms of energy (such as mechanical, electrical, or chemical energy), and, by extension, of the relationships between all forms of energy.

TRANSCENDENTAL EQUATION — A transcendental equation is an equation containing a transcendental function of the variable being solved for. Such equations often do not have closed-form solutions.

TURBO-PASCAL — Turbo Pascal is a software development system that includes a compiler and an integrated development environment for the Pascal programming language running on CP/M, CP/M-86, and DOS. It was originally developed by Anders Hejlsberg at Borland, and was notable for its extremely fast compiling times.

TURBOMACHINERY ENGINEER — Turbomachinery, in mechanical engineering, describes machines that transfer energy between a rotor and a fluid, including both turbines and compressors. While a turbine transfers energy

	from a fluid to a rotor, a compressor transfers energy from a rotor to a fluid.
VENTURI FLOW CONTROLS	A venturi is a device which converts pressure to kinetic energy, then converts it back.
VERNIER CALLIPER	A vernier scale is a visual aid to take an accurate measurement reading between two graduation markings on a linear scale by using mechanical interpolation; thereby increasing resolution and reducing measurement uncertainty by using vernier acuity to reduce human estimation error.
VON KÁRMÁN'S INTEGRAL BOUNDARY LAYER	An integral fundamental to many of the approximation methods commonly employed to calculate boundary layer thicknesses on the surfaces of general obstacles placed in high Reynolds number flows.

As defined by Wiki and Britannica Encyclopedia.

Made in the USA
Coppell, TX
06 February 2023